Table of Contents

Month 1 Checklist

Hands-on activities to help prepare your child for school!

SELF-CONCEPT

Self-Awareness: pages 5-8

Being aware of how we look, recognizing our place in the family, and knowing our age are important skills because they help us understand who we are. Many preschools spend part of each day on self-awareness activities. The following activities will prepare your child for this work:

- ❑ Complete the worksheets.
- ❑ Have your child look in a mirror as you discuss his or her hair color, facial features, and so on.
- ❑ Thumb through a calendar—pointing out months and days of the week—as you discuss birthdays and your child's age.
- ❑ Look through a family album and discuss immediate and extended family.
- ❑ Let your child help plan his or her birthday party—invitations, games, food, decorations.
- ❑ Use white paper plates to draw funny faces of family members and post on the refrigerator.

PREREADING AND PREWRITING

Visual Discrimination: pages 9-12

Classification: pages 13-17, 33-34

Learning to look at a printed page and identify what's happening on it is the beginning stage of learning to read. Telling which items on a page go together, moreover, helps children learn to group similar ideas—a thinking skill important in reading and other areas. And drawing, circling, and other paper-and-pencil skills are the first steps in learning to write.

- ❑ Complete the worksheets.
- ❑ Play "I Spy." One person chooses an object easily seen and says, "I spy something red" or "I spy something square." The other players must guess which thing is meant. The player who guesses the right object gets to say "I spy" next.
- ❑ Sort household objects such as clothing, silverware, building blocks, and toys into like groups.
- ❑ Match socks when doing laundry.
- ❑ Play a game in which the goal is to find what's missing in a space. For example, remove a salt shaker from the table before your child comes in the room and give clues about the missing object—"Something that's glass and small is missing from the table. What is it?"

LANGUAGE

Color Words: pages 18-21

Among the first sight words that children learn to read are those for colors. Use the following activities to help your child learn to identify colors:

- ❑ Complete the worksheets.
- ❑ Declare a color day. For example, have your child complete the worksheet for red (p. 18). Then off and on over the next day, encourage him or her to point out red things: tomatoes, cherries, apples, stop lights, fire engines, and so on.
- ❑ Use a deck of colored flash cards to play "Color Concentration." Start with two cards for each color. Lay them color side down on a surface. Take turns flipping them over, two at a time. If the colors match, the player keeps the cards. If they don't, he or she flips them back over and it's the next player's turn.

MATH

Shapes: pages 22-25

Sizes: pages 26-28

In addition to learning words about relative sizes—long/short, large/small, and so on—early math learning also includes recognizing basic shapes and their names. Help your child with these skills through the following activities:

- ❑ Complete the worksheets.
- ❑ Have a shapes day during which your child looks for a particular shape in everyday places—e.g., square buttons, square sides on boxes, square window panes.
- ❑ With clay, make long snakes and short snakes.
- ❑ Let your child help bake cookies—making big ones, small ones, and cookies that are the same size.
- ❑ Use building blocks to help your child learn relative sizes. Ask him or her to separate the large.

READING

Drawing Conclusions: pages 29-32

Learning to draw conclusions from what one sees in pictures or hears when listening to the text of a storybook is an important part of reading comprehension. Foster this skill with the following activities:

- ❑ Pull out and read the story, "Who Am I?" As you read, pause for your child to answer each riddle before turning the page. Talk about the clues that helped the child answer each question.
- ❑ Make up riddles about people or TV characters well known to the child and ask "Who is it?"
- ❑ Encourage your child to make up animal riddles like the ones in this month's storybook.

My Picture

My name is Marqus.

Parents: Encourage your child to talk about the bear's features and discuss his or her own features. Then ask your child to fill in the blank face and color it. Print your child's name on the line, and have him or her use a finger to trace the letters.

My Birthday

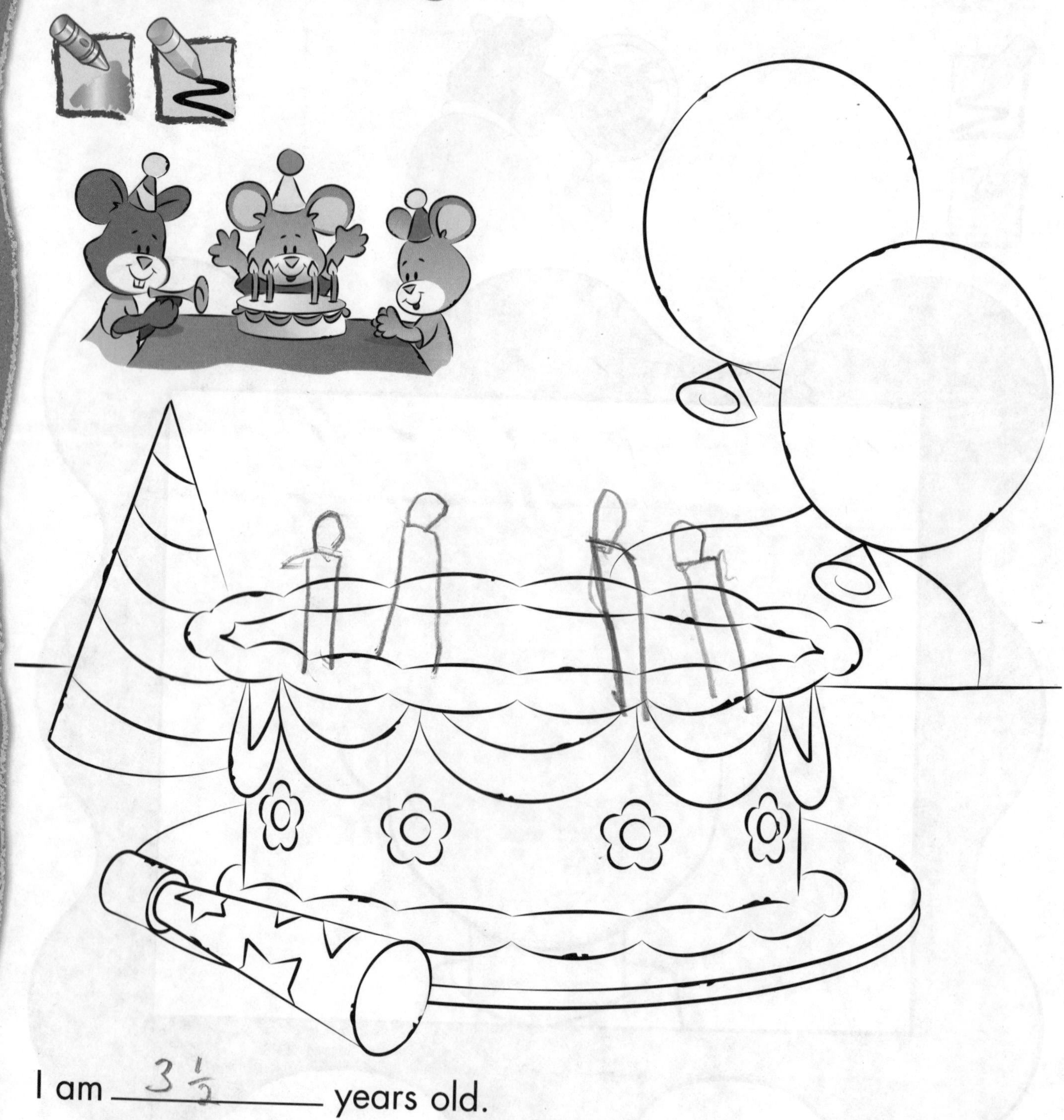

I am 3 1/2 years old.

My birthday is on Nov 14.

Parents: Discuss birthday celebrations and your child's age. Ask your child to draw the correct number of candles on the cake, and then to color the picture. Write your child's age and birth date and read the sentences aloud. Then have your child "read" with you.

My Family

Draw your family.

There are 6 people in my family.

Parents: **Discuss the cat family portraits and ask your child how the cats are related. Then ask your child to identify each of his or her family's members, and draw a family portrait in the picture frame. Discuss what number goes in the sentence.**

My Favorite Pets

Circle your favorite pets.

fish

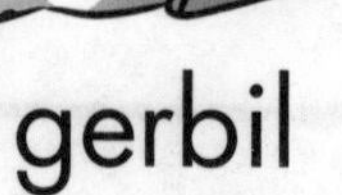

gerbil

bird

My favorite pet is the dog.
His name is Ruff Ruff

Parents: **Discuss the picture at the top of the page. If your child does not have a pet, ask for the names of his or her favorite animals. Then ask your child to circle his or her favorite pets. Discuss which kind of pet (or pet name) goes in the sentence.**

Forest Animals

Circle these animals in the picture.

Parents: Ask your child to point to and name each animal at the top of the page. Then ask him or her to find and circle those animals in the picture.

PREREADING

Jungle Animals

Circle these animals in the picture.

Parents: Ask your child to point to and name each animal at the top of the page. Then ask him or her to find and circle those animals in the picture. Ask, "Where are these animals?"

Sea Animals

Circle these animals in the picture.

Parents: **Ask your child to point to and name each animal at the top of the page. Ask him or her to find and circle those animals in the picture. Ask, "Where are these animals?"**

PREREADING

Fire Station

Circle these objects in the picture.

Parents: Ask your child to point to and name each object at the top of the page. Then ask him or her to find and circle those objects in the picture. (Two of the items appear more than once in the larger picture.) Ask, "What is this place?"

The Bedroom

Parents: Have your child point to the boxes above that show what belongs in each blank. Help your child cut out the sweater and lamp and paste them in the correct spaces. (Note: Be careful not to cut the boxes for page 14.)

PREREADING

The Garden

Parents: Have your child point to the boxes above that show the things that belong in the blanks. Help your child cut out the flower and lettuce and paste them in the correct spaces.

Make A Match

Parents: **Ask your child to point to and name each item in the left-hand column and then to draw a line to connect each of those items with the matching item on the right.**

PREREADING

Clothing Go-Togethers

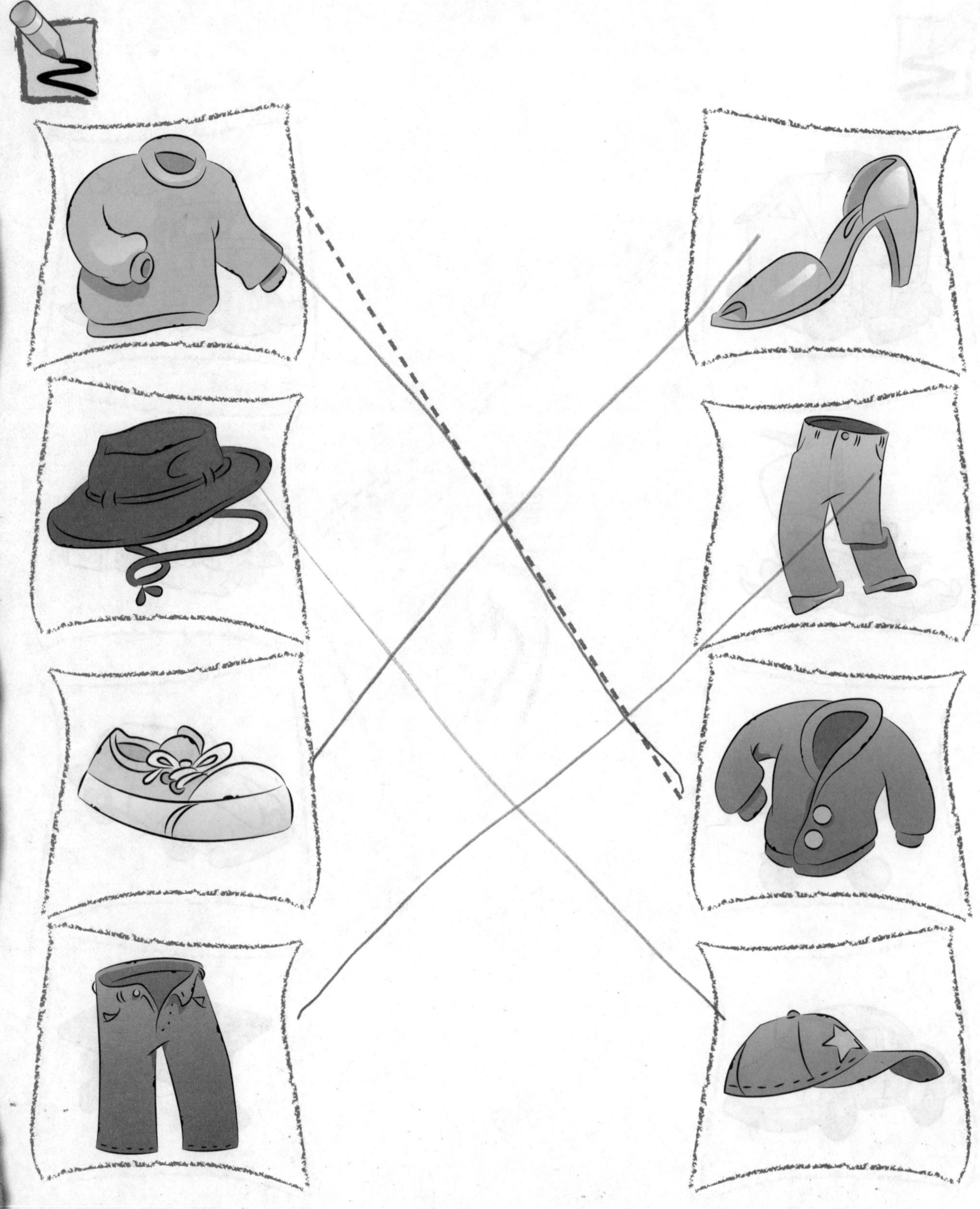

Parents: Ask your child to point to and name each item in the left-hand column. Discuss how each item is used. Then ask your child to draw a line to connect each of those items with an item on the right that is used in the same way.

Food Go-Togethers

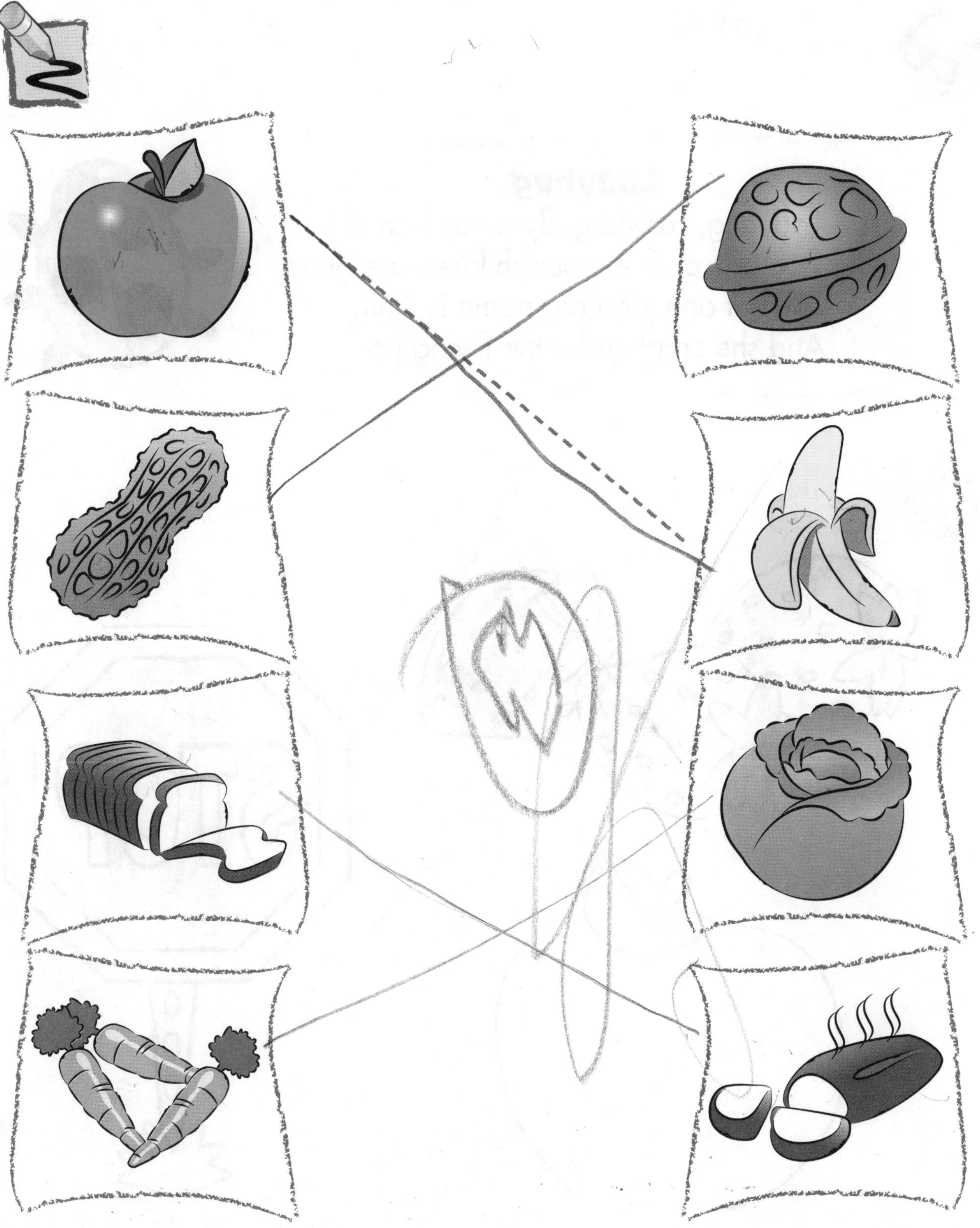

Parents: Ask your child to point to and name each item in the left-hand column. Have your child identify the fruit, the nut, the bread, and the vegetable. Then say, "Draw a line to connect each of the items that go together."

Red

Ladybug

Ladybug, Ladybug, fly away home!
Your house is on fire, your children are gone.
All but one, and her name is Ann,
And she crept under the frying pan.

Parents: Read the rhyme. Have your child point to the ladybug and tell what it is and its color. Ask your child to identify each of the items pictured at the bottom of the page and then color them red.

Yellow

Sally Go Round the Sun

Sally go round the sun,
Sally go round the moon,
Sally go round the chimney-pots
On a Sunday afternoon.

Parents: Read the rhyme. Have your child point to the sun and tell what color it is. Ask your child to identify each of the items pictured at the bottom of the page and then color them yellow.

LANGUAGE

Blue

Little Boy Blue

Little Boy Blue, come blow your horn;
The sheep's in the meadow,
the cow's in the corn.
Where is the boy who looks after the sheep?
He's under the haystack, fast asleep.

Parents: Read the rhyme. Ask, "What color is the little boy's clothes?" Then discuss which parts of the pictures at the bottom of the page should be blue, and have your child color them.

Green

Peter Piper

Peter Piper picked a peck of pickled peppers;
A peck of pickled peppers Peter Piper picked.
If Peter Piper picked a peck of pickled peppers,
Where's the peck of pickled peppers
Peter Piper picked?

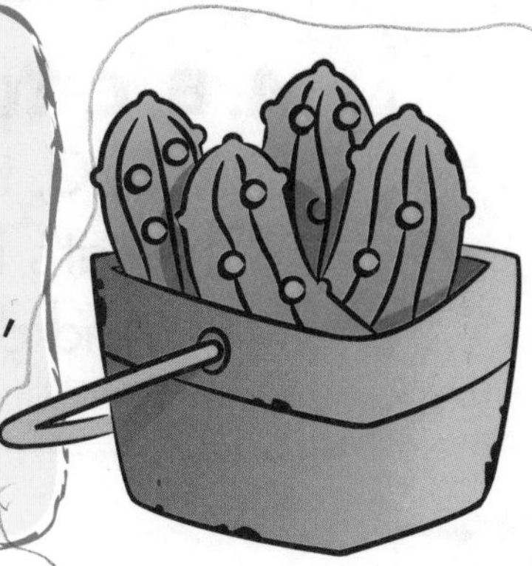

Parents: Read the rhyme. Ask, "What color are the pickles?" Then have your child color the items at the bottom of the page green.

MATH

Square

A, B, C, Tumble-Down D

A, B, C, tumble-down D,
The cat's in the cupboard
And can't see me!

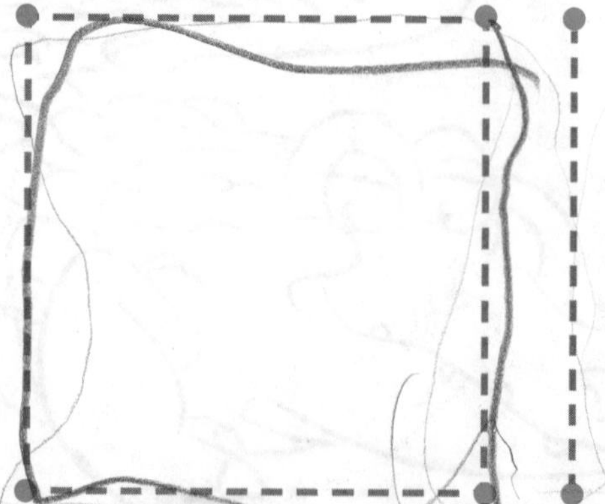

Parents: Read the rhyme. Then say, "This is a square. It has four sides—all the same length. "Have your child color the row of squares. Then have your child use a finger to trace the first square in the bottom row, and a pencil to trace and draw the next two squares.

Circle

Hickory, Dickory, Dock

Hickory, dickory, dock!
The mouse ran up the clock.
The clock struck one, the mouse ran down,
Hickory, dickory, dock.

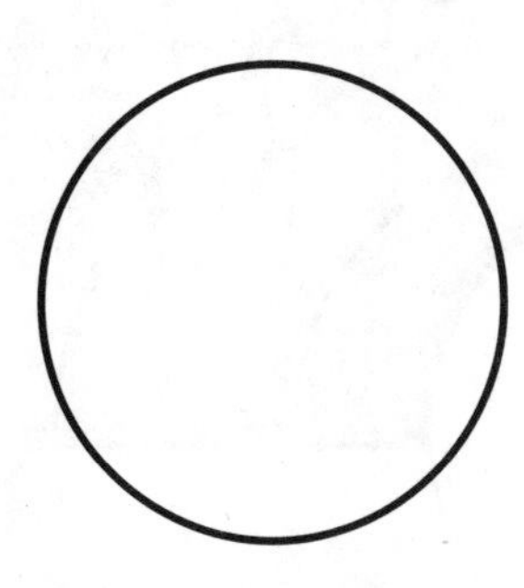

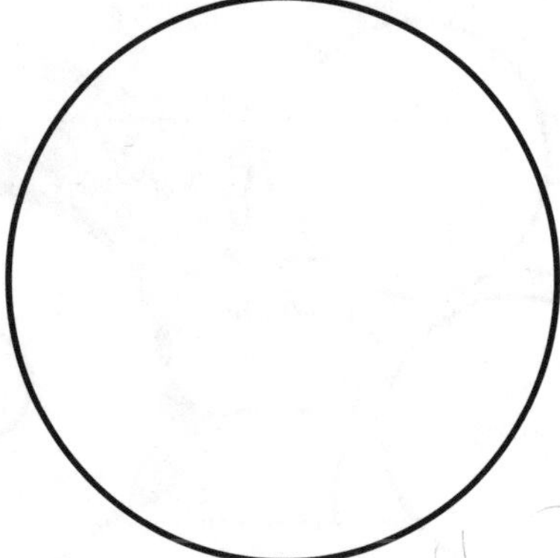

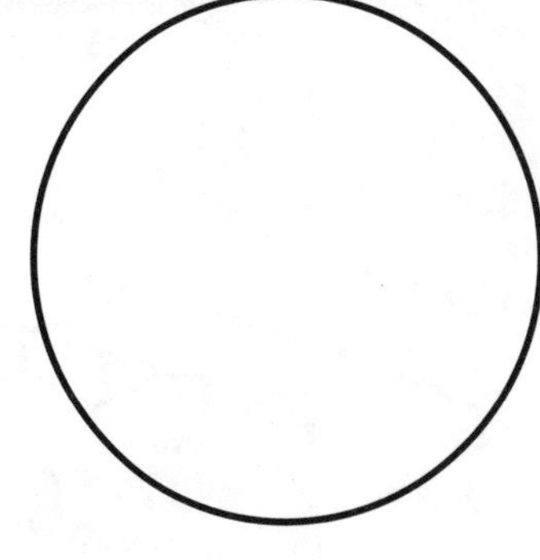

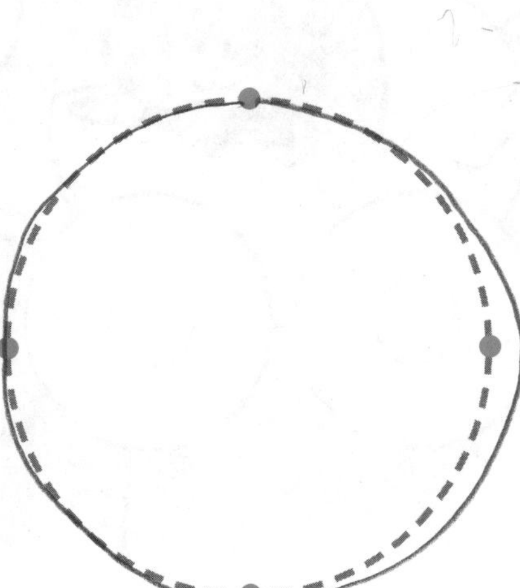

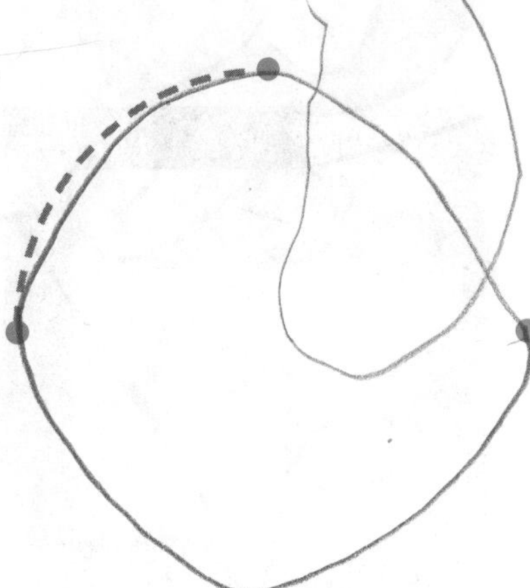

Parents: Read the rhyme. Then say, "This is a circle—all the lines are curved. "Have your child color the row of circles. Then have him or her trace the first circle in the bottom row with a finger, and then use a pencil to trace over the next two circles.

Round World

Color the ◯.

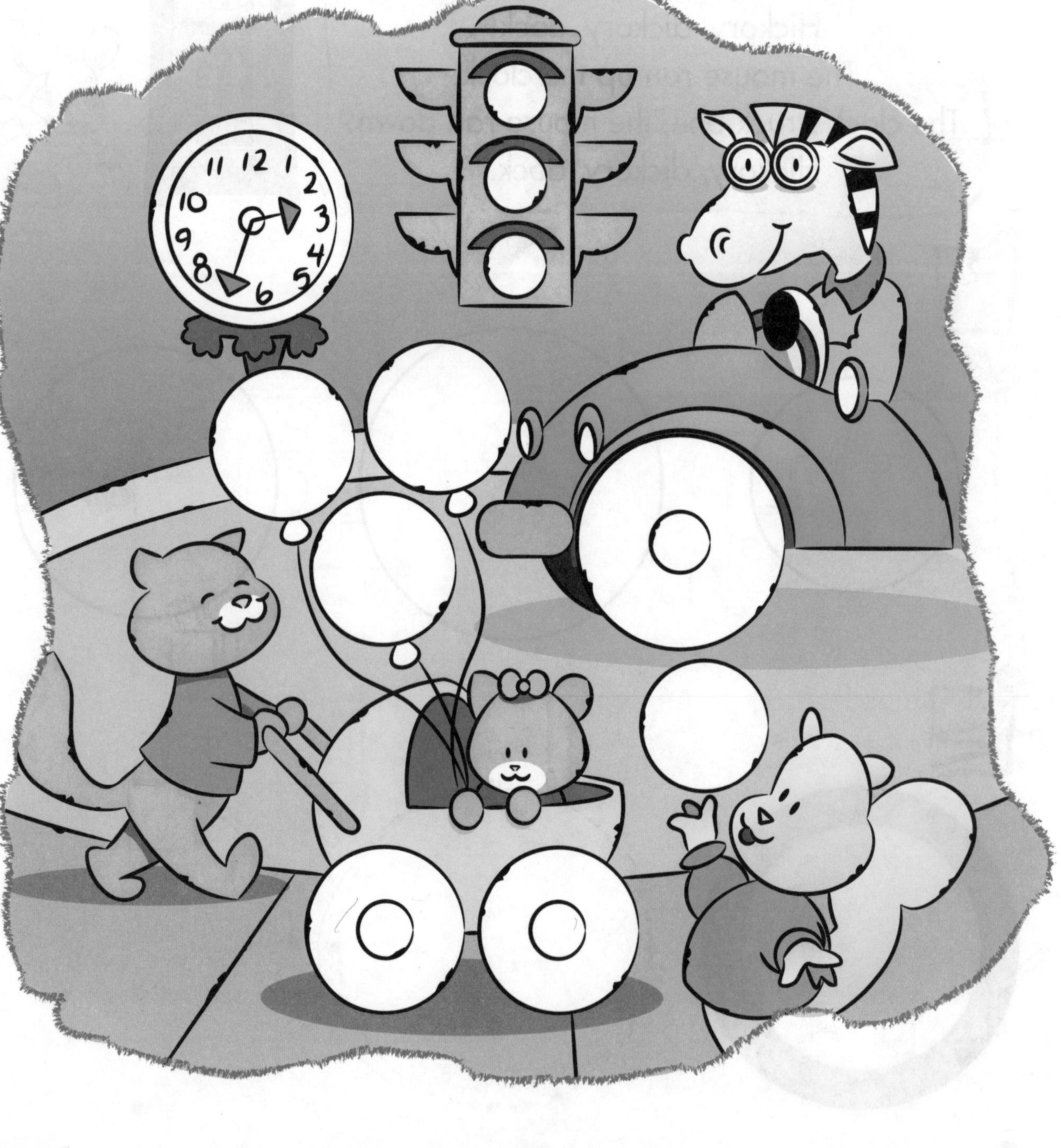

Parents: Ask your child to point out all the circles in the scene and then color them.

Square World

Color the □.

Parents: **Ask your child to point out the squares in the scene and then color them.**

Large and Small

Circle what is small.

Parents: Have your child point to the large rabbit and then the small rabbit. Then point to one of the rabbits and have your child identify it as large or small. At the bottom of the page, have your child tell which vegetable is small and circle it.

Long and Short

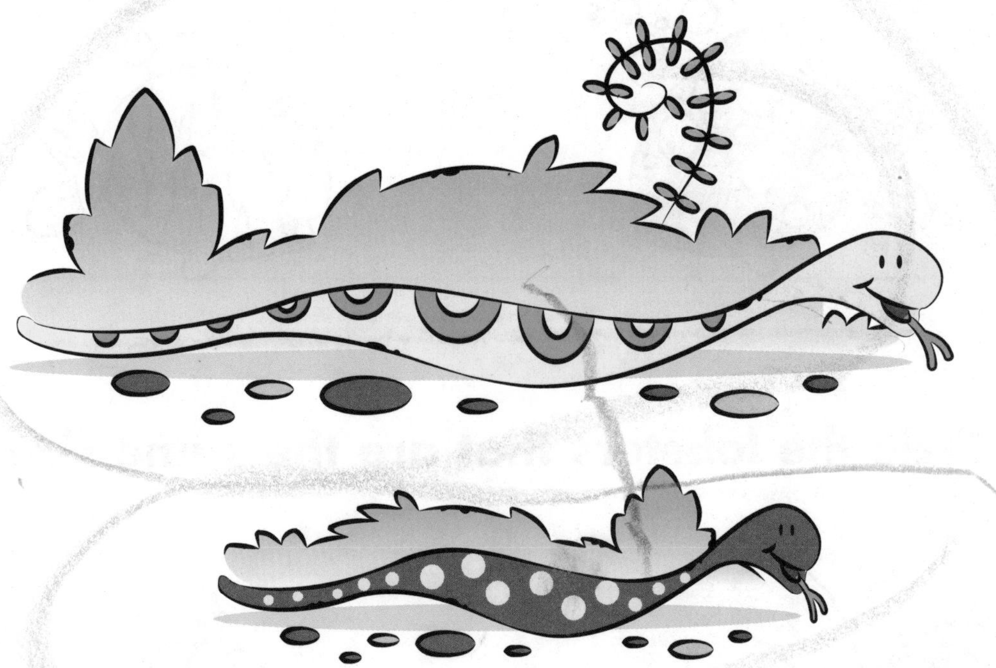

Circle what is long.

Parents: Have your child point to the long snake and then the short snake. Then point to one of the snakes and have your child identify it as long or short. At the bottom of the page, have your child tell which animal is long and which is short. Say, "Circle what's long."

Same Size

Circle the lobsters that are the same size.

Circle the seahorses that are the same size.

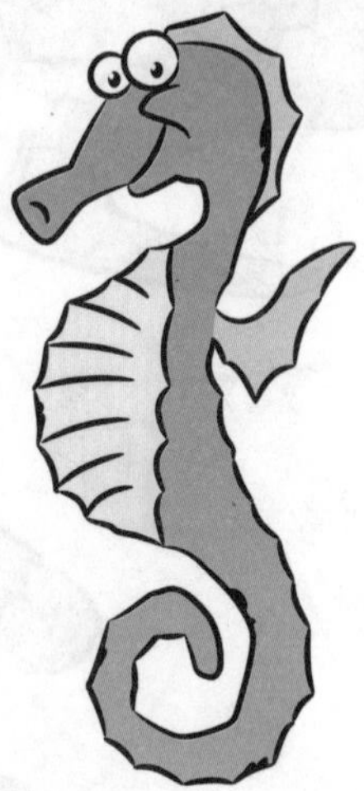

Parents: Have your child point to the two fish and compare them. Ask: "How are the two fish different? How are they the same?" Help your child see that the fish are the same size. Then have your child circle the lobsters and then the seahorses that are the same size.

inside of the front cover.

I am a pig!

Who am I?

Who am I?

I am a frog!

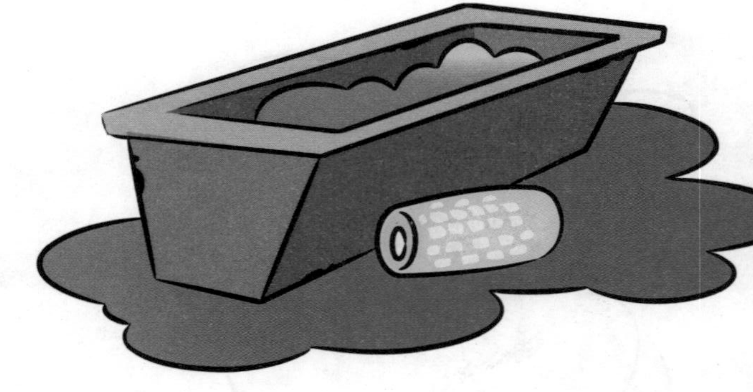

I am pink.
I have a short, curly tail.
I roll in the mud and say,
"Oink! Oink!"

Who am I?

I am a bird!

I live on a farm. I give milk for you to drink. When I am happy, I say, "Moooooo!"

Who am I?

I am a cow!

I can fly. I have feathers that keep me warm. I live in a nest up high in a tree.

Who am I?

Bird

We Belong Together

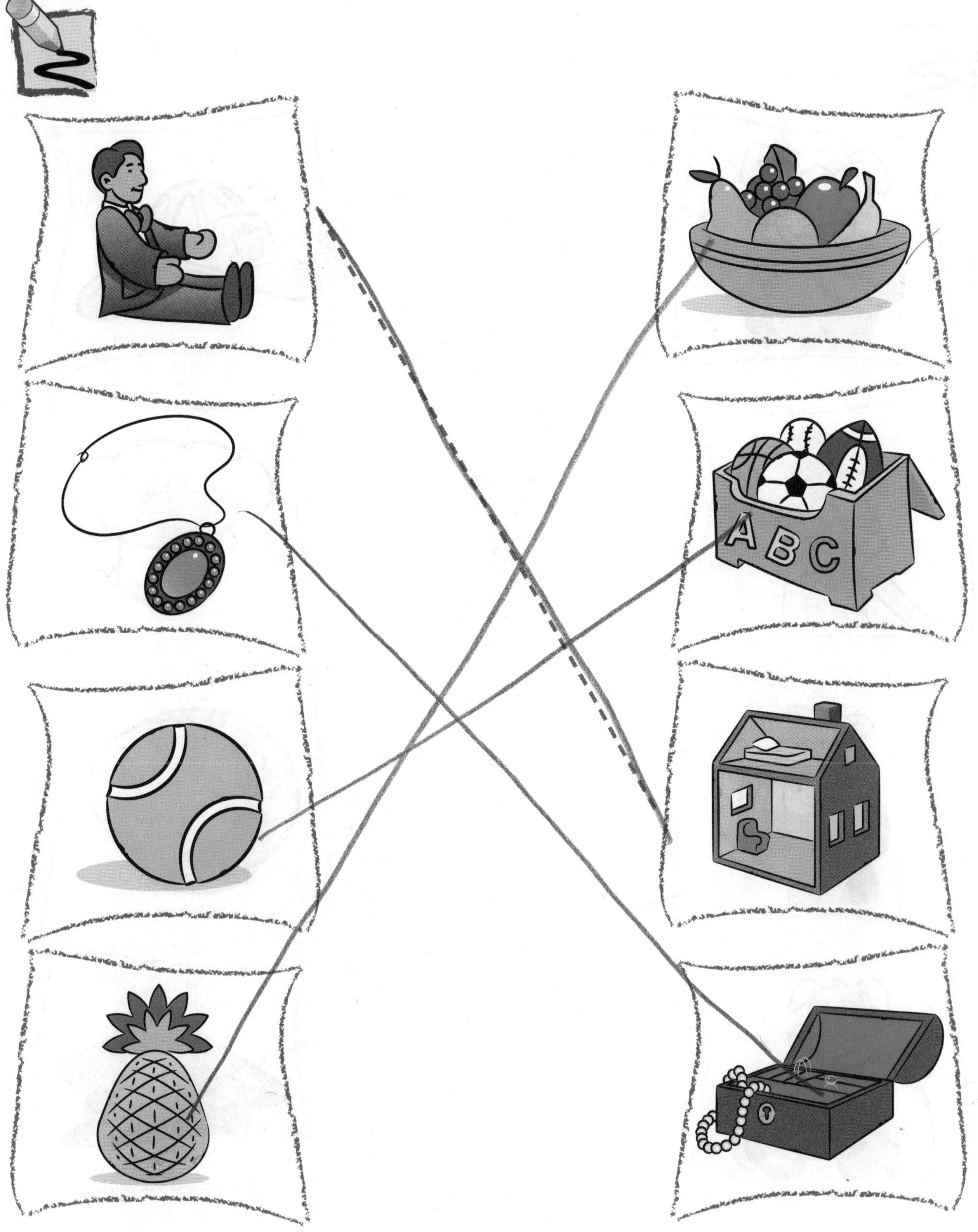

Parents: Have your child identify each picture in both columns. Discuss why a dashed line connects the doll with the doll house. Ask your child to trace that dashed line, and then to draw a line from each of the other items on the left to the correct item on the right.

PREREADING

Hats Off

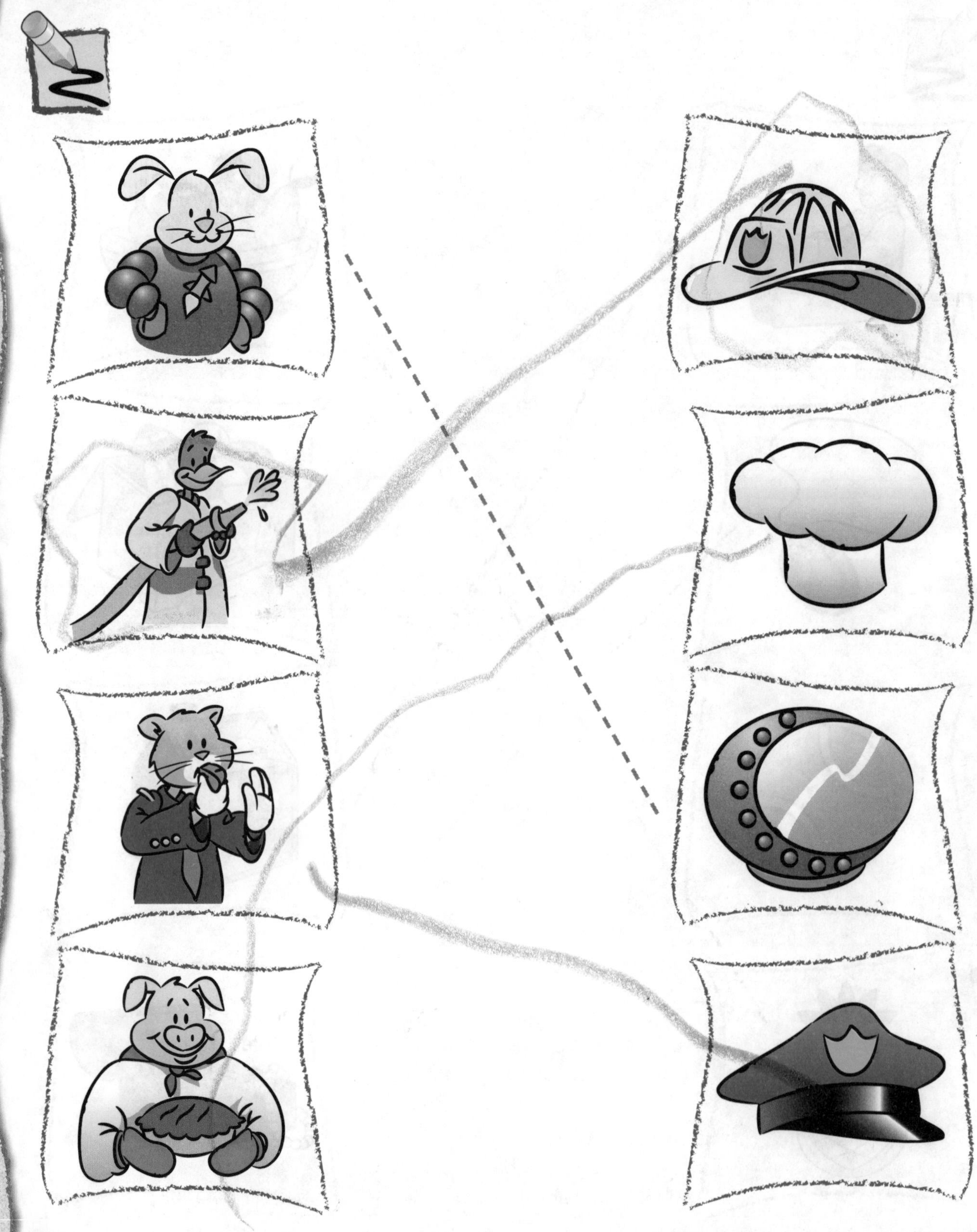

Parents: Have your child identify each picture in both columns. Discuss why a dashed line connects the astronaut with the helmet. Ask your child to trace that dashed line, and then to draw a line from each of the other workers on the left to the matching hat on the right.

Month 2 Checklist

Hands-on activities to help prepare your child for school!

SELF-CONCEPT

Senses: page 37
Hands and Feet: pages 38-41

Body parts and their functions are important pieces of information for preschoolers. Use the following ideas to teach your child about the five senses and hands and feet:

- ❑ Complete the worksheets.
- ❑ Make handprints and footprints on a piece of flattened clay or clay dough. For fun, make the pet's prints next to them. How are the prints alike? How are they different?
- ❑ Lacing boards or lacing shoes are good ways to practice fine motor skills at the same time that the child is reminded of all the wonderful things hands can do.
- ❑ Play games or activities, but call the child's attention to how the hands or feet are used—for example, "Let's clap to the rhythm of this song with our hands" or "Try doing some jumping jacks! What are your feet doing?" Play "Simon Says" and have Simon say things such as "Take three big steps with your feet."

PREREADING AND PREWRITING

Sorting, Classifying: pages 42-46, 49-52
Visual Discrimination: pages 47-48
Fine Motor Skills: page 64

Understanding that various things in the world share characteristics, that they are alike in specific ways, helps children understand organization. In addition to the activities listed on page 3, here are some everyday ways to help your child learn to classify:

- ❑ Complete the worksheets.
- ❑ Sort blocks, beads, or counters into color groups.
- ❑ Play a game in which you name two items, such as piano and guitar, and ask the child to name a third item that might go with that group, such as fiddle. Explain why the third item does or does not go with the first two.
- ❑ In addition to the maze in this section, you can help your child with prewriting skills by drawing several simple zigzag lines on a piece of paper and letting the child trace over them in pretty colors. Learning to stay on a line is a prerequisite skill for printing.

LANGUAGE

More Color Words: pages 53-56

Use any of the color activities on page 3 along with the ones below to teach the colors presented in this section.

❑ Complete the worksheets.

❑ Children love to mix things, so let them mix colors to see how we get many hues from the four primary colors: red, blue, yellow, and black. The colors featured in this section (orange, purple, and brown) are all formed by combining colors introduced in Month 1. Help your child combine red and yellow food coloring to make orange; red and blue to make purple; and red, blue, and yellow to make brown. You can also use water-based markers to do the same thing.

❑ Point out color words in the environment, on crayons and markers, in ads, and so on.

❑ Write a color word (such as orange) using (orange) colored ink on a sheet of paper. Prepare several sheets. Then have your child sort colored beads or blocks onto the different sheets. Once your child can recognize the color words, write the words in black ink to make the activity more difficult.

MATH

Shapes: pages 57-60

Sizes: pages 61-63

In addition to the activities on page 3, the ones that follow are fine hands-on activities to teach beginning math skills:

❑ Complete the worksheets.

❑ Have your child make a triangle-shaped placemat out of construction paper. Then at breakfast or lunch, cut some foods into triangles—toast, sandwiches, cheese slices. Serve on the placemat. [Use this same activity with other shapes.]

❑ Work with blocks of various shapes and sizes to help your child understand long/short, big/little, and tall/short. For example, hold up two blocks of different lengths and ask, "Which is the long one?"

❑ Brainstorm a list of things that can be tall or short with your child (e.g., people, buildings, Ferris wheels, etc.). Have your child draw examples of each kind of thing.

Touch

Circle what's soft.

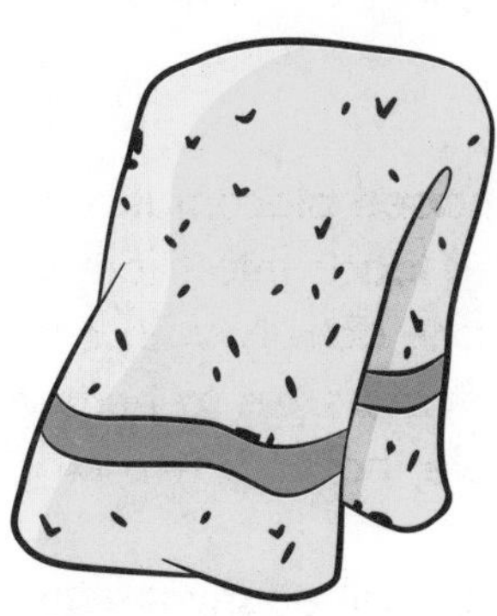

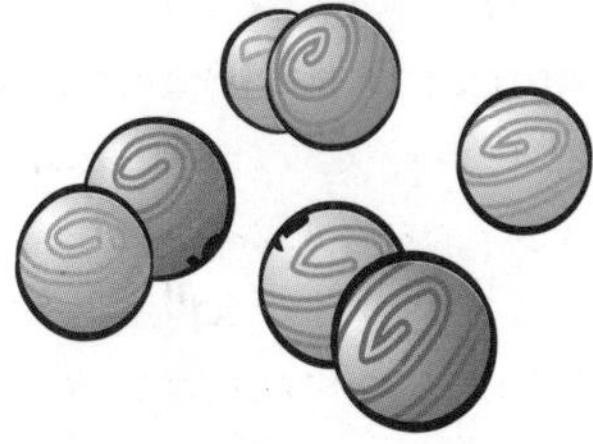

Parents: Explain that our hands have nerves just under the skin to help us feel things, so that we know when they are hard, soft, smooth, bumpy, hot, cold, and so on. Ask your child to circle the things that feel soft.

My Hands

Draw your (hand) **.**

I have ________ fingers on each hand.

Parents: Have your child place his or her hand on the page and trace around it with an index finger. Then help him or her trace around it with a crayon, count the number of fingers, and write the numeral in the sentence. Together, read the completed sentence.

Using My Hands

Circle the ones using their hands.

Parents: Discuss what the children at the top of the page are doing. Comment on how the children are using their hands. Discuss what each child is doing in the other pictures on the page. Then have your child circle the ones that show children using their hands.

My Feet

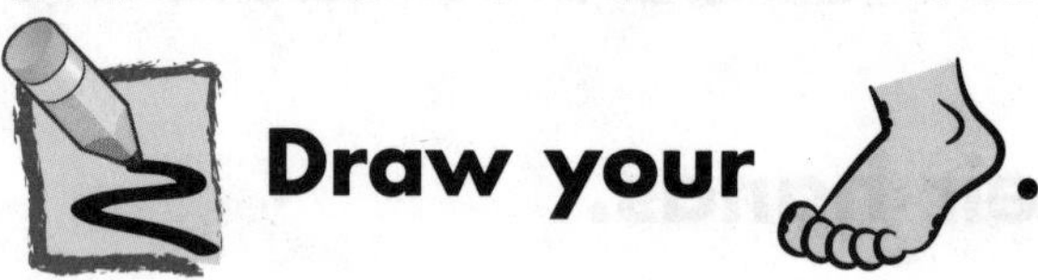

Draw your .

I have________ toes on each foot.

Parents: Have your child place his or her foot on the page and trace around it with an index finger. Then help him or her trace around it with a crayon, count the number of toes, and write the numeral in the sentence. Together, read the completed sentence.

Using My Feet

Circle the ones using their feet.

Parents: Discuss what each child is doing in the pictures on the page. Then have your child circle the pictures that show children using their feet.

What Goes Where?

Use cutouts from page 45.

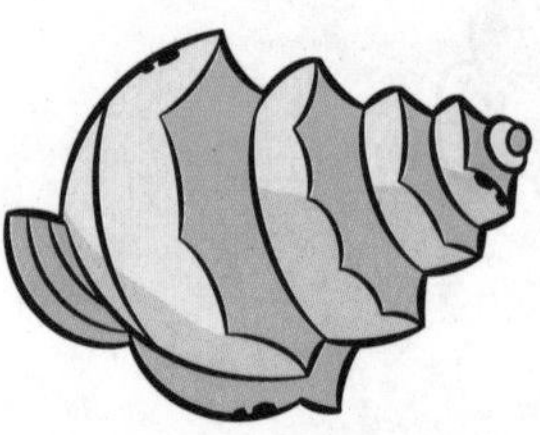
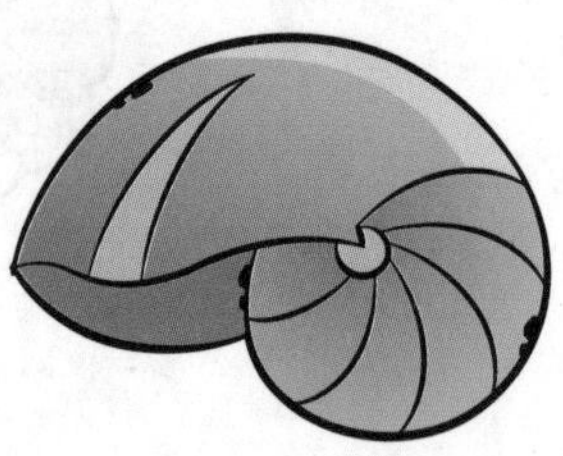

Parents: Have your child name the pictures in each row and tell how they are alike (all are chairs, dogs, etc.). Turn to page 45 and help your child find, cut out, and paste the pictures that belong in the empty boxes in each row.

Grouping

Use cutouts from page 45.

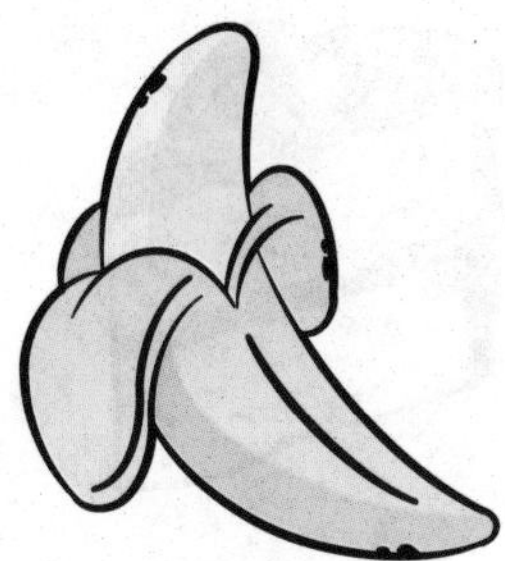

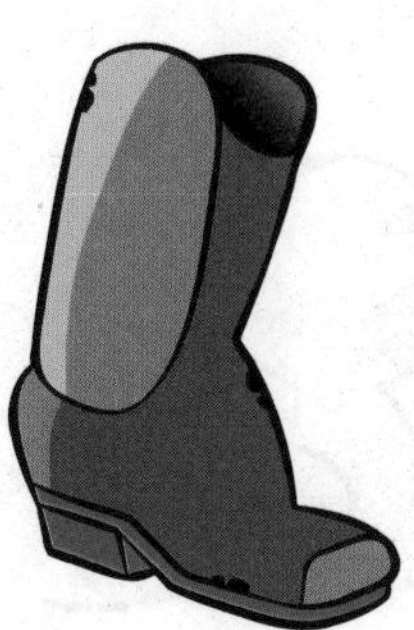

Parents: Have your child name the pictures in each row and tell how they are alike (all are fruits, footwear, etc.). Turn to page 45 and help your child find, cut out, and paste the pictures that belong in the empty boxes.

PREREADING

What's Alike?

Use cutouts from page 45.

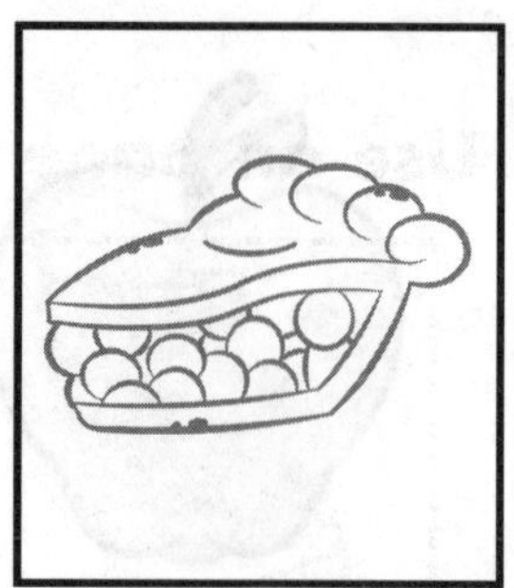

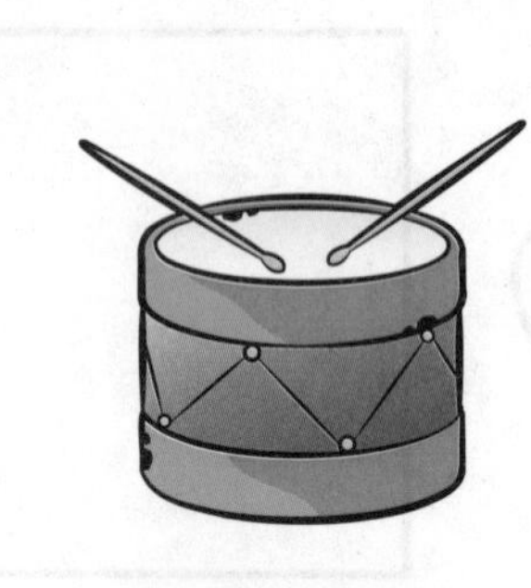

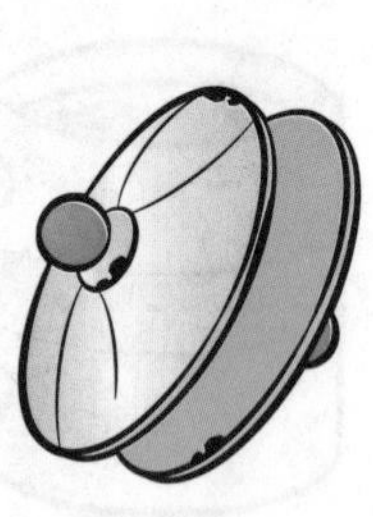

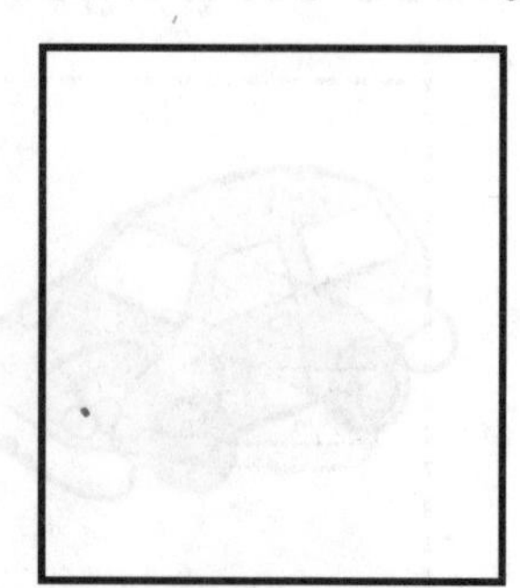

Parents: Have your child name the pictures in each row and tell how they are alike (all are desserts, musical instruments, etc.). Turn to page 45 and help your child find, cut out, and paste the pictures that belong in the empty boxes.

Cutouts

Use on page 42.

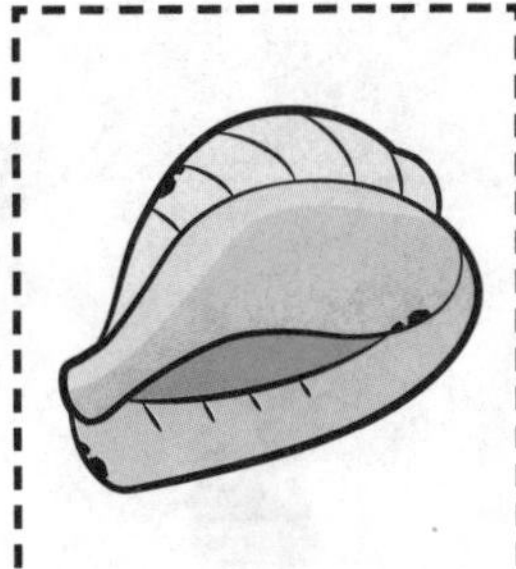

Use on page 43.

Use on page 44.

Fish or Bird?

Circle the one that's different in each group.

Parents: Ask your child to identify the animals in each group, and then find and circle the animal that is different.

PREREADING

Frogs and Turtles

Circle the one that's different in each group.

Parents: Ask your child to identify the animals in each group, and then find and circle the animal that is different. Discuss what makes it different.

Toys

 **Circle what belongs in the**  **.**

Parents: Ask your child to name all the pictures on the page. Then say, "Circle all the pictures of things that belong in the toy box."

PREREADING

Tools

Circle what belongs in the [tool box].

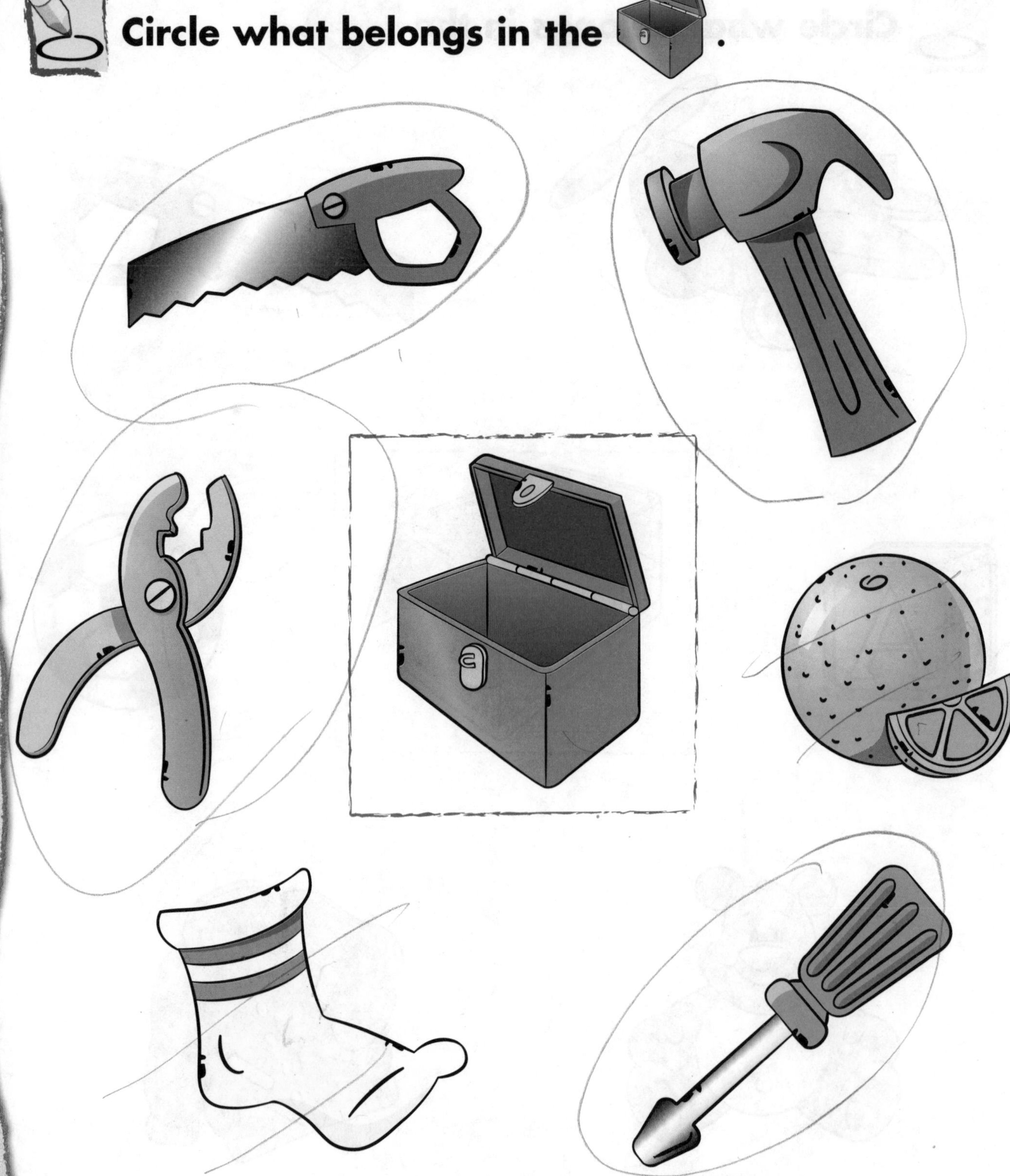

Parents: Ask your child to name all the pictures on the page. Then say, "Circle all the pictures of things that belong in the tool box."

Food

Circle what belongs in the  **.**

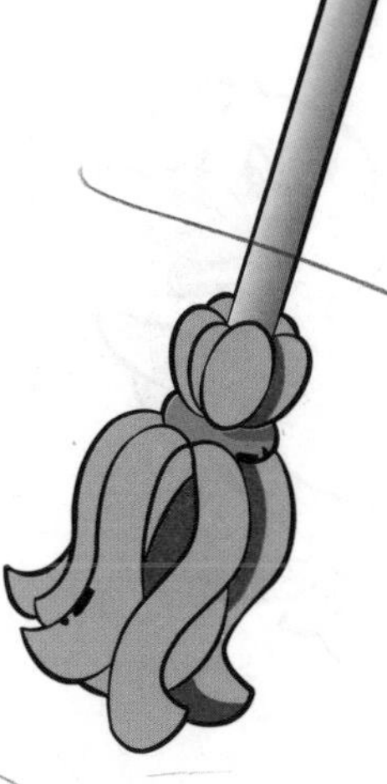

Parents: Ask your child to name all the pictures on the page. Then say, "Circle all the pictures of things that belong in the picnic basket."

Animals

Circle the ones that belong in the  **.**

Parents: Ask your child to name all the pictures on the page. Then say, "Circle all the animals that belong in the barn."

Orange

Peter, Peter, Pumpkin Eater

Peter, Peter, pumpkin eater,
Had a wife and couldn't keep her;
He put her in a pumpkin shell
And there he kept her very well.

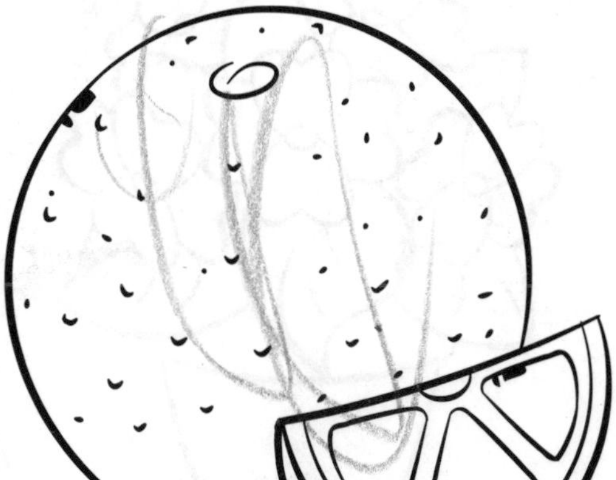

Parents: Read the rhyme. Have your child point to the jack-o-lantern and tell what it is and what color it is. Ask your child to identify each of the items pictured at the bottom of the page and color them orange.

Purple

Little Jack Horner

Little Jack Horner sat in a corner,
Eating a Christmas pie;
He put in his thumb, and pulled out a plum,
And said, "What a good boy am I!"

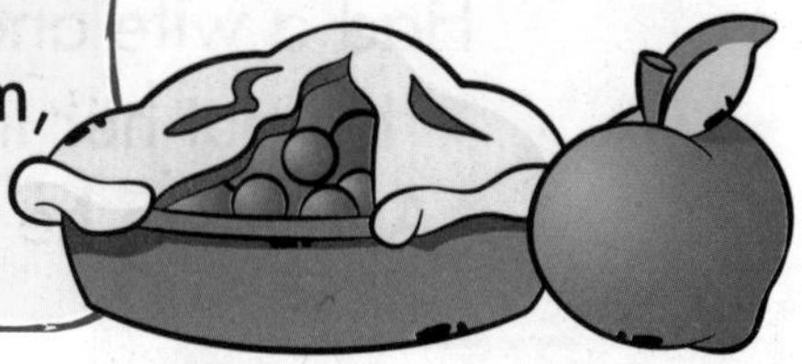

Parents: Read the rhyme. Have your child point to the plum and tell what it is and what color it is. Then discuss which parts of the pictures at the bottom of the page should be purple and have your child color them.

Brown

Old Woman in a Shoe

There was an old woman who lived in a shoe.
She had so many children she
didn't know what to do.
She gave them some broth without any bread,
And sang to them sweetly, and sent them to bed.

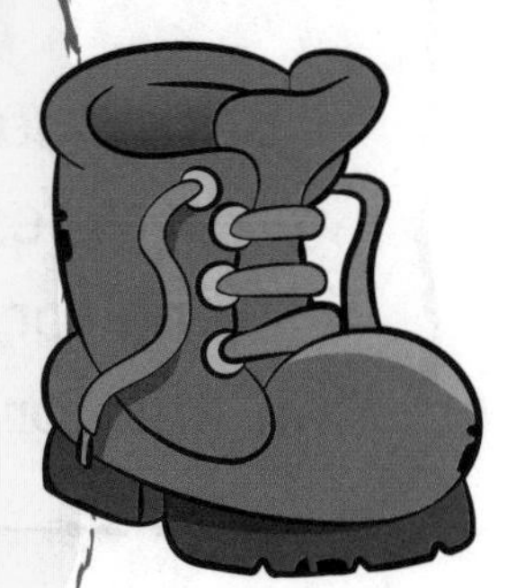

Parents: Read the rhyme. Have your child point to the shoe and tell what it is and what color it is. Then discuss which pictures at the bottom of the page could be brown and have your child color them.

Black

Baa, Baa, Black Sheep

Baa, Baa, black sheep, have you any wool?
Yes, sir, yes, sir, three bags full;
One for my master and one for my dame,
And one for the little boy who lives down the lane.

Parents: Read the rhyme. Have your child point to the black sheep and black wool and say the name of their color. Then ask your child to identify each of the items pictured at the bottom of the page and color them black.

Triangle

Simple Simon

Simple Simon met a pie man,
Going to the fair;
Says Simple Simon to the pie man,
"Let me taste your ware."

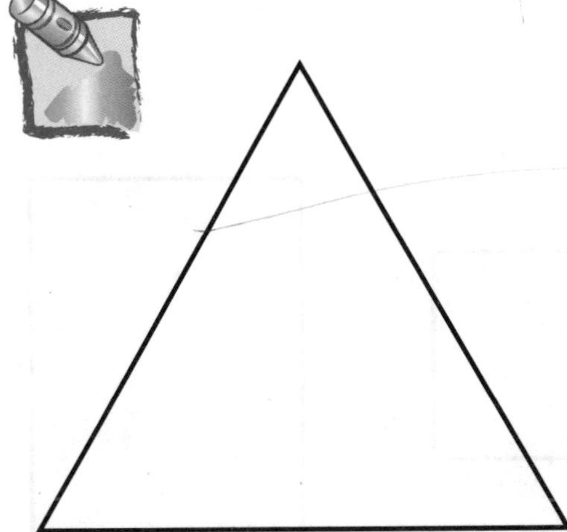

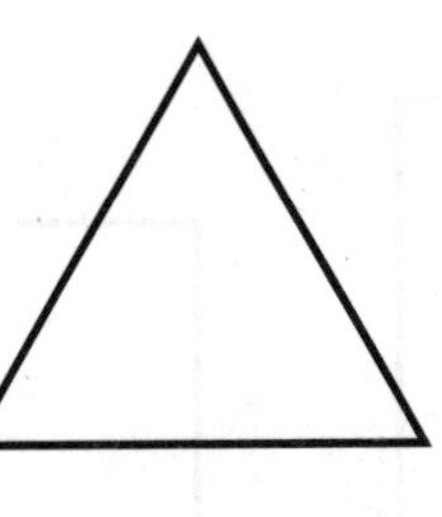

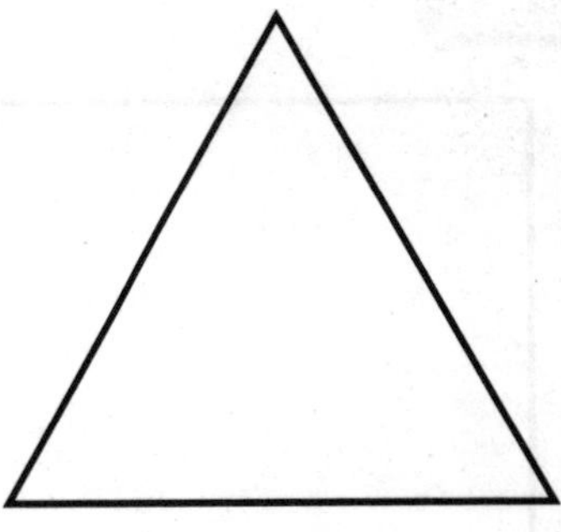

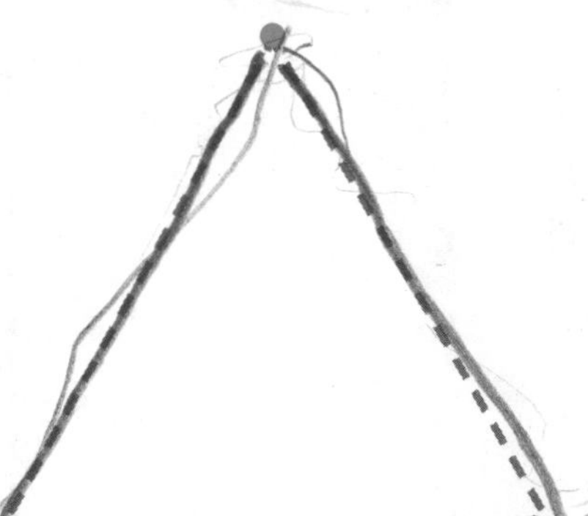

Parents: Read the rhyme. Then say, "This pie slice is a triangle. It has three sides." Have your child color the row of complete triangles. Then have him or her use a finger to trace the first triangle in the bottom row, and a pencil to draw the next two triangles in that row.

Rectangle

Mary at the Cottage Door

One, two, three, four,
Mary at the cottage door;
Five, six, seven, eight,
Eating cherries off a plate.

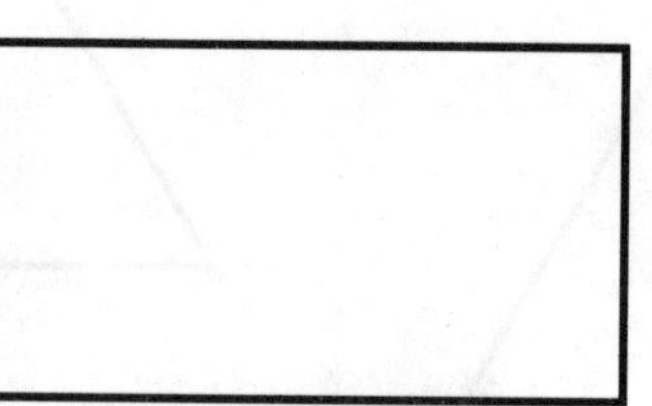

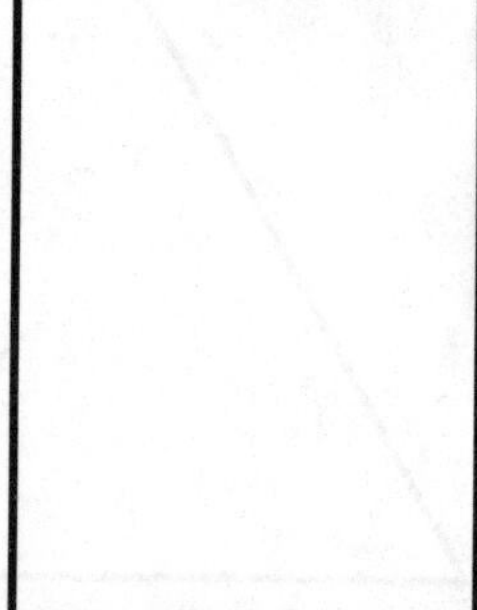

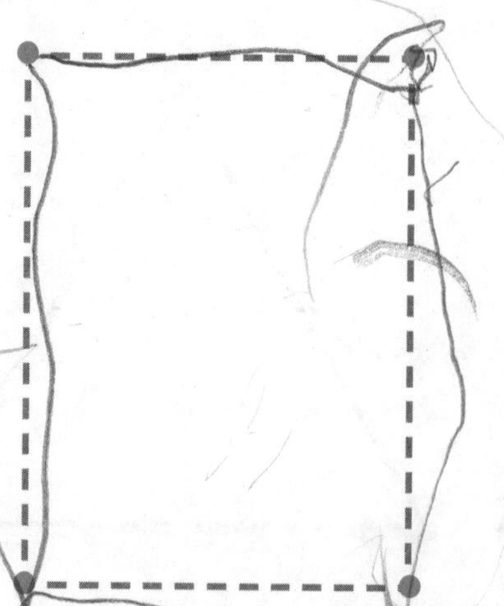

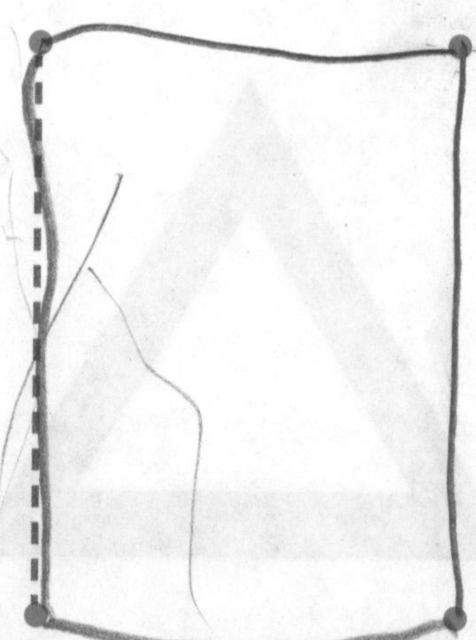

Parents: **Read the rhyme. Then say, "This door is a rectangle. It has four sides—but two sides are long and two are short." Have your child color the row of complete rectangles, use a finger to trace the first rectangle in the bottom row, and a pencil to draw the next two.**

Find the Rectangles!

Color all the ▭.

Parents: Discuss the scene with your child. Then ask him or her to point out all of the rectangles and color them.

MATH

Triangle Fun

Color all the △.

Parents: **Discuss the scene with your child. Then ask him or her to point out all the triangles and color them.**

Long and Short

Oats and Beans and Barley
Oats and beans and barley grow,
Oats and beans and barley grow.
Do you or I or anyone know,
How oats and beans and barley grow?

Color the long ones.

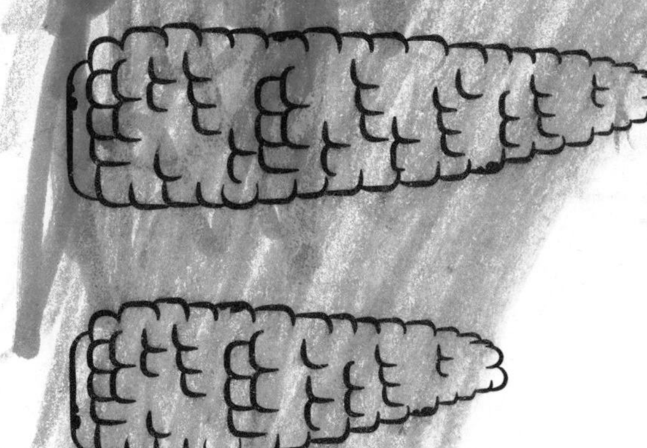

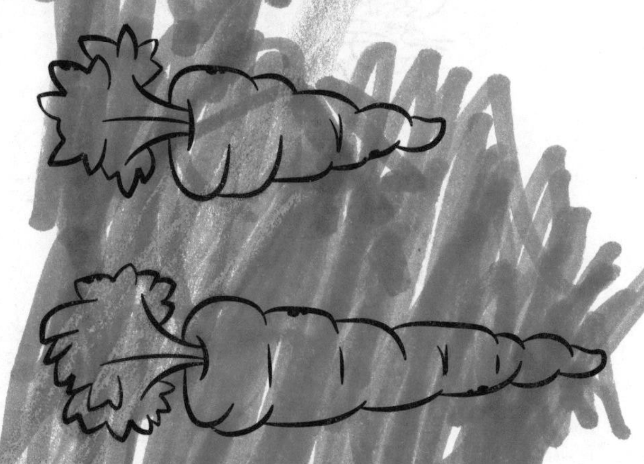

Parents: Read the rhyme. Tell your child that the picture at the top of the page shows two stalks of wheat. Ask him or her to point to the long wheat and then to the short wheat. Then have your child color the long vegetable in each box.

Big and Little

Pussycat, Pussycat

Pussycat, pussycat, where have you been?
I've been to London to visit the Queen.
Pussycat, Pussycat, what did you there?
I frightened a little mouse under her chair.

Color what's big in each row.

Parents: Read the rhyme. Ask your child to point to the big cat and then to the little cat. Then have him or her color the big object in each row.

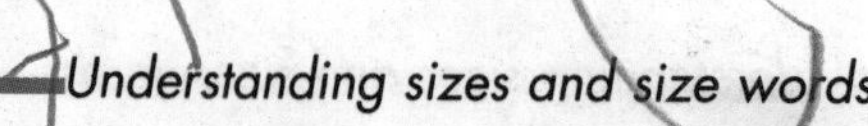

Tall and Short

Mary, Mary

Mary, Mary quite contrary
How does your garden grow?
With silver bells and cockle shells,
And pretty maids all in a row.

Color the short ones.

Parents: Read the rhyme. Ask your child to point to the tall girl and then to the short girl. Then have him or her color the short object in each box.

Birdy's Clouds

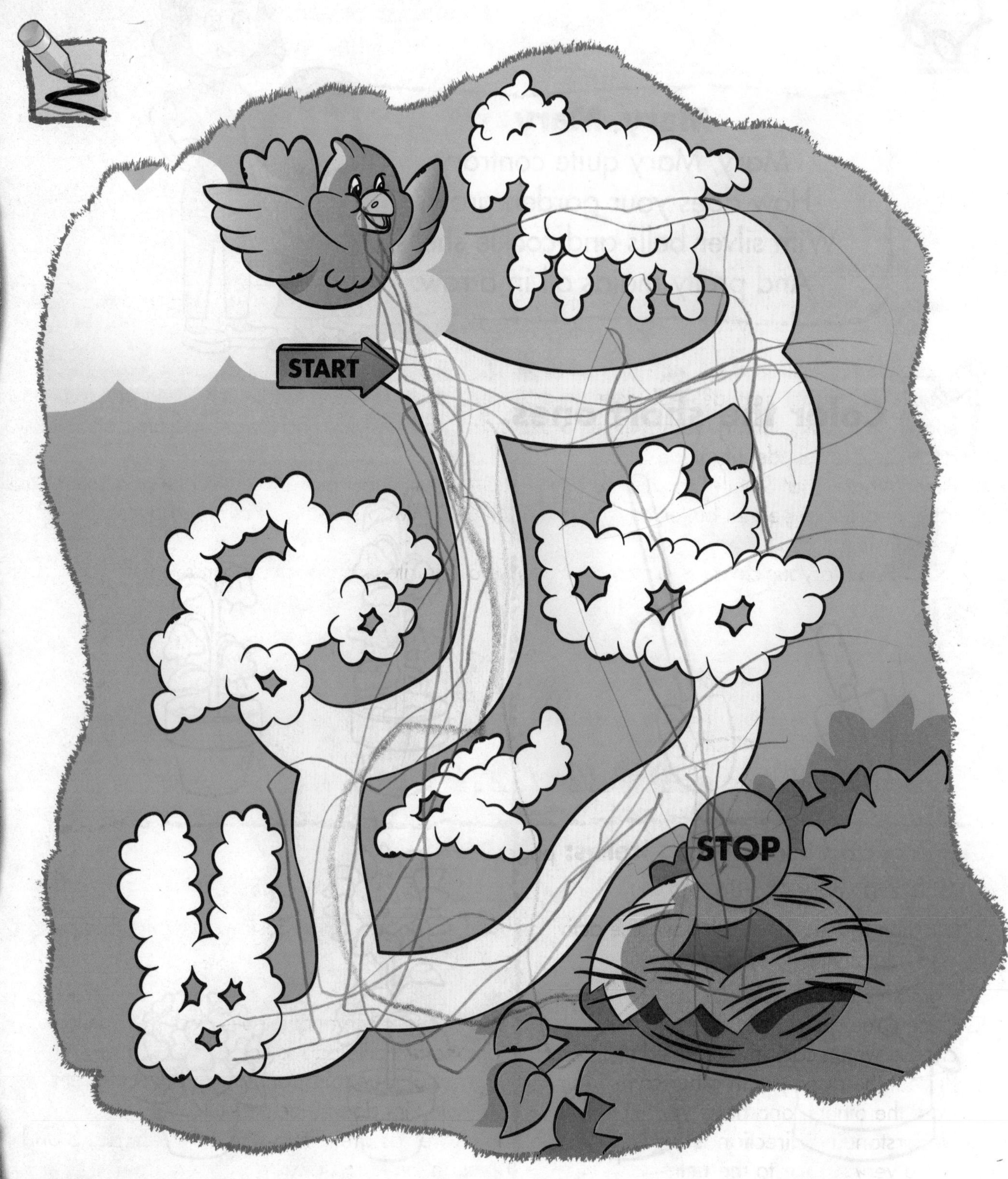

Parents: Ask your child to use his or her index finger to follow the path between the bird and the nest. Then have him or her use a pencil or crayon to draw the path the bird should take.

Month 3 Checklist

Hands-on activities to help prepare your child for school!

SELF-CONCEPT

The Senses: pages 67-72

All learning relies on the senses. That's why most preschools spend part of the year helping children learn all about the five senses. Here are some ways to have fun:

- ❑ Complete the worksheets.
- ❑ Play "What's That Sound?" Ask your child to close his or her eyes and listen. Then make a sound—such as running water, hitting a piano key, opening/closing the refrigerator, etc.—and ask your child to identify it.
- ❑ Play "What's That Smell?" In each of three or four small cups, place a few drops of a scent: such as vanilla, orange, peanut butter, and so on. Ask your child to smell each cup and guess the scent inside.
- ❑ Point to your child's eye and say, "Name a favorite thing that you can see with your eyes."

PREREADING AND PREWRITING

Sorting and Classifying Items: pages 73-78

Direction: pages 85-86

In addition to the activities below, use activities listed on pages 3 and 33 to help your child master sorting, classifying, and direction:

- ❑ Complete the worksheets.
- ❑ Place three quarters in one pile and a penny and a quarter in another pile. Ask your child to choose which coin in the mixed pile belongs with the first pile and to say why. Repeat the activity with other coins. Also, make a set of four coins, one of which is different from the others, and have your child identify the coin that doesn't belong.
- ❑ Understanding direction is a critical prereading as well as prewriting skill. For example, *b* and *d* are very similar to the untrained eye—even though the hump faces a different direction on each letter. Also, we move from left to right across a printed page—something that children who are read to usually pick up quickly. You can help your child learn about direction with a simple activity: place three toy figures in a row but have one face a different direction from the others. Ask your child to tell which one is facing a different direction. Repeat the activity as long as there's interest.

MATH

Comparing Sizes: pages 79-84
Counting from 1 to 5: pages 87-96

In the worksheets for this month, children continue working on comparing items for size and begin working on numbers—with the focus on learning that each numeral represents a quantity.

- ❑ Complete the worksheets.
- ❑ Give your child practice choosing the longest, shortest, tallest, biggest, and littlest of three items in everyday situations. For example, when cooking asparagus, you might remove three stems and ask, "Which one is the longest? Shortest?"
- ❑ When teaching numbers and helping your child understand the quantities they represent, it's best to use "hands-on" activities. For example, when teaching one—show your child two sets of items (jelly beans, dried beans, toy cars, etc.), one with one member and the other with more than one member. Have your child choose the set with one. As the child counts each set, make sure he or she says the number names as each item is counted (one car, two cars, etc.). This will help him or her see that there is one item for each number.
- ❑ Note: Learning to print numbers can be very difficult for small children until they've developed adequate fine motor skills. Don't despair. Most children eventually learn to print just fine. Give lots of practice with mazes and tracing over prewritten lines to help your child develop this important skill.

Five Senses

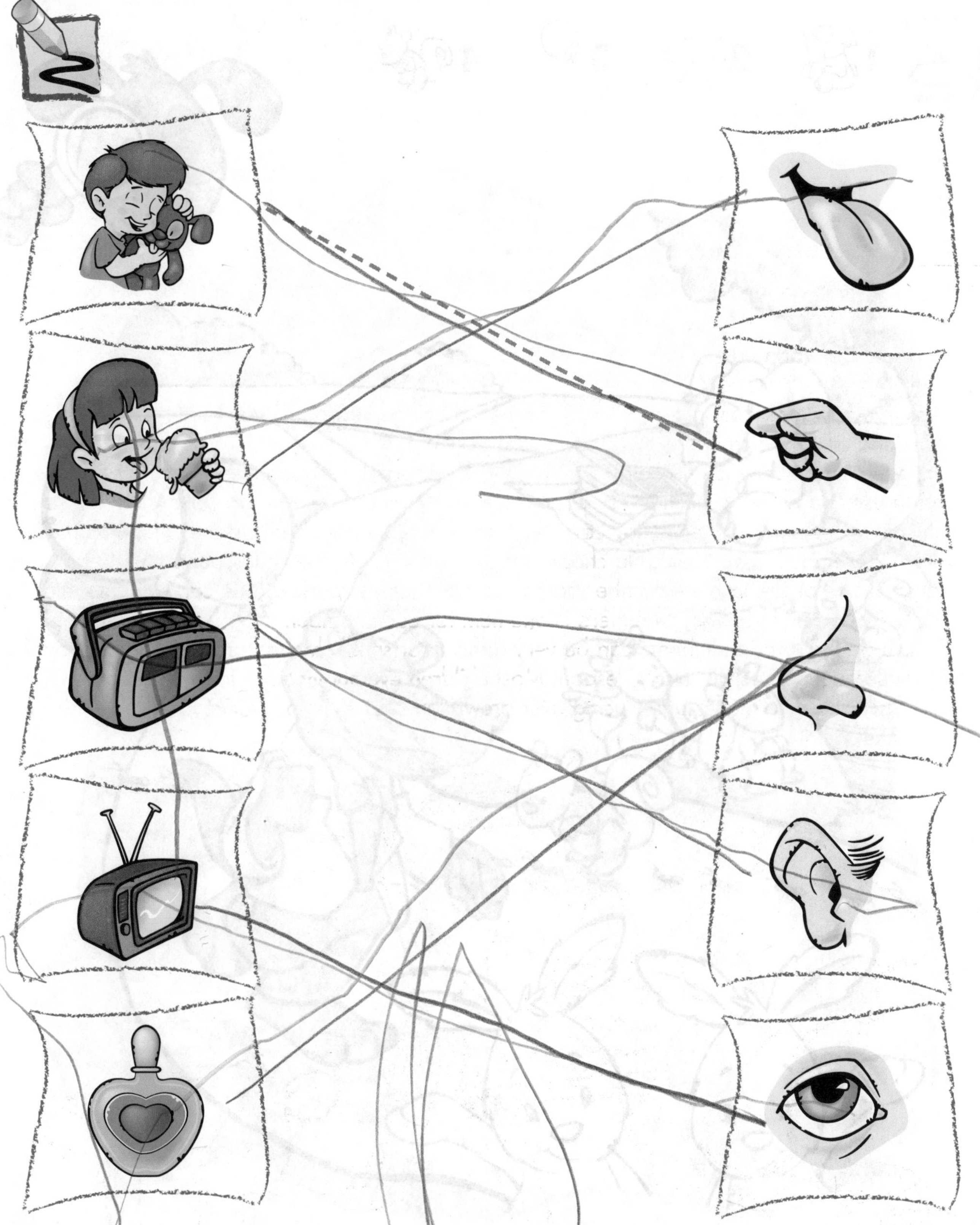

Parents: Explain that people have five senses that they use daily—touch, taste, smell, hearing, and sight. Ask your child to draw a line from each picture on the left to the body part it goes with on the right.

SELF-CONCEPT

I Can See

1 2 3 4

Parents: Ask your child to find and circle four squirrels, two rabbits, one elephant, and three balloons.

Understanding the senses; recognizing differences (visual discrimination)

I Can Hear

Circle what you can hear.

Parents: **Ask your child to name the pictures below the elephant and circle the things that can be heard.**

SELF-CONCEPT

I Can Smell

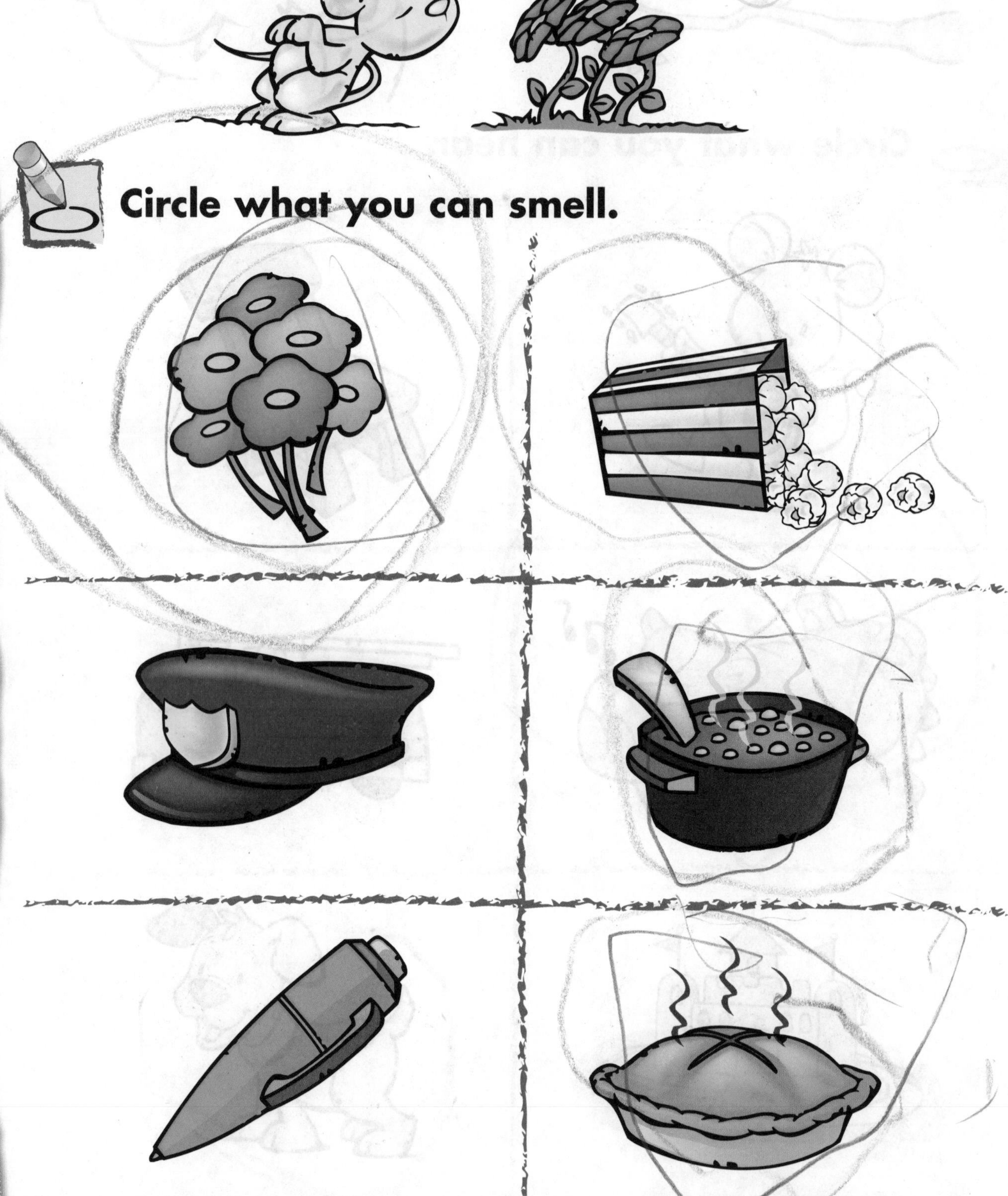

Circle what you can smell.

Parents: Ask your child to name the pictures below the mouse and circle the things that can be smelled.

I Can Touch

Circle what you can touch.

Parents: **Ask your child to name the pictures below the boy and circle the things that can be touched.**

SELF-CONCEPT

I Can Taste

Circle what you can taste.

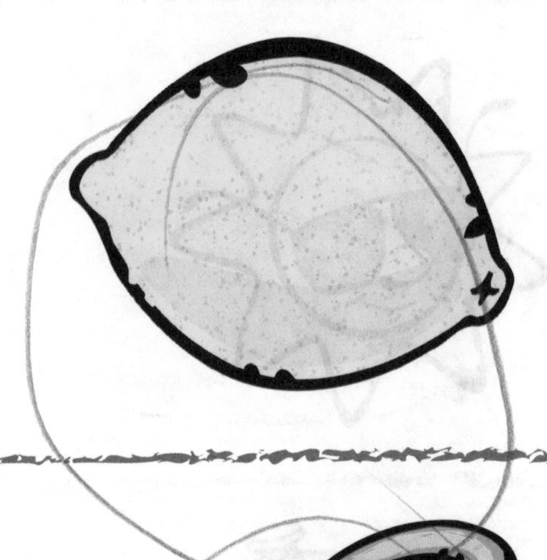

Parents: **Ask your child to name the pictures below the frog and circle the things that people enjoy tasting.**

We Go Together

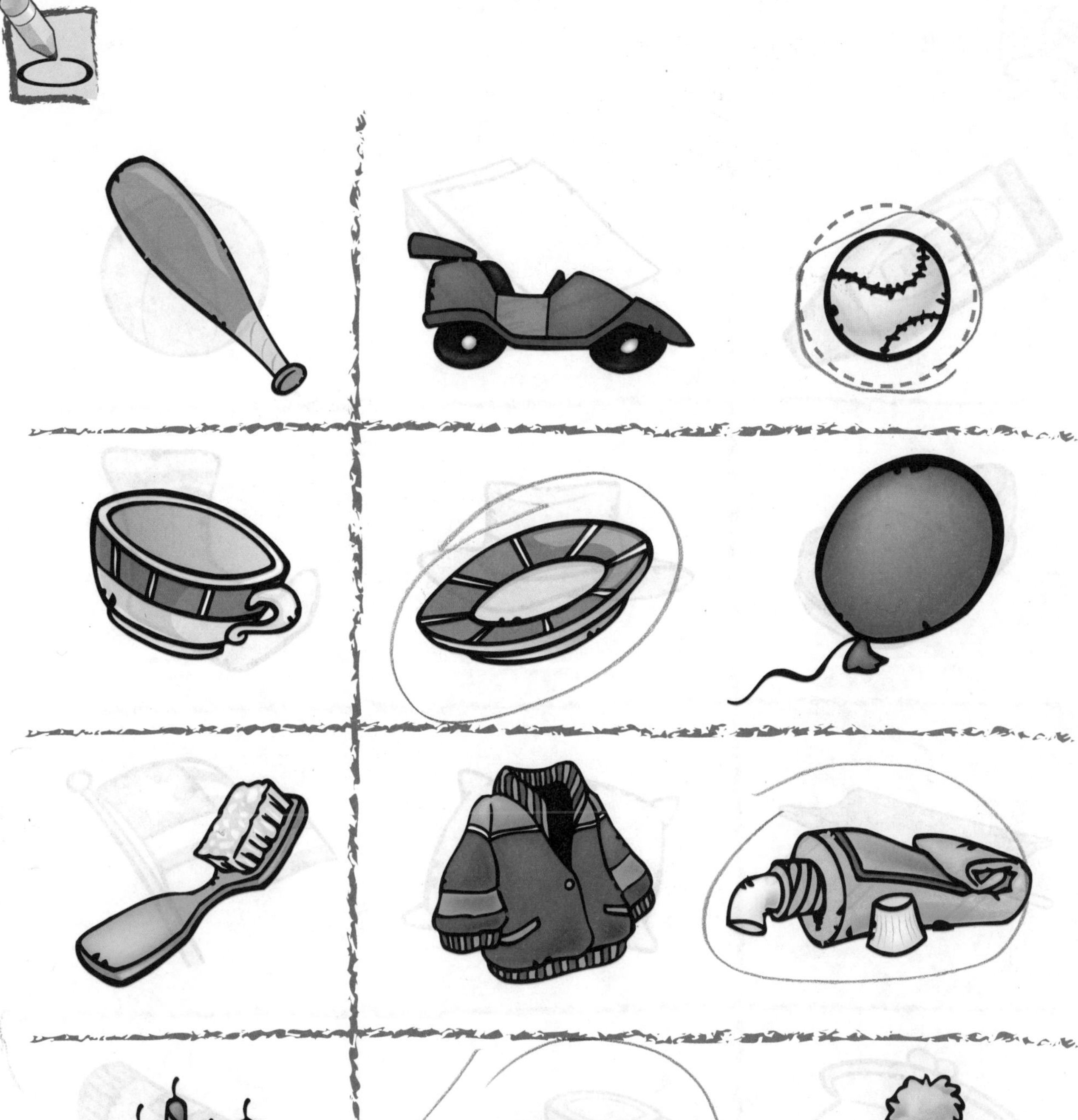

Parents: **Ask your child to name the first picture in each row, and then circle the other picture in that row that goes with it. Encourage your child to explain how the two items go together.**

PREREADING

Companions

Parents: **Ask your child to name the first picture in each row and then circle another picture in the row that goes with it. Encourage your child to explain how the two items go together.**

What Doesn't Belong at the Zoo

Circle what's not at the zoo.

    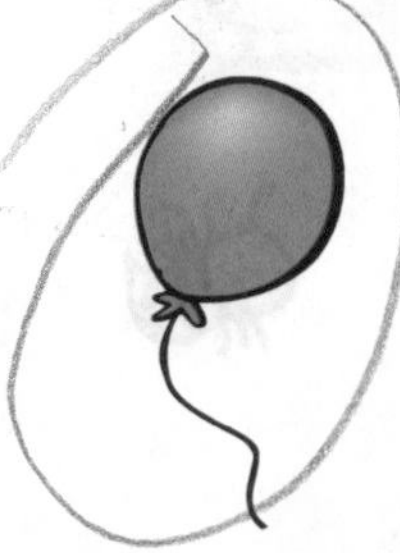

Parents: (Top) Ask your child to tell you about the zoo picture. (Bottom) Then point to the items below the picture and say, "Circle the things that are not at the zoo."

What Doesn't Belong at the Park?

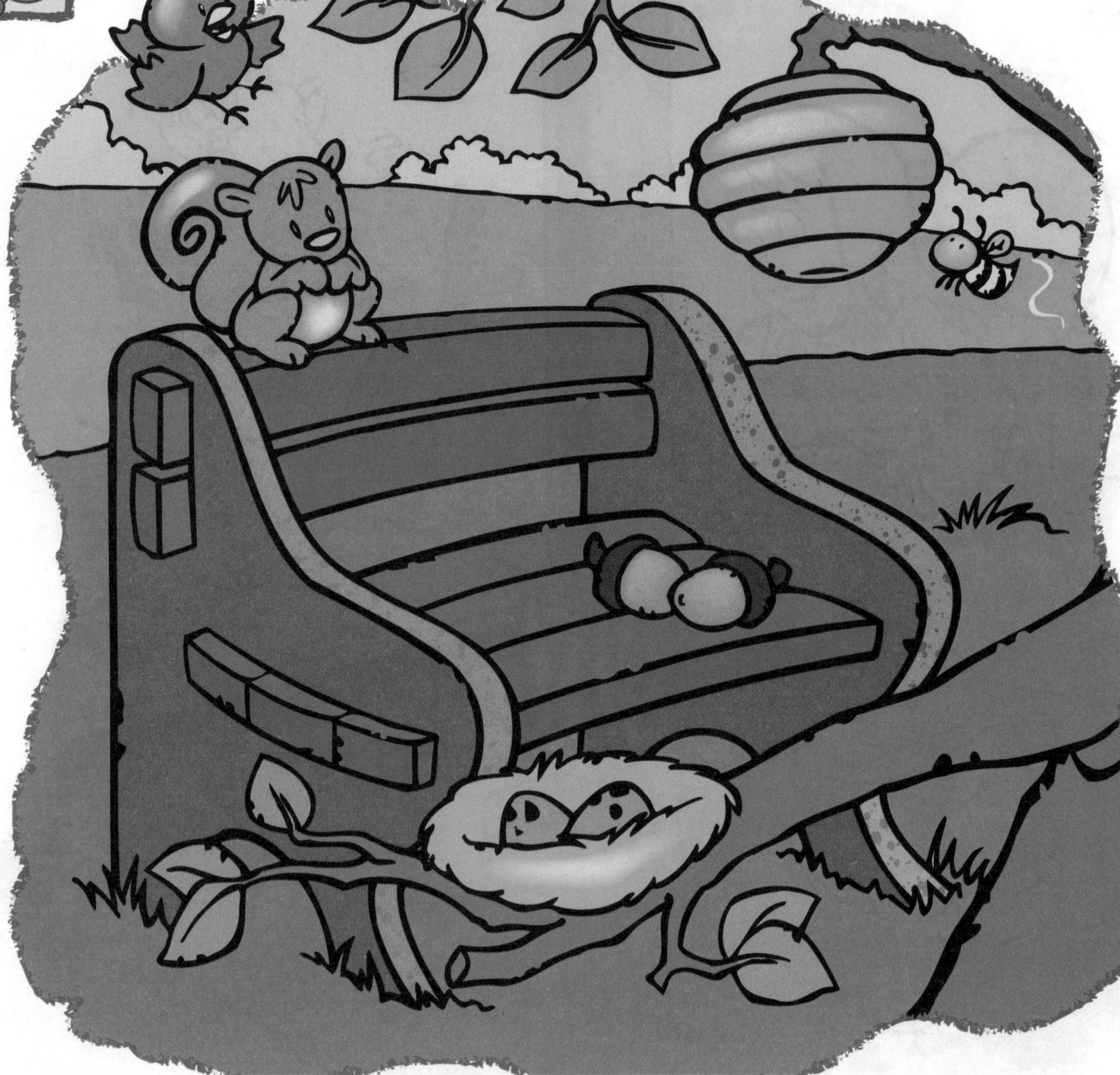

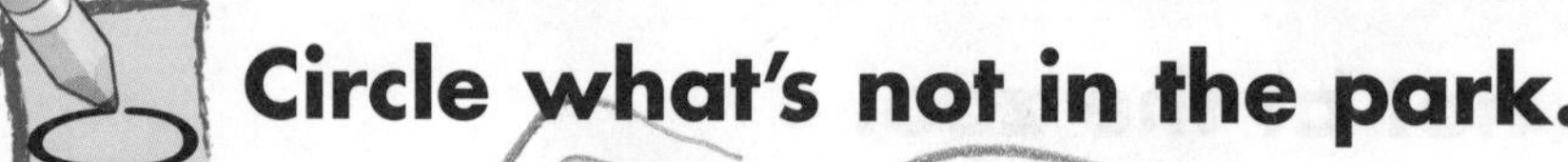

Circle what's not in the park.

Parents: (Top) Ask your child to tell you about the park picture. (Bottom) Then point to the items below the picture and say, "Circle the things that are not in the park."

Does It Belong?

Circle what doesn't belong.

Parents: Ask your child to name the items in each row and circle the picture that does not belong. Encourage your child to say why it doesn't belong.

What Doesn't Belong?

Circle what doesn't belong.

Parents: **Ask your child to name the items in each row and circle the picture that does not belong. Encourage your child to say why it doesn't belong.**

Longest and Shortest

Cackle, Cackle

Cackle, cackle, Mother Goose,
Have you any feathers loose?
Truly have I, pretty fellow,
Half enough to fill a pillow.

Color the longest.

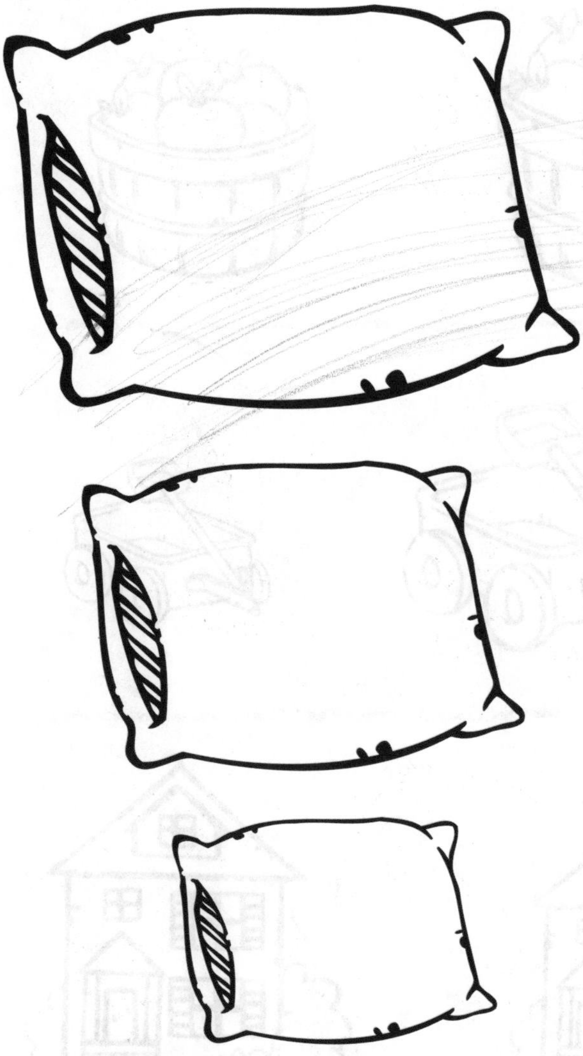

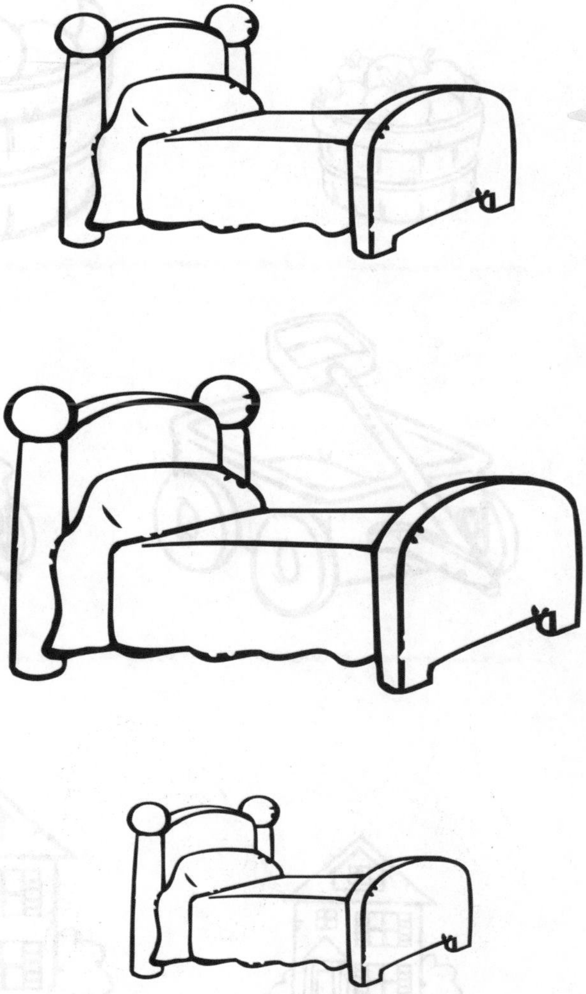

Parents: Read the rhyme. Ask your child to point to the longest feather and then to the shortest feather. Then have your child color the longest object in each column.

MATH

Biggest and Littlest

To Market, To Market
To market, to market,
To buy a fat pig;
Home again, home again,
Jiggety-jig.

Color the biggest.

Circle the littlest.

Parents: **Read the rhyme. Ask your child to point to the biggest pig and then to the littlest pig. Then have your child color the biggest object in each row and circle the littlest object.**

Tallest and Shortest

I'm a Little Teapot
I'm a little teapot, short and stout.
Here is my handle, here is my spout.
When I get all steamed up, then I shout:
"Tip me over and pour me out!"

Color the tallest.

Circle the shortest.

Parents: Read the rhyme. Ask your child to point to the tallest teapot and then to the shortest teapot. Then have your child color the tallest object in each row and circle the shortest object.

Size Review

Pat-a-Cake

Pat-a-cake, pat-a-cake, baker's man!
Bake me a cake as fast as you can;
Roll it and pat it and mark it with a B,
And put it in the oven for baby and me.

short?

big?

long?

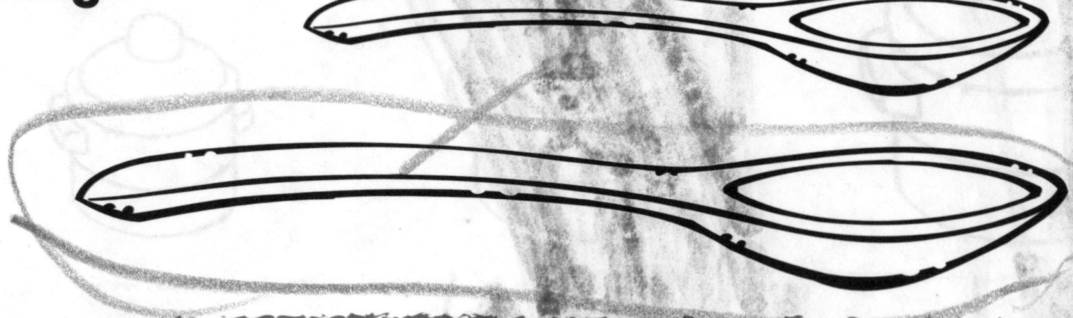

biggest?

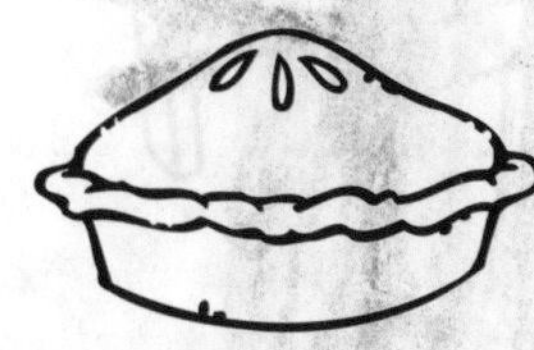

Parents: Read the rhyme and help your child follow these directions: Color the short pitcher; color the big cupcake; color the long spoon; color the biggest pie.

Same Size Concentration

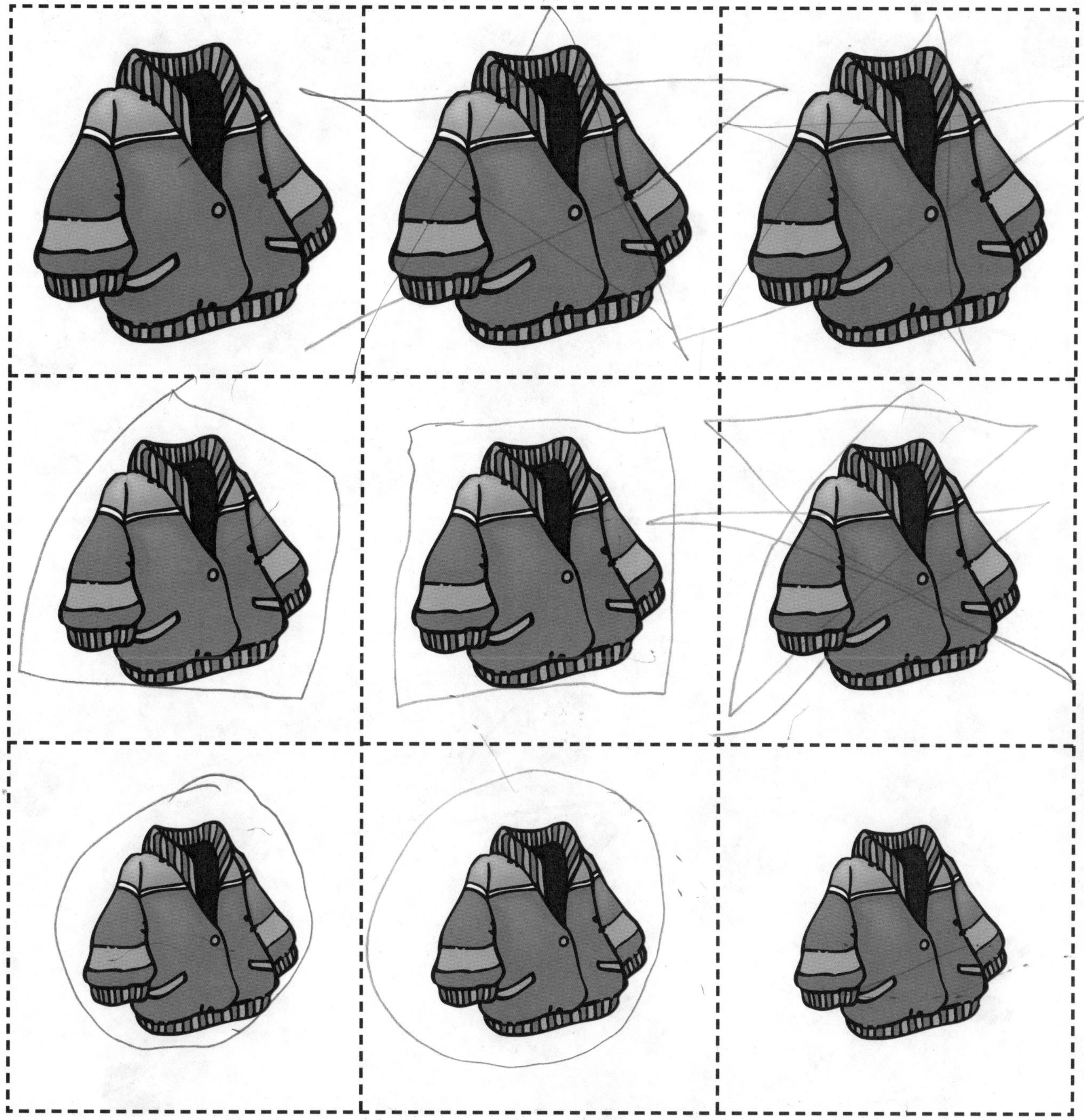

Parents: **(1) Cut out the playing cards. (2) Place all cards faceup, point to one, and ask your child to say whether it shows the biggest, smallest, or middle-size jacket. Have your child find the other two jackets that match in size. (3) Then lay all cards facedown. In turn, each player flips over two cards. If the cards show the jacket in different sizes, the player returns the cards to their original places, facedown. If the two cards show the jacket in the same size, the player keeps the cards and takes a second turn. Play ends when there are no more matches.**

Same Amount

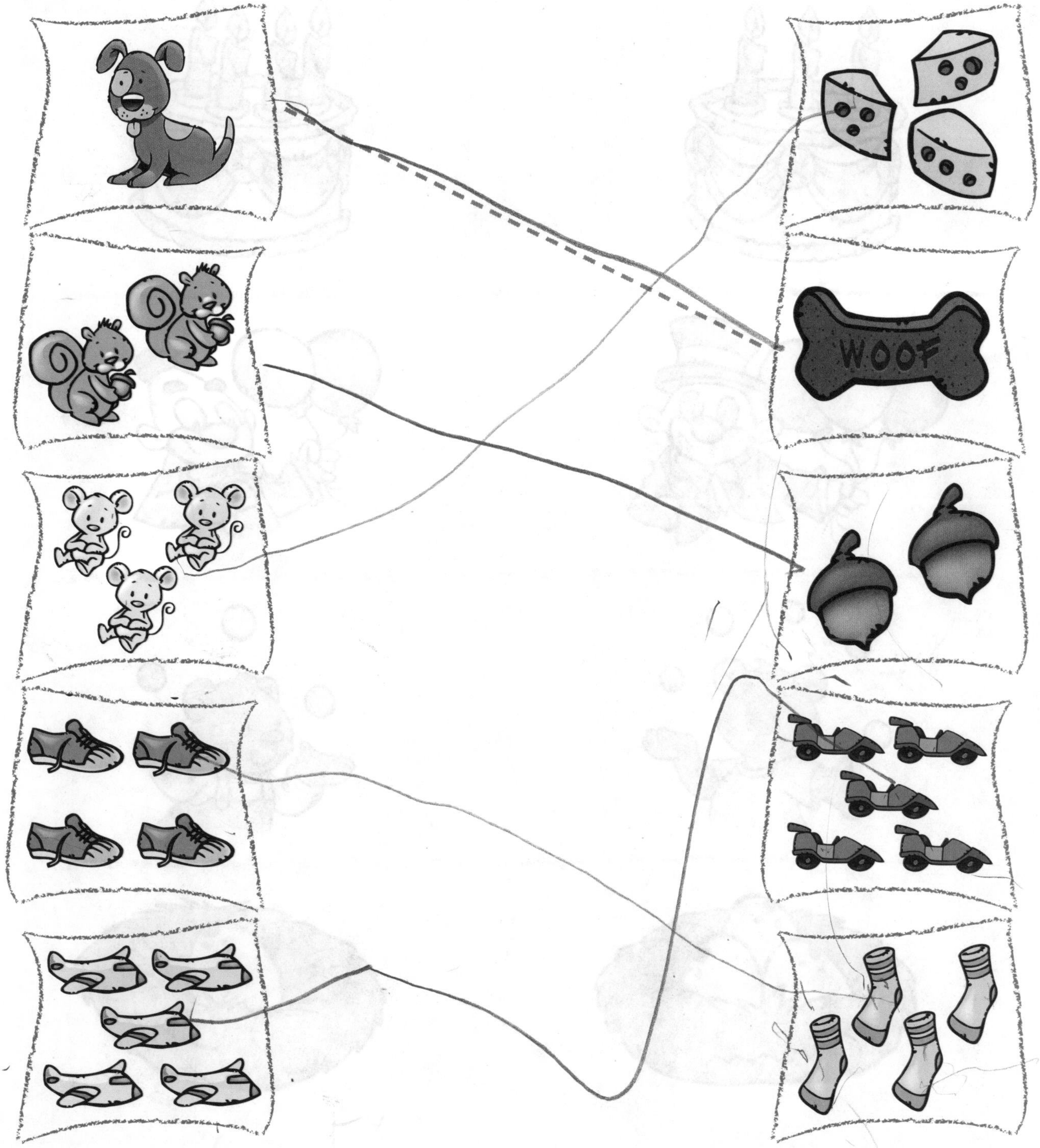

Parents: Help your child count the items in the first box at the left and then trace the line between the dog and the bone. Ask, "Why do the dog and bone go together?" (Dogs gnaw bones; there is one bone and one dog). Continue with the rest of the page.

MATH

More

Circle the one with more.

Parents: **Help your child count the number of candles on each cake. Have your child circle the picture that has more candles. Repeat these steps on the other rows, discussing the number of balloons, balls, and eggs.**

Fewer

Circle the group with fewer.

Parents: Have your child identify the objects pictured in each row. Then help your child count the number of objects in each group and circle the group that has fewer.

One

1 **one**

Parents: (Top) Ask your child to say "one" as he or she points to the numeral and number word, and then counts the one zebra. (Middle) Ask your child to count and color one hippo. (Bottom) Have your child trace the numerals.

Two

Parents: (Top) Ask your child to say "two" as he or she points to the numeral and number word, and then counts the two umbrellas. (Middle) Ask your child to count and color two clowns. (Bottom) Have your child trace the numerals.

M A T H

Three

3 three

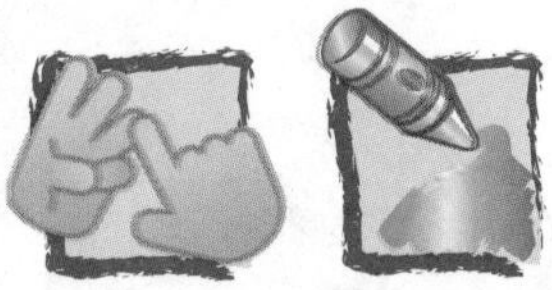

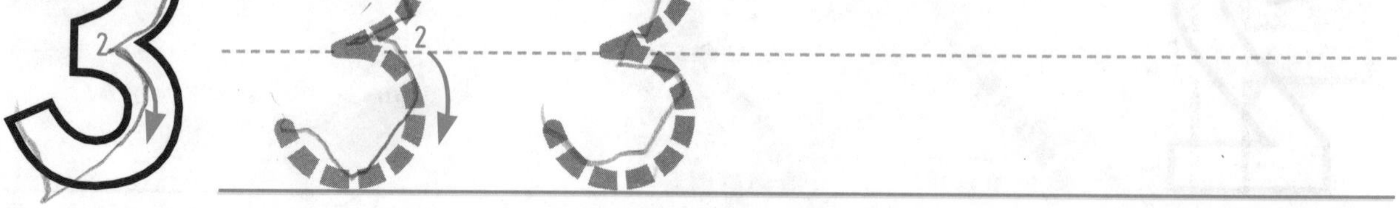

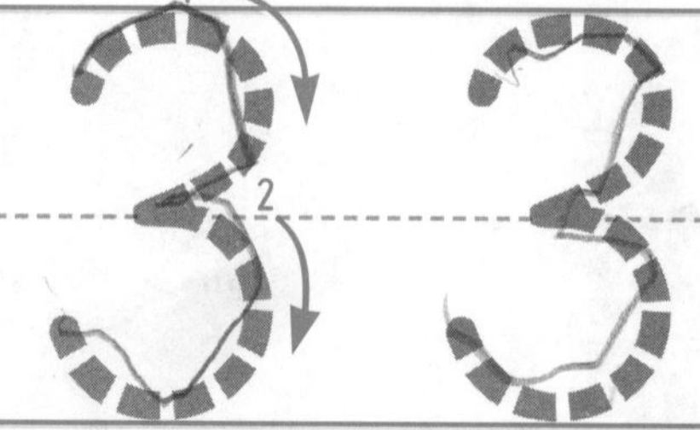

Parents: (Top) Ask your child to say "three" as he or she points to the numeral and number word, and then counts the three hand puppets. (Middle) Ask your child to count and color three toys. (Bottom) Have your child trace the numerals.

Four

Parents: (Top) Point out the numeral and the number word. Ask your child to say "four" as he or she points to the numeral and number word, and then counts the four belts. (Middle) Ask your child to count and color four sweaters. (Bottom) Have your child trace the numerals.

Five

5 five

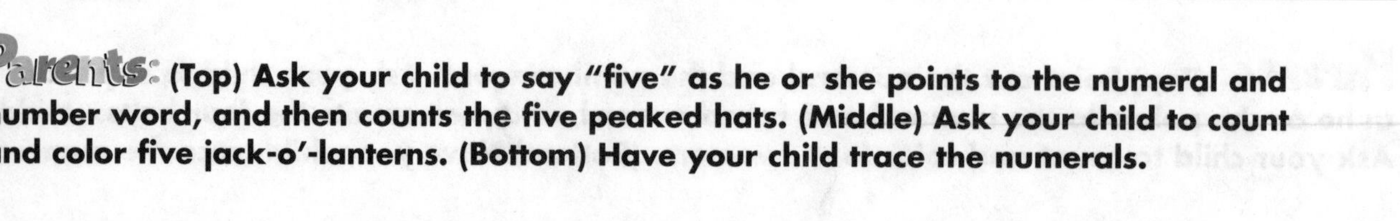

1 3 2

3 1 2

Parents: (Top) Ask your child to say "five" as he or she points to the numeral and number word, and then counts the five peaked hats. (Middle) Ask your child to count and color five jack-o'-lanterns. (Bottom) Have your child trace the numerals.

Color by Number

Parents: Have your child point to and read the numerals on the crayons and then identify the color of each crayon. Then ask your child to color the paint cans using the crayon code.

Number Review

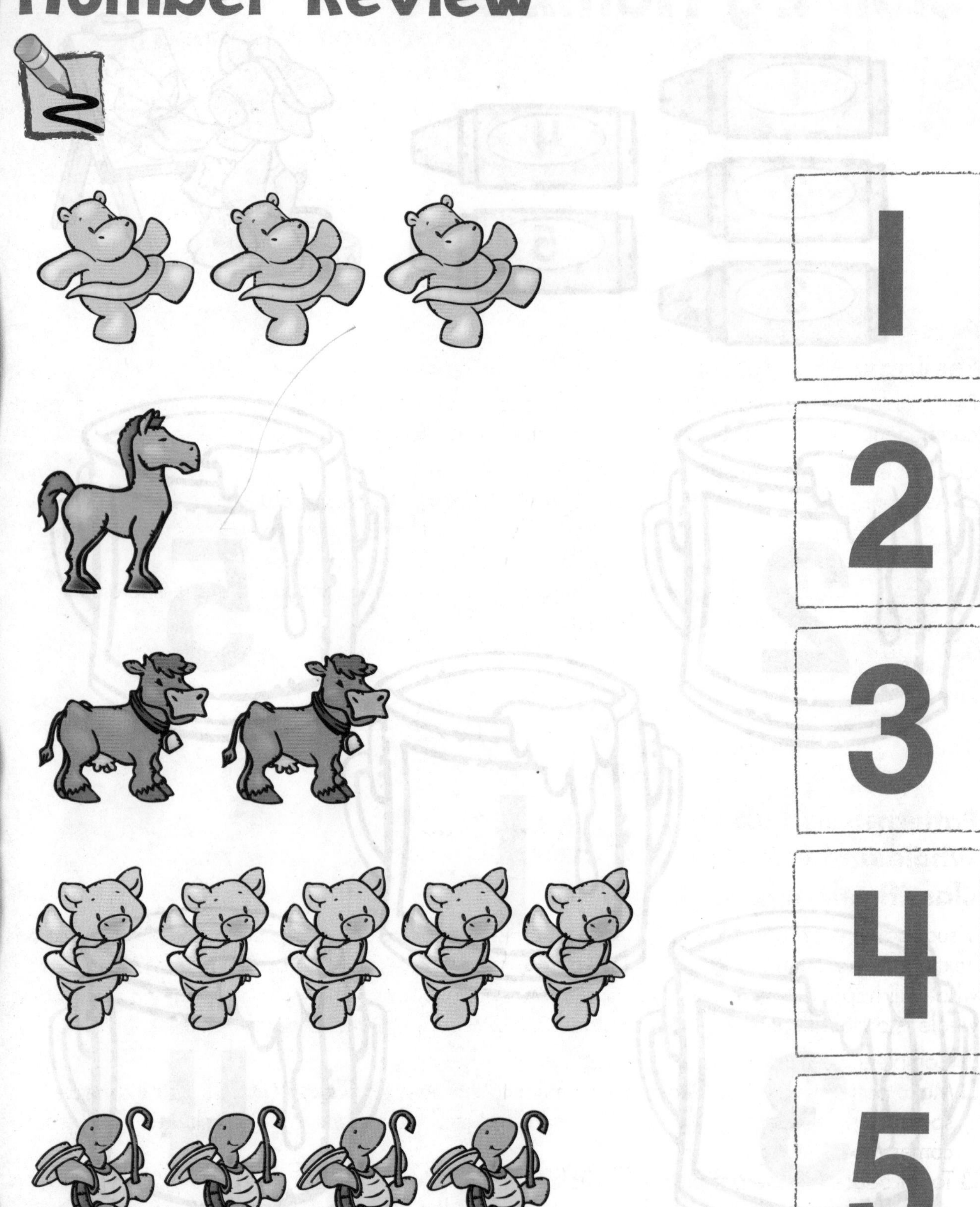

Parents: Have your child count the objects in each set at the left and draw a line to the correct number.

Month 4 Checklist

Hands-on activities to help prepare your child for school!

SELF-CONCEPT

Personal Interests: pages 99-101
Feelings: pages 102-103

Being able to discuss favorite activities and describe how we feel in various situations are important components of self-awareness that every preschooler needs.

- ❑ Complete the worksheets.
- ❑ Ask your child to draw pictures of his or her favorite indoor and outdoor activities.
- ❑ Say a list of three favorite things (e.g., amusement park, zoo, going for ice cream) and ask, "Which is your most favorite? Second most favorite?"
- ❑ Have your child use dolls to act out experiences that have made him or her happy or sad.

PREREADING AND PREWRITING

Patterns: pages 104-110
Whole and Part: pages 111-113
Classification: pages 123-124

Visual patterns are introduced in this month. Being able to look at a pattern and tell what comes next is an important thinking skill. In reading, for example, children are often asked to predict what will happen next in a story based upon what has happened thus far. Identifying parts of a whole is a classification skill, which entails looking carefully (visual discrimination).

- ❑ Complete the worksheets.
- ❑ Make patterns with household items similar to the ones on pages 104-106. For example: spoon, fork, spoon, ______ ; or white cup, red cup, white cup, ______. Ask your child what comes next.
- ❑ To introduce the idea of part and whole in a playful way, find two full-page magazine ads and cut the bottom third off each. Have your child match each bottom part with the correct top part.

LANGUAGE

First, Next, and Last: pages 114-116

The events in stories happen in a specific sequence. Being able to remember the sequence is a part of reading comprehension. The activities below will help your child work on speaking skills as well as sequencing:

❑ Complete the worksheets.

❑ Have your child tell about his or her morning or afternoon activities using the words *first, next,* and *last*. If possible, record the account and play it back for your child.

MATH

Shapes: pages 117-122

The worksheets this month review the four basic shapes: circle, square, triangle, and rectangle. Use any of the activities from Months 1 and 2 (pages 3 and 35) or the activities below as you revisit shapes with your child:

❑ Complete the worksheets.

❑ Cut out circles, squares, triangles, and rectangles in different sizes from construction paper. Help your child arrange them to form pictures similar to the caterpillar or train (pages 117-118). Make favorite pictures permanent by pasting the shapes on a backing sheet.

READING

Book Skills: pages 125-128

Many things important about reading are picked up as we first hear our favorite books read—how to hold the book, turn the pages, and read (or look at the pages) from front to back. Let your child practice these maneuvers with the pull-out storybook for this month and with other books you read aloud:

❑ Pull out and read aloud the storybook, *Count the Ducks*, pages 125-128.

❑ When reading a book to your child, have him or her find its front, back, title page, and several specific page numbers.

❑ As you read to your child, regularly draw his or her attention to the title on the first page and the page number at the bottom of each subsequent page.

Seasons

Parents: Identify each season. Talk about what the children are doing in each scene. Ask your child which season is his or her favorite. Then let him or her finish coloring the pictures.

Indoor Fun

Circle 3 things you like to do.

Parents: Discuss what each of the animals is doing. Ask your child to circle the three activities he or she likes best. Encourage your child to tell why he or she chose those activities.

Outdoor Fun

Circle 3 things you like to do.

Parents: Discuss what each of the animals is doing. Ask your child to circle the three activities he or she likes best. Encourage your child to tell why he or she chose those activities.

How I Would Feel

Parents: **Have your child circle the face that shows how he or she would feel (happy or sad) in each situation, and then color the pictures.**

Happy or Sad?

Parents: Have your child circle the face that shows how he or she would feel (happy or sad) in each situation, and then color the pictures.

SELF-CONCEPT

PREREADING

Animal Parade

Use cutouts from page 107.

 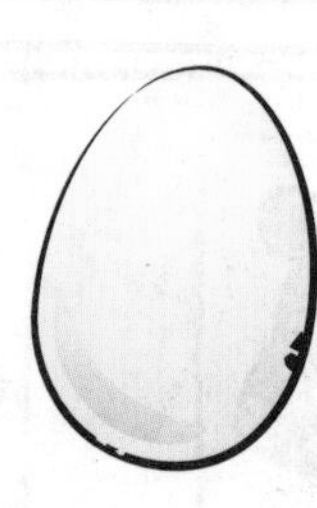  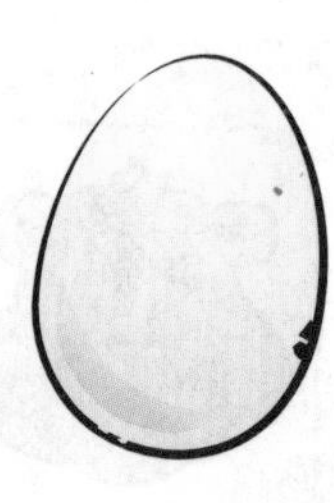 

Parents: **Have your child name the animals pictured in the first row and discuss the pattern that the pictures follow. Ask, "Which animal comes next?" Then help your child cut out the pictures on page 107 and paste them in the correct spaces.**

Toy Parade

Use cutouts from page 107.

 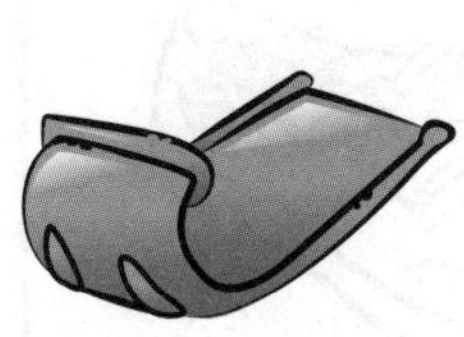  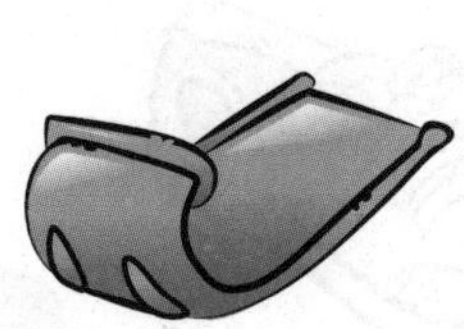 

Parents: Have your child name the toys pictured in the first row and discuss the pattern that the pictures follow. Ask, "Which toy comes next?" Then help your child cut out the pictures on page 107 and paste them in the correct spaces.

PREREADING

Clothes on Parade

Use cutouts from page 107.

    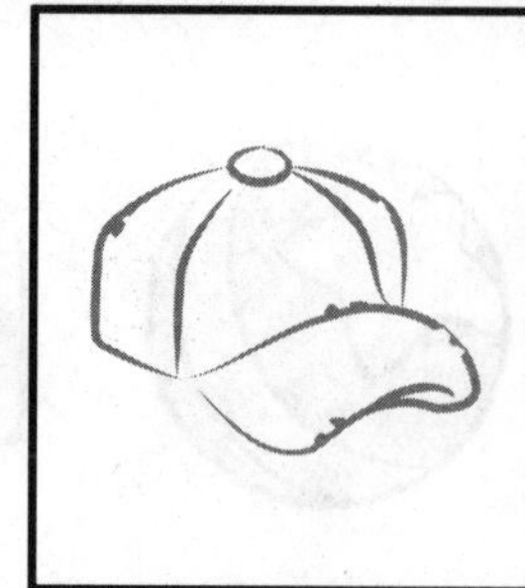

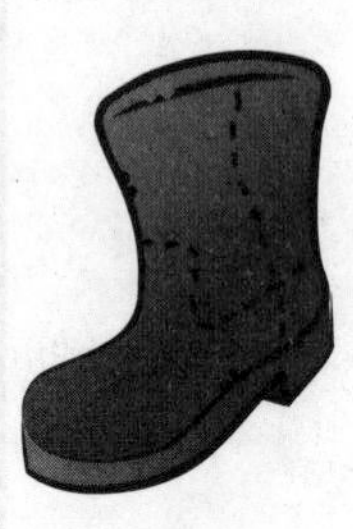  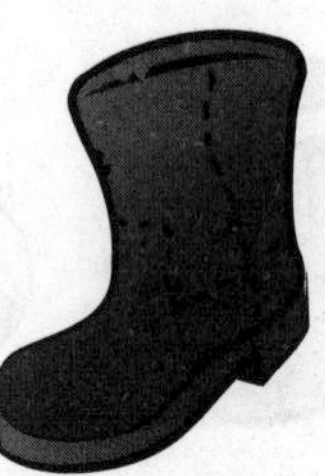  

Parents: Have your child name the clothes pictured in the first row and discuss the pattern that the pictures follow. Ask, "What comes next—hat or sweater?" Then help your child cut out the pictures on page 107 and paste them in the correct spaces.

Use on page 104.

Use on page 105.

Use on page 106.

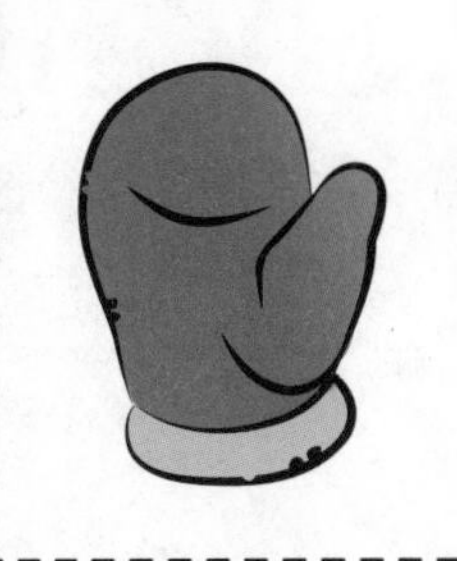

Color Patterns

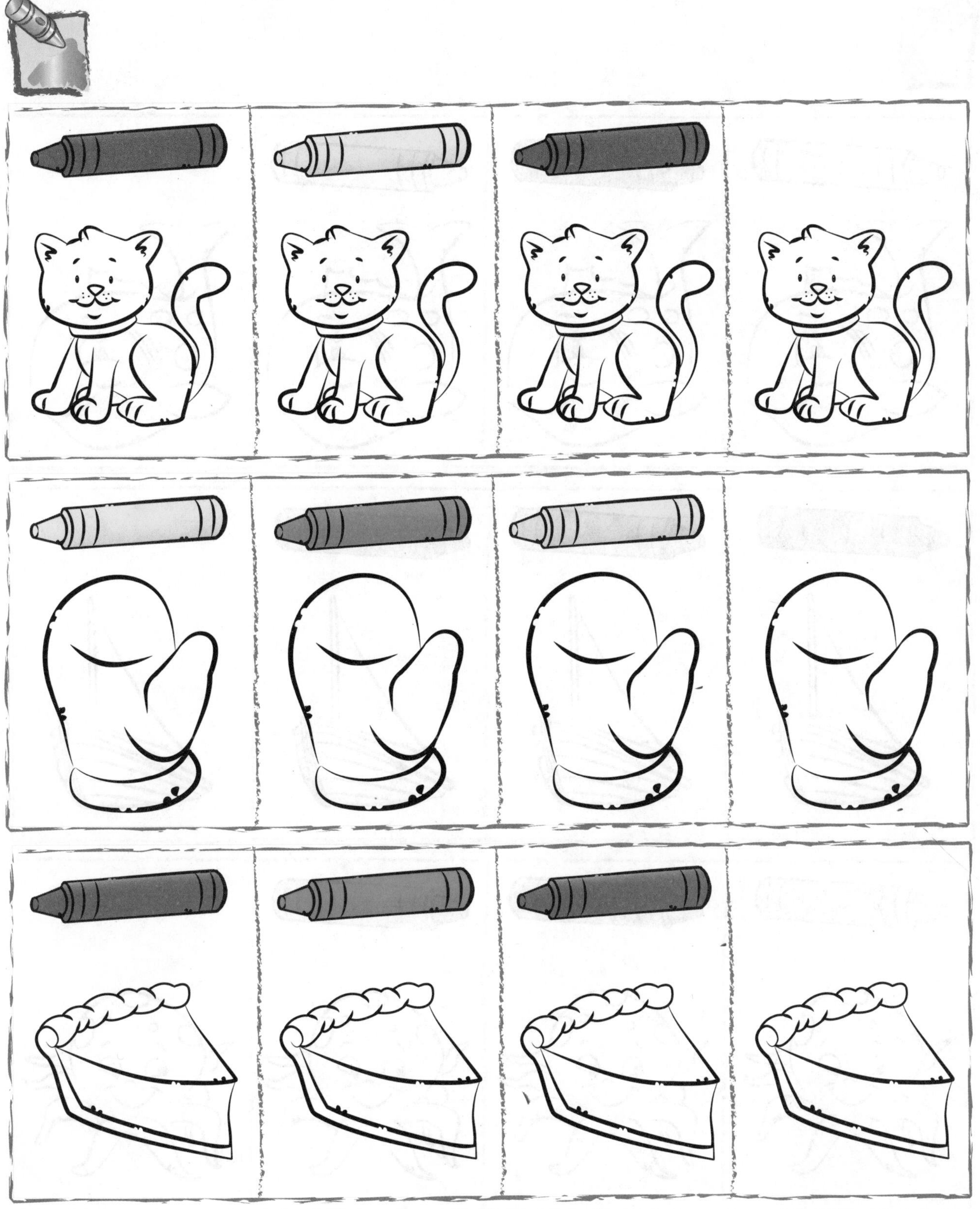

Parents: **In each row, have your child name the crayon color above each picture and color accordingly. Then discuss the "color pattern" of the row to help your child decide which color to use on the last picture.**

PREREADING

Sea Colors

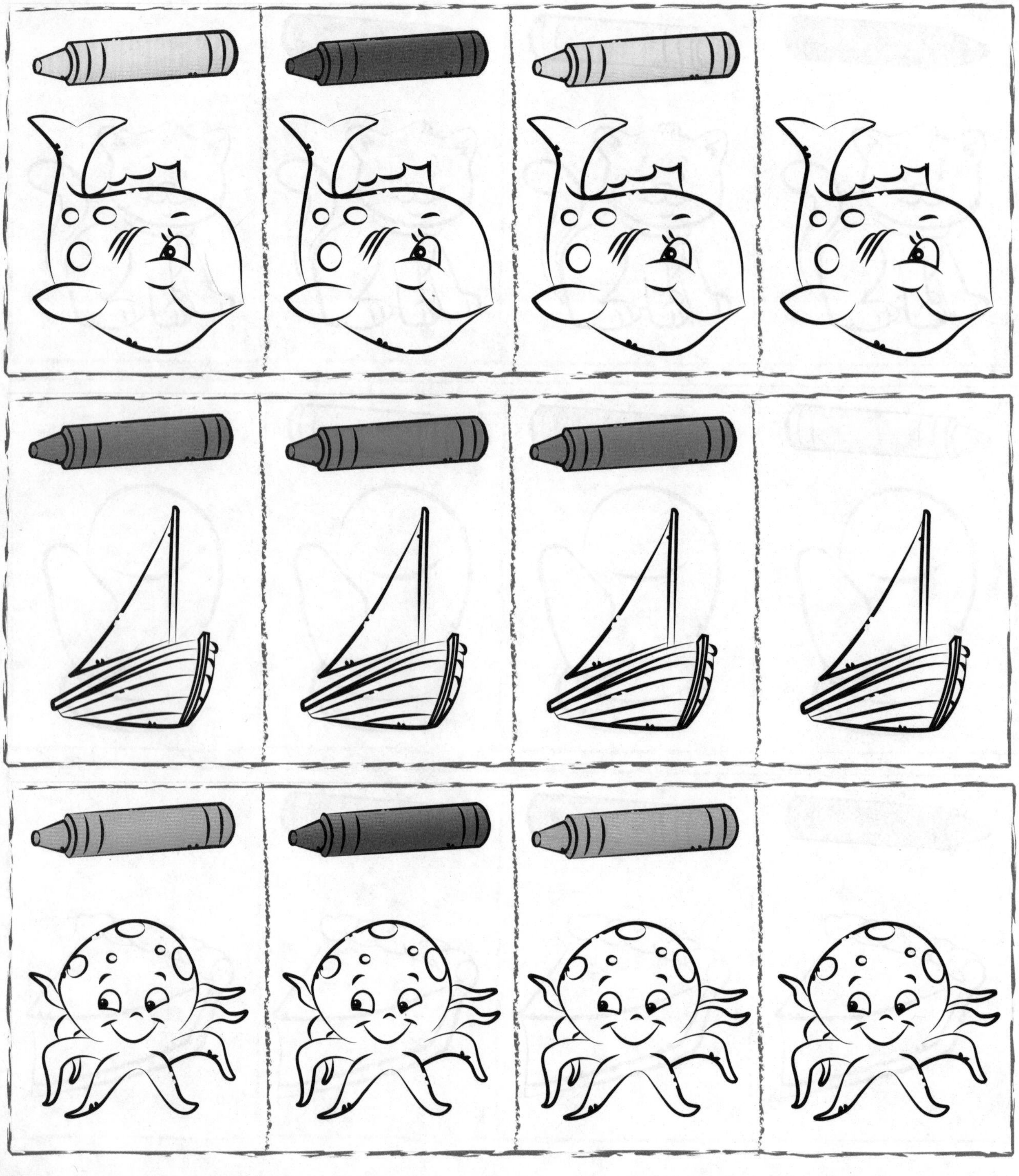

Parents: In each row, have your child name the crayon color above each picture and color accordingly. Then discuss the "color pattern" of the row to help your child decide which color to use on the last picture.

Whole to Part

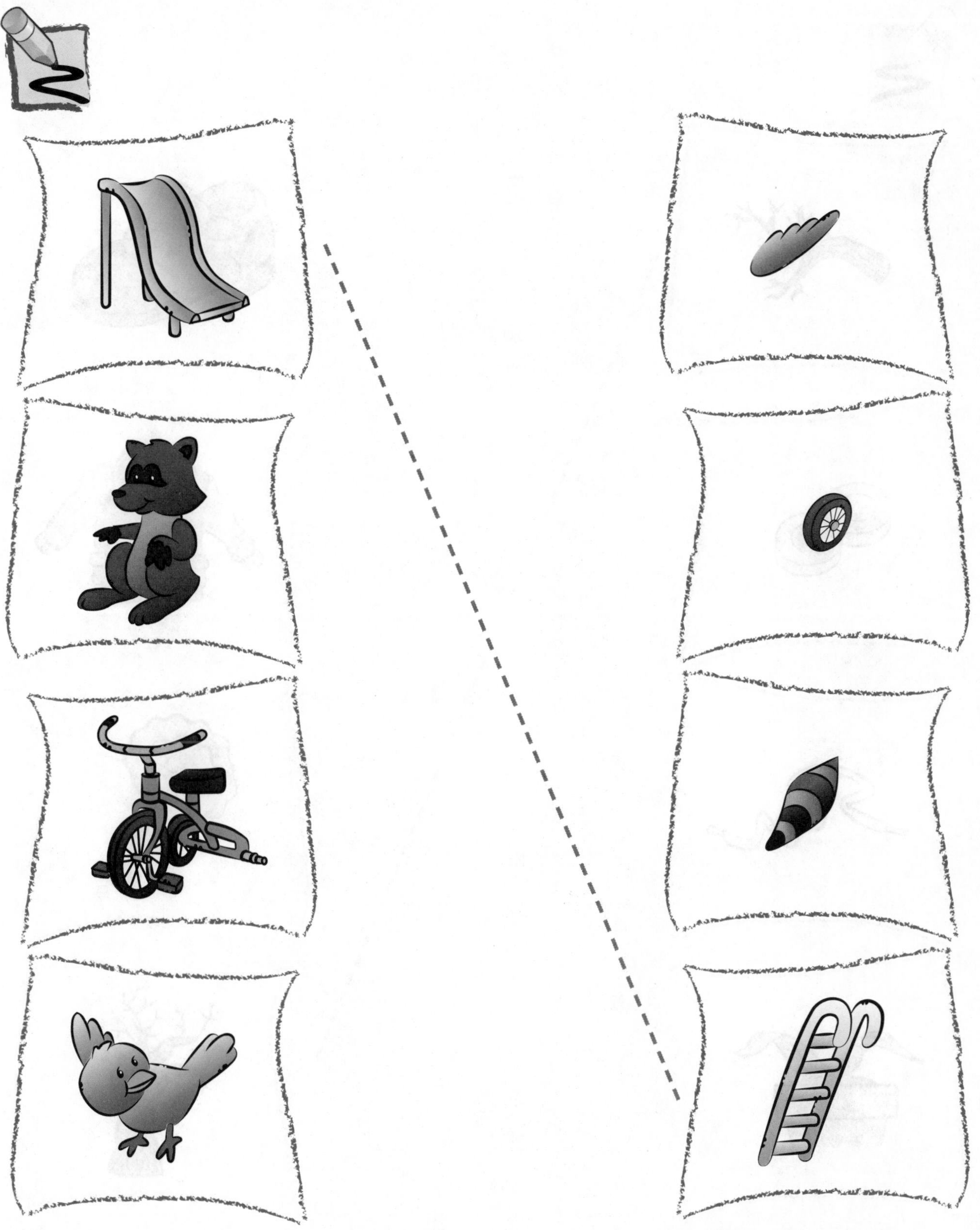

Parents: Say, "Look at the slide. What's missing? Draw a line to the missing part." Then have your child continue with the other items. Discuss where the missing parts fit on the whole.

Pieces

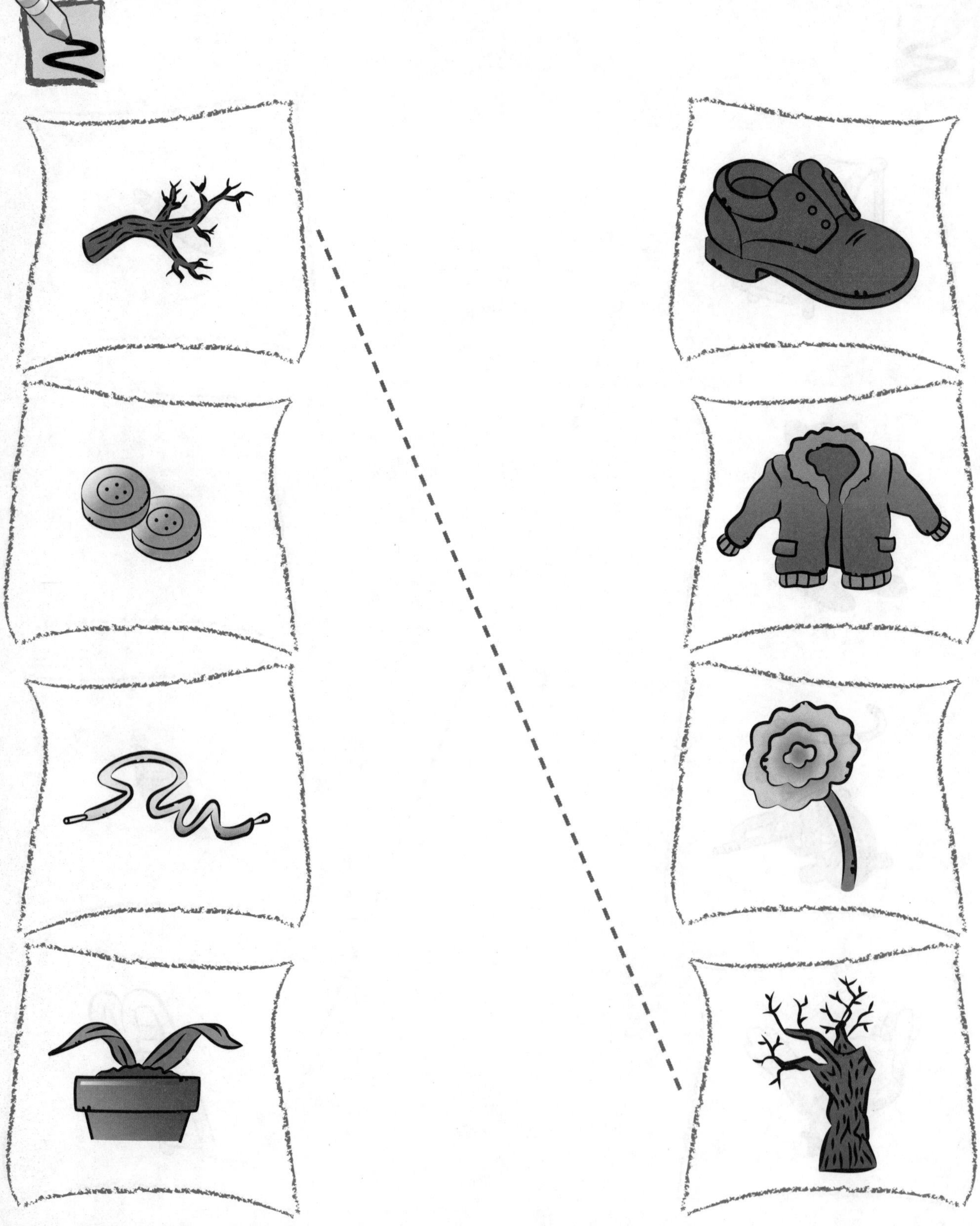

Parents: Say, "Look at the branch. What's missing? Draw a line to what it goes with." Then have your child continue with the other items. Discuss where the missing parts fit on the whole.

More Pieces

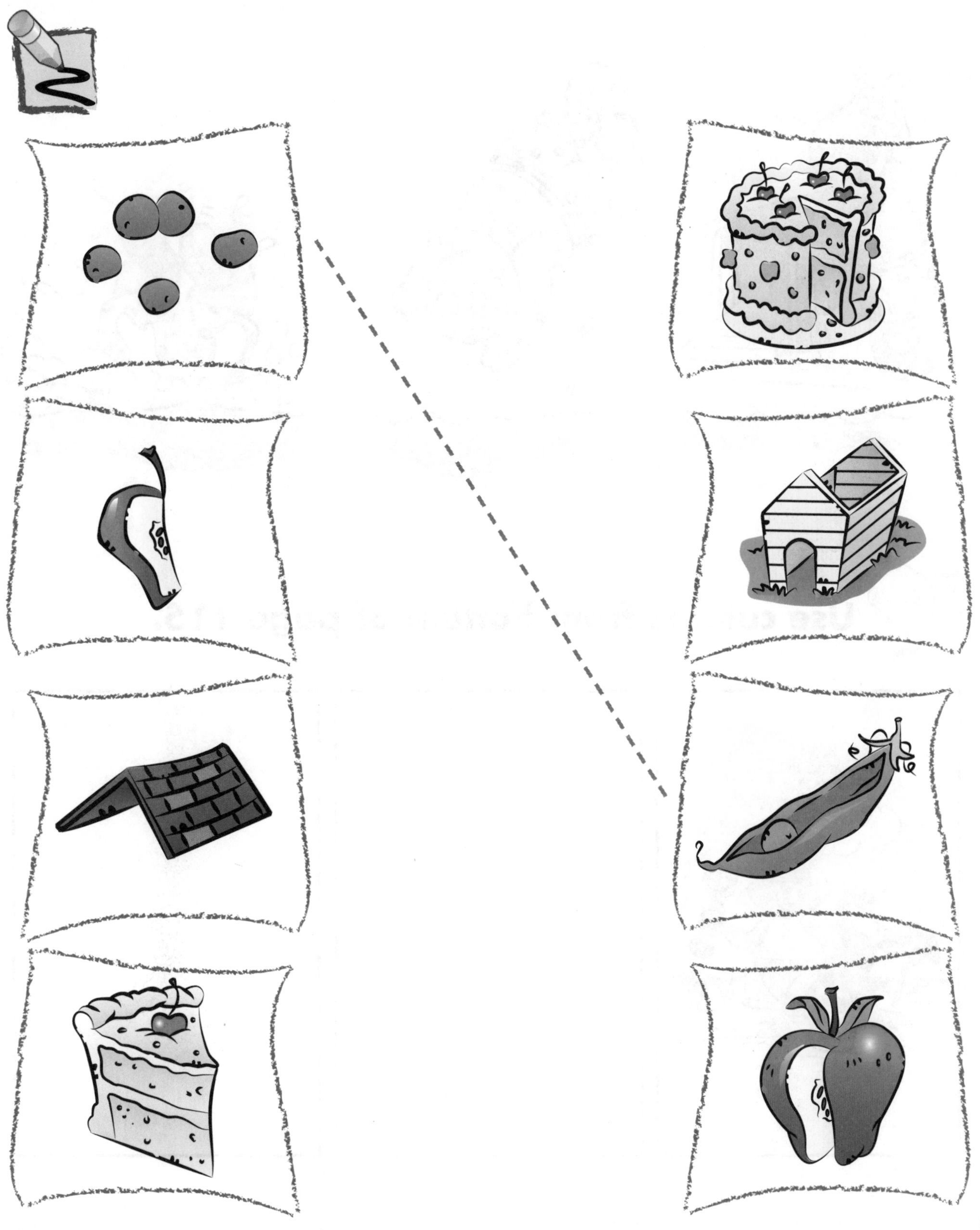

Parents: Say, "Look at the peas. Draw a line to what they go with." Then have your child continue with the other items. Discuss where the missing parts fit on the whole.

In the Swim

Use cutouts from bottom of page 115.

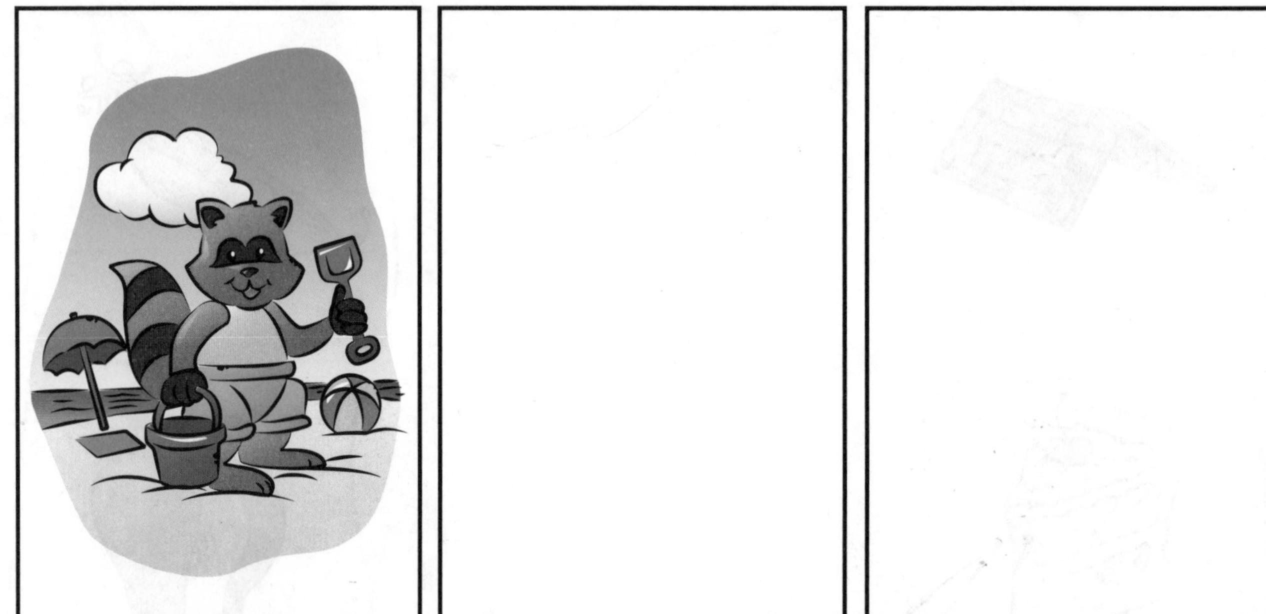

Parents: Encourage your child to use the words *first, next,* and *last* to tell a story about the pictures at the top of the page. Then have him or her paste the pictures from page 115 in a logical order on this page, and tell the raccoon's story.

Ready for School

Parents: **Have your child cut out the pictures in the top two rows, put each set in order to show what happened, and tell a story about the pictures using the words *first, next,* and *last.* Use the bottom row of pictures on page 114.**

Eating and Skating

Parents: Have your child cut out the pictures, put each set in order to show what happened, and tell a story about the pictures using the words *first, next,* and *last.*

Circle & Caterpillar

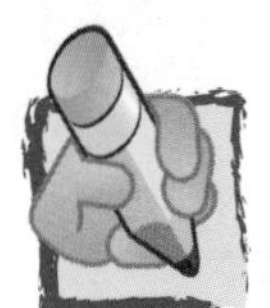

circle

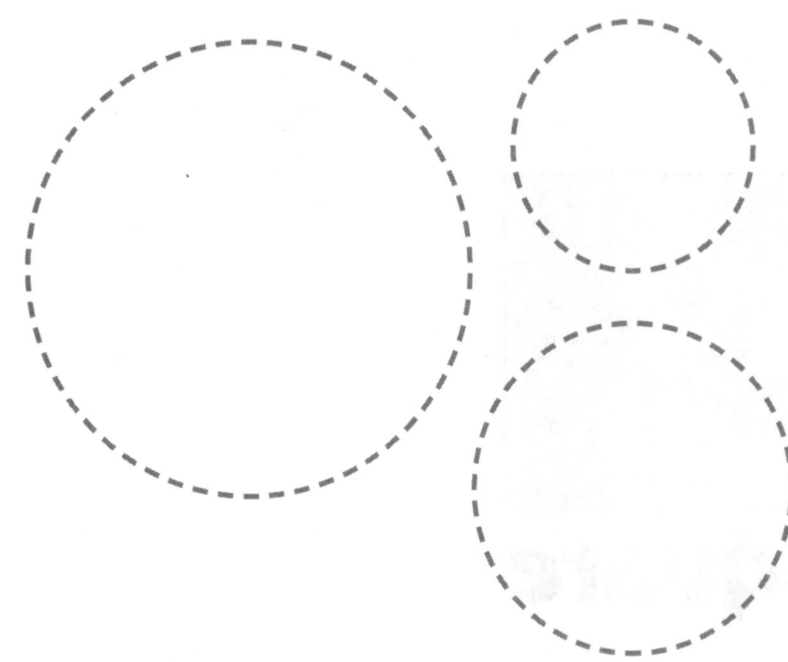

Parents: (Top) Have your child point to the red circle, name its shape, and then trace over the dotted-line circles. (Bottom) Ask your child to color the circles.

MATH

Square & Train

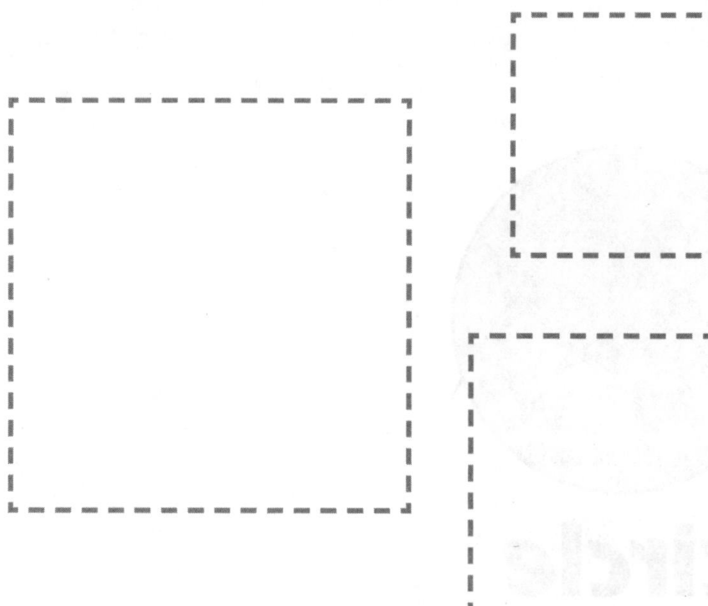

Parents: (Top) Have your child point to the blue square, name its shape, and then trace the dotted-line squares. (Bottom) Ask your child to color the squares.

Triangle & Bird

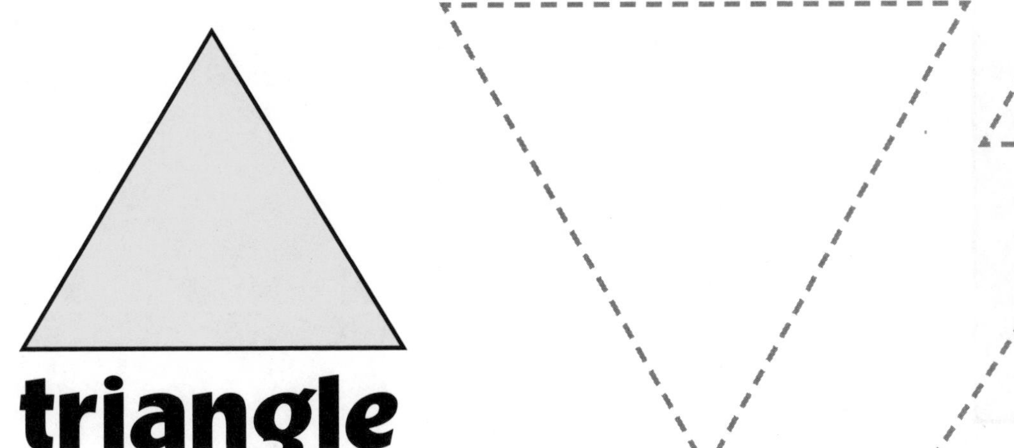

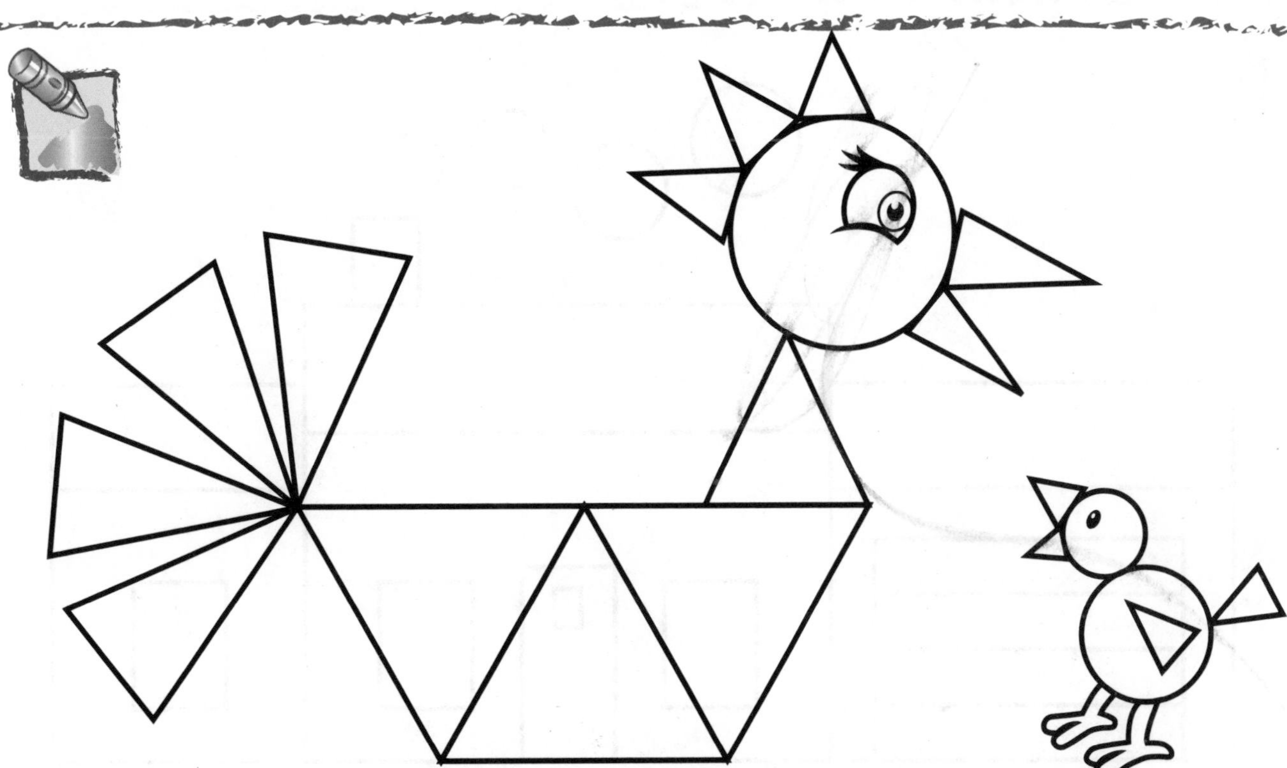

Parents: (Top) Have your child point to the yellow triangle, name its shape, and trace the dotted-line triangles. (Bottom) Ask your child to color the triangles.

Rectangle & House

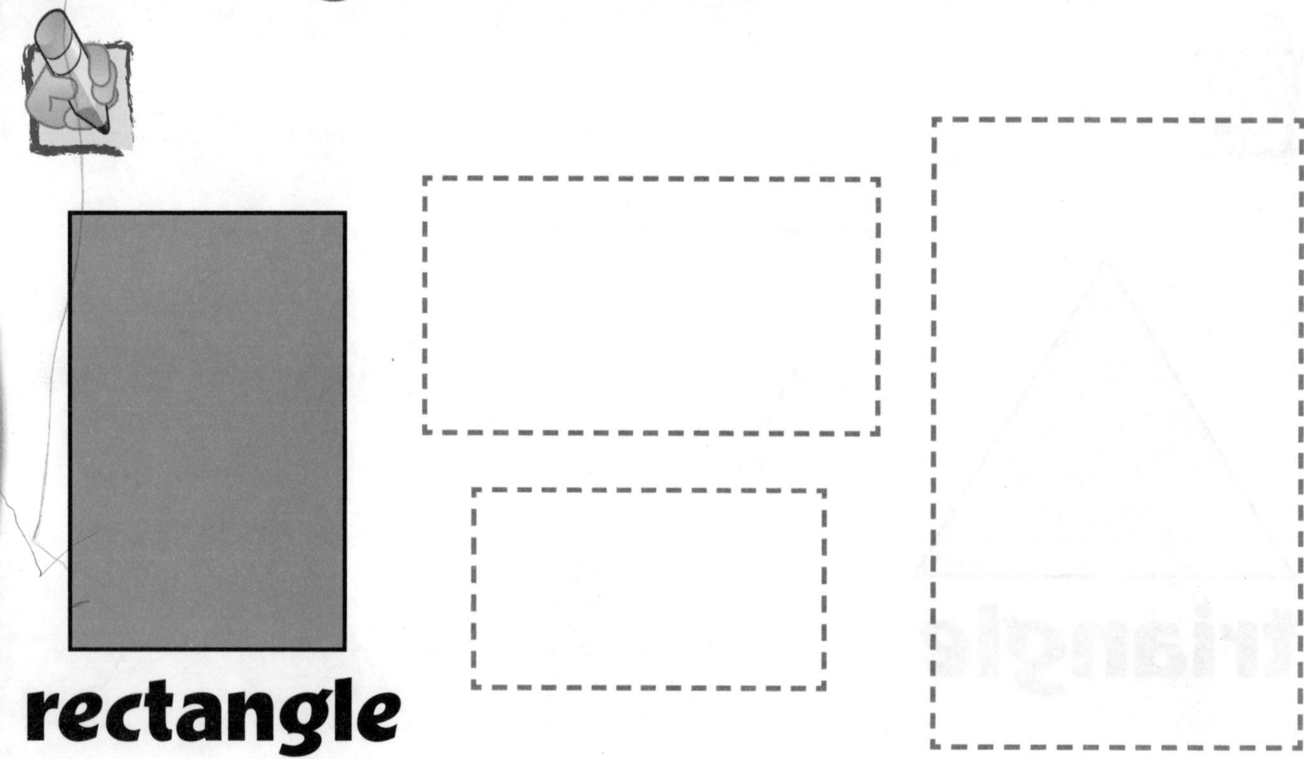

rectangle

Parents: (Top) Have your child point to the green rectangle, name its shape, and then trace the dotted-line rectangles. (Bottom) Ask your child to color the rectangles.

One-color Patterns

Draw and color what comes next in each row.

Parents: At the top of the page, ask your child to point to each bead and name its shape. Then ask, "What shape would come next?" Have your child draw and color the shape that continues the pattern in each row.

Two-color Patterns

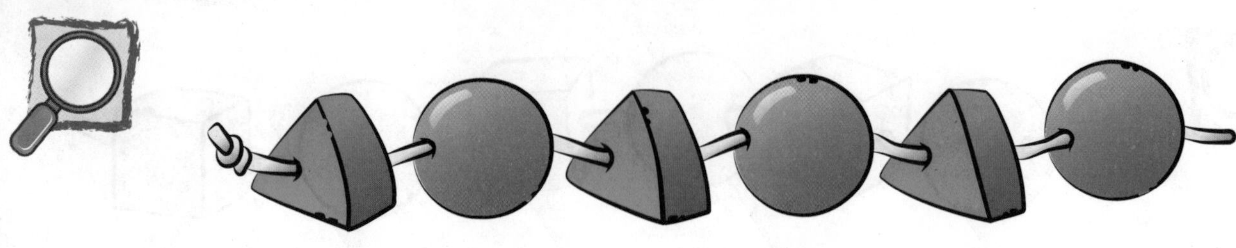

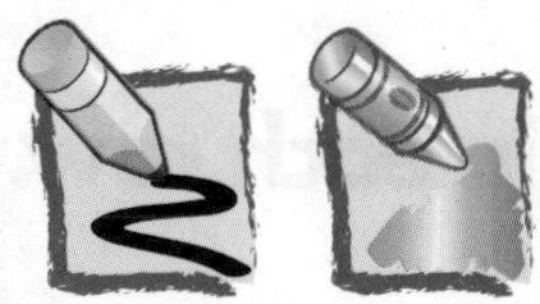

Draw and color what comes next in each row.

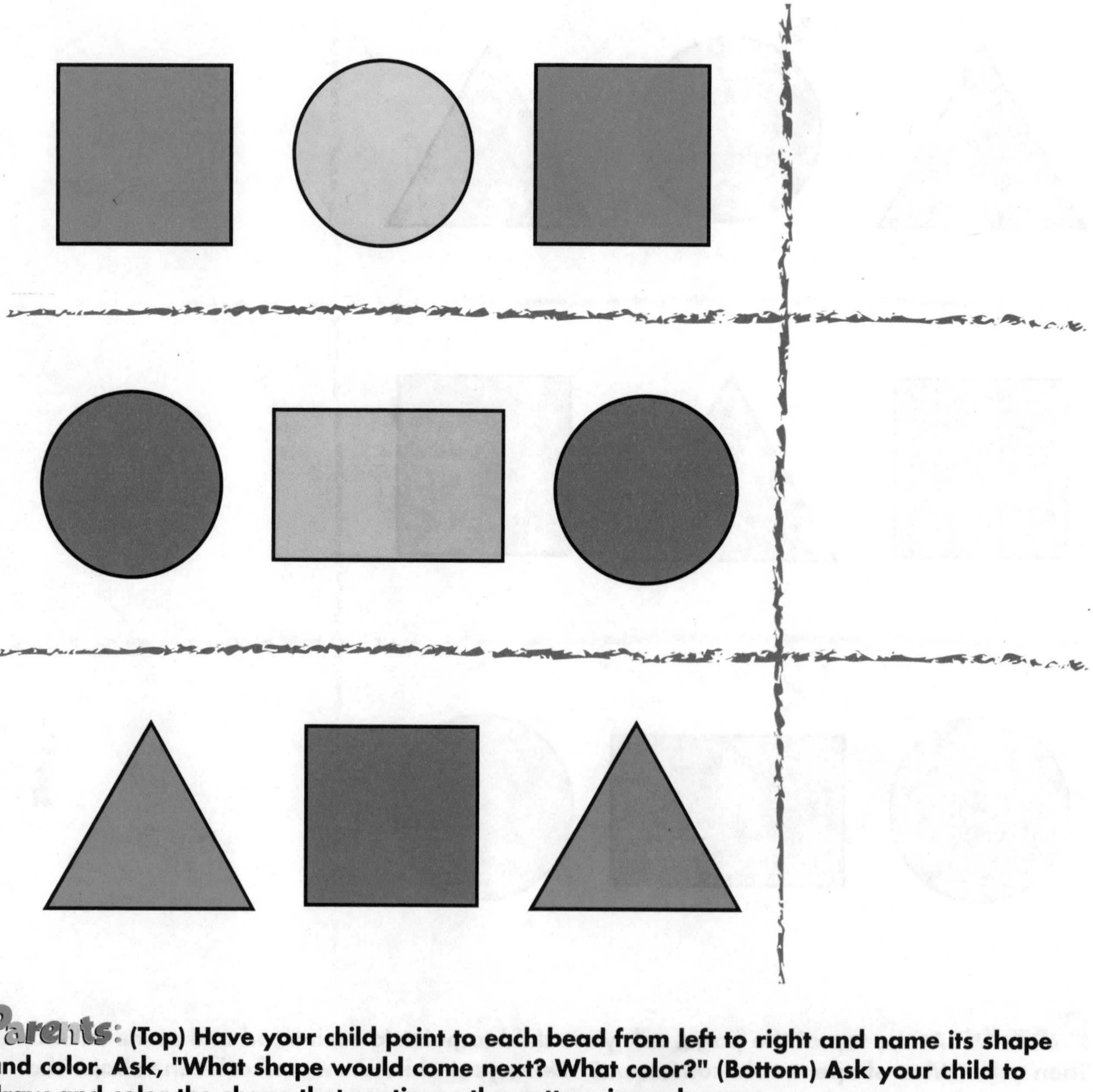

Parents: (Top) Have your child point to each bead from left to right and name its shape and color. Ask, "What shape would come next? What color?" (Bottom) Ask your child to draw and color the shape that continues the pattern in each row.

Animal Fun

Parents: (Top) Ask your child to draw a line between the dog and its dish. Ask, "What will the dog do with the bones?" (Bottom) Have your child draw lines between things that go together. Discuss what each animal will do with the object it is connected to.

Animal Homes

Parents: (Top) Ask your child to draw a line between the dog and its home. Ask, "What will the dog do in his home?" (Bottom) Have your child draw lines between things that go together. Discuss why the things go together.

inside of the front cover.

1

2

3

4

5

6

7

8

9

10

Count the Ducks

Rub-a-dub
Rubber ducky in the tub.

1 one duck

Rub-a-dub-dub
Dotted ducky in the tub.

2 two ducks

Rub-a-dub-dub-dub
Dapper ducky in the tub.

3 three ducks

One more thing before you're done.
Count the ducks from 10 to 1.

Rub-a-dub-dub-dub-dub-dub-
dub-dub-dub-dub-dub
Dripping ducky in the tub.

10 ten ducks

Let's do it again.
Count the ducks from 1 to 10.

1 2 3 4 5

6 7 8 9 10

Rub-a-dub-dub-dub-dub
Dainty ducky in the tub.

4 four ducks

Rub-a-dub-dub-dub-dub-dub
Dancing ducky in the tub.

5 five ducks

Rub-a-dub-dub-dub-dub-dub-dub
Dirty ducky needs the tub.

6 six ducks

Rub-a-dub-dub-dub-dub-dub-dub-dub
Dizzy ducky in the tub.

7 seven ducks

Rub-a-dub-dub-dub-dub-dub-dub-dub-dub
Drumming ducky in the tub.

8 eight ducks

Rub-a-dub-dub-dub-dub-dub-dubdub-
dub-dub
Detective ducky in the tub.

9 nine ducks

Month 5 Checklist

Hands-on activities to help prepare your child for school!

SELF-CONCEPT

Self-Awareness, Feelings: pages 131-137

Some of the pages for this month offer additional opportunities to help your child talk about his or her favorite things and feelings:

- ❑ Complete the worksheets.
- ❑ Make a sign on construction paper that says, "(Child's name)'s Favorite Foods." Have your child trace over the letters with glue and sprinkle with glitter. Then look through magazines with your child, talk about his or her favorite foods, and cut out pictures that you can post—along with the sign—on the refrigerator. You can also use this activity to encourage your child to try different foods.
- ❑ Play a game of hide and seek. Each time someone is found, ask "Were you surprised? Why? What did it feel like?"

LANGUAGE

Words for Shapes: pages 138-141
Following Directions: pages 143, 158

Use any of the hands-on activities for shapes or directionality from previous checklists in addition to the activities below:

- ❑ Complete the worksheets.
- ❑ Let your child help make cookies using shaped cutters—stars, circles, squares, rectangles, triangles, crescents, and so on. As you work, talk about the names of the various shapes. Then, if you like, let your child help sort the cookies into paper bags marked with shape names.

MATH

Counting to 5, Matching Numerals with Amounts, Writing Numerals: pages 146-157

It is a good idea to review counting skills frequently. These activities and the ones listed on other checklists provide excellent practice:

- ❑ Complete the worksheets.
- ❑ Place six or seven spoons on a table in a pile. Ask your child to count out five. Increase or decrease the number counted as appropriate.
- ❑ Flashcards that show a numeral, number word, and a given number of items are a good way to practice number skills—especially number recognition and number word identification. You can use the cut-out cards provided in this book on pages 209-210 or buy a deck of cards. Wait until your child has nearly mastered 1 to 5 before increasing the numbers counted.

PREREADING AND PREWRITING

Fine Motor Control: pages 142, 159-160
Directionality: pages 144-145

Use any of the prewriting and visual discrimination activities provided in other checklists and try these:

- ❑ Complete the worksheets.
- ❑ Spread flour over a baking sheet or newspaper. Encourage your child to draw shapes, letters, or numbers in the flour.
- ❑ Buy or make simple stencils—stars, circles, squares, etc.—and let your child practice using the stencils to draw shapes.
- ❑ Line up four chairs, all but one facing the same direction. Then tell the child, "Sit in the one facing a different direction from the others." Repeat as long as there is interest. You can use this activity as part of a game of musical chairs if you have several children. Each time the music stops, everyone sits. The person who sits in the wrong-direction chair two times in a row gets to turn the music on and off next.

Sweet Fun

Parents: **Remind your child that too many sweets are not good for people, but that almost everyone likes them and has a favorite. Discuss your child's favorite. Then ask him or her to follow directions to color the sweets on the page.**

SELF-CONCEPT

My Favorite Foods

Circle 5 of your favorite foods.

Parents: Have your child identify and discuss his or her feelings about the foods shown and name other foods that he or she likes. Then ask your child to circle five favorite foods on the page.

Angry or Surprised I

Circle the faces that show how you would feel.

Color the pictures.

Parents: Discuss times when your child has felt angry and other times when he or she has felt surprised. Then have your child circle the face that shows how he or she would feel in each situation before coloring the picture.

SELF-CONCEPT

Angry or Surprised II

Circle the faces that show how you would feel.

Color the pictures.

Parents: Discuss times when your child has felt angry and other times when he or she has felt surprised. Then have your child circle the face that shows how he or she would feel in each situation before coloring the picture.

My Favorite Animal

All About Me

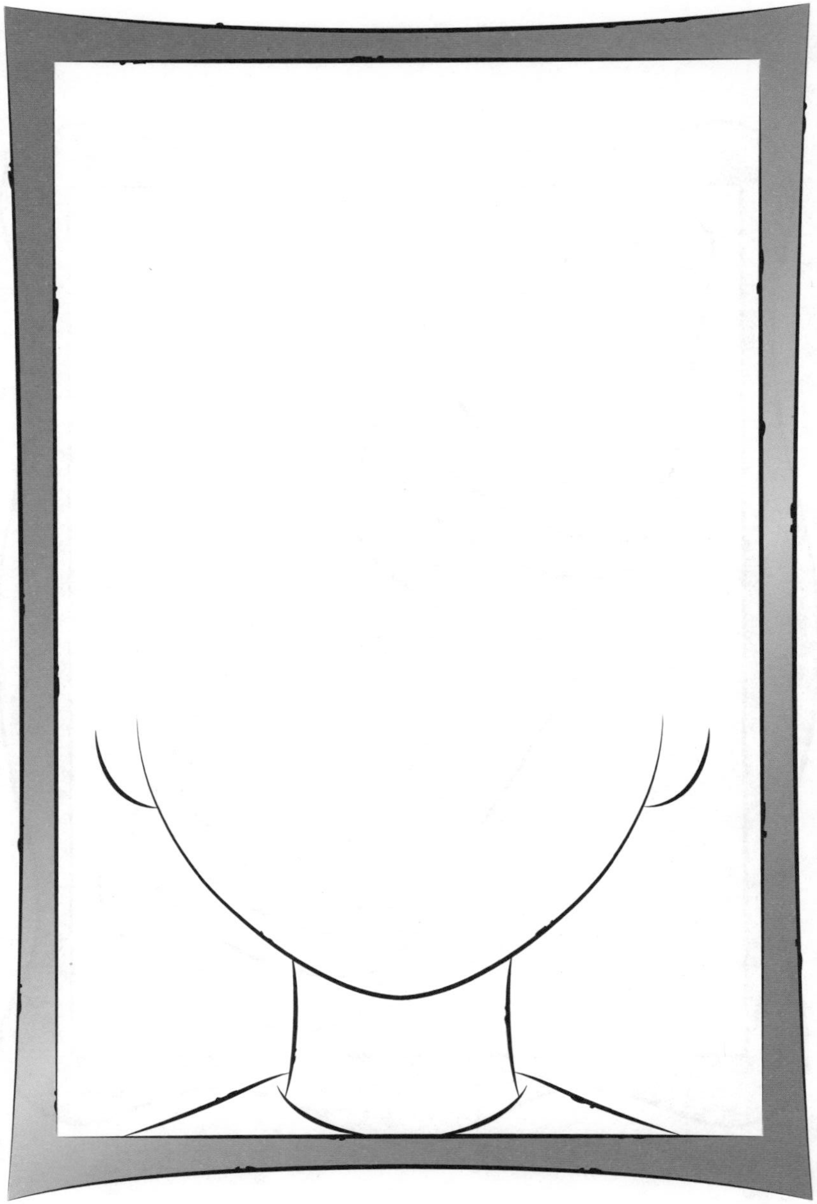

My Favorite Color

My Favorite Toy

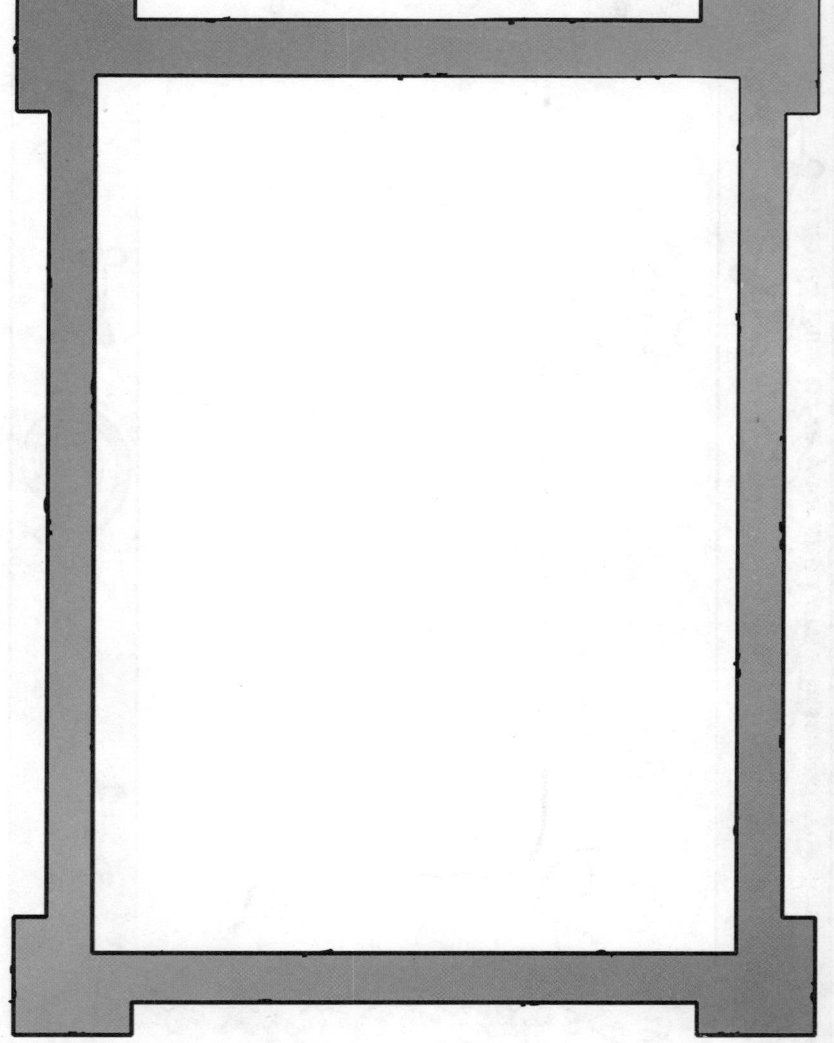

Best Friends

Parents: Read aloud the title of the page and encourage your child to name several best friends—people, pets, or even dolls. Then have your child draw a self-portrait that includes one of his or her best friends.

Diamond

Little Girl

Little girl, little girl, where have you been?
Gathering roses to give to the queen.
Little girl, little girl, what gave she you?
She gave me a diamond as big as my shoe.

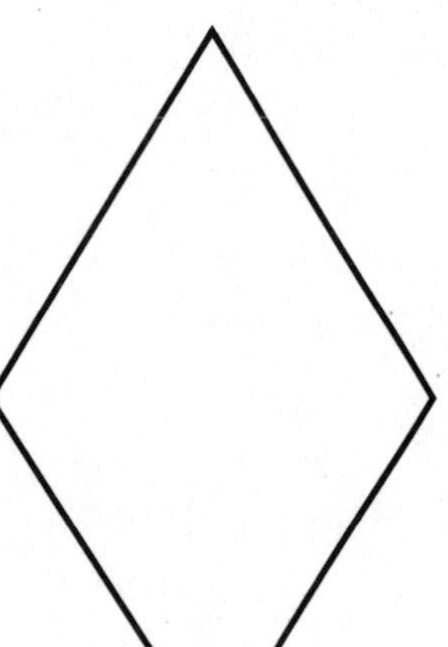

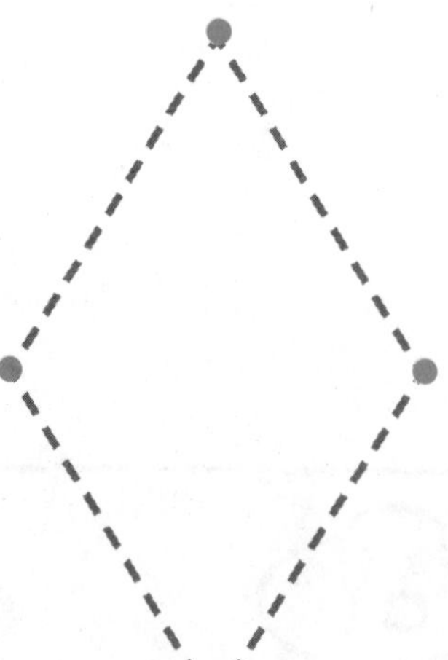

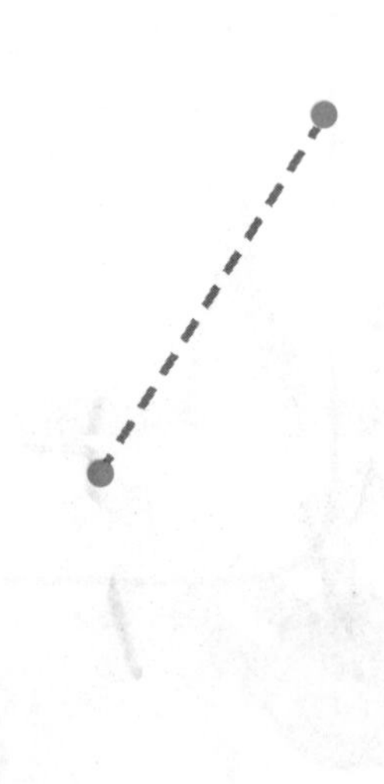

Parents: Read the rhyme. Then point to the diamond and say, "This is a diamond." Have your child color the row of three diamonds. Then have your child use a finger to trace the first diamond in the bottom row and a pencil to trace and draw the next two diamonds.

Star

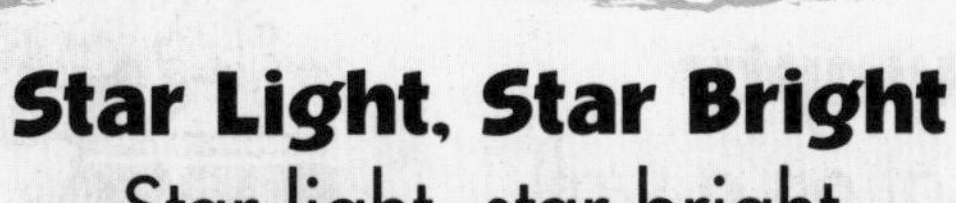

Star Light, Star Bright

Star light, star bright
The first star I see tonight;
I wish I may, I wish I might
Have the wish I wish tonight.

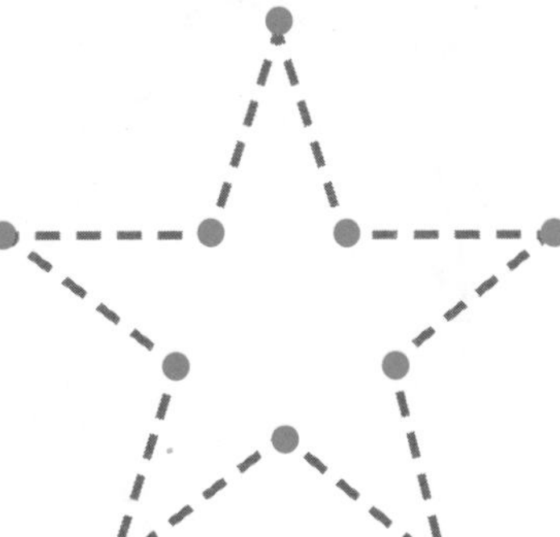
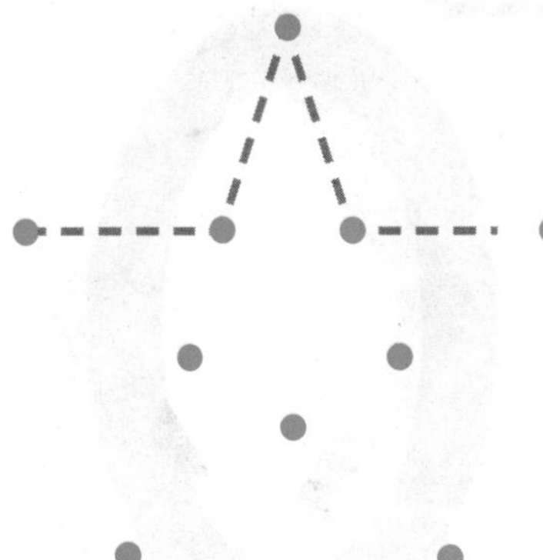

Parents: Read the rhyme. Then point to the star and say, "Do you know this shape? It's a star." Have your child color the row of three stars. Then have him or her use a finger to trace the first star in the bottom row and a pencil to trace and draw the next two stars.

Oval

Humpty Dumpty

Humpty Dumpty sat on a wall,
Humpty Dumpty had a great fall;
All the king's horses and all the king's men
Couldn't put Humpty together again.

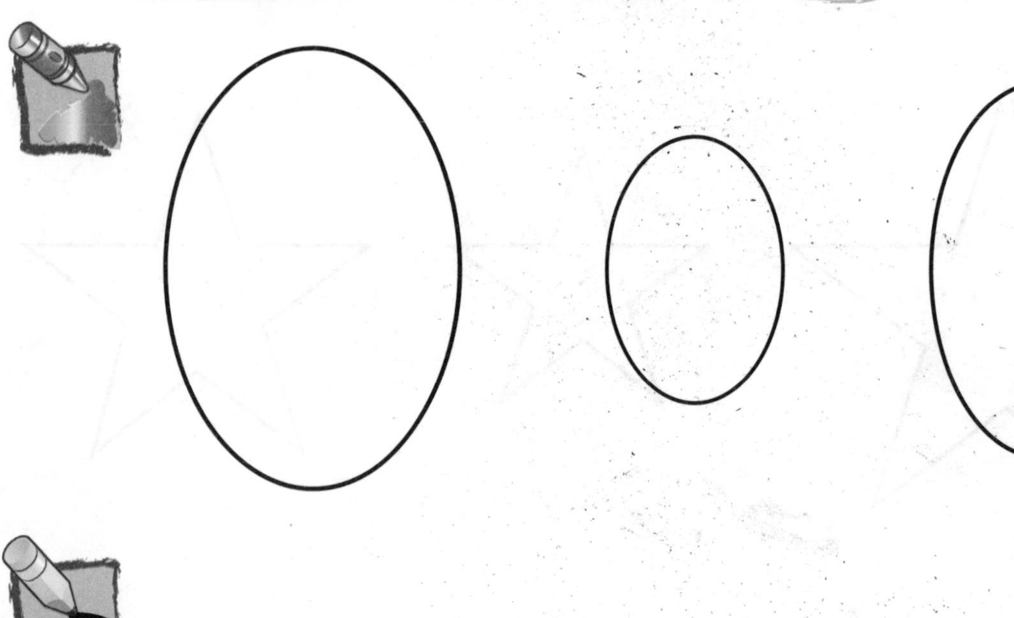

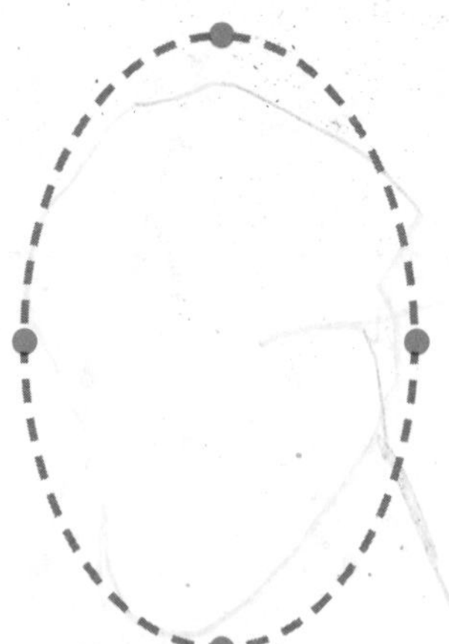

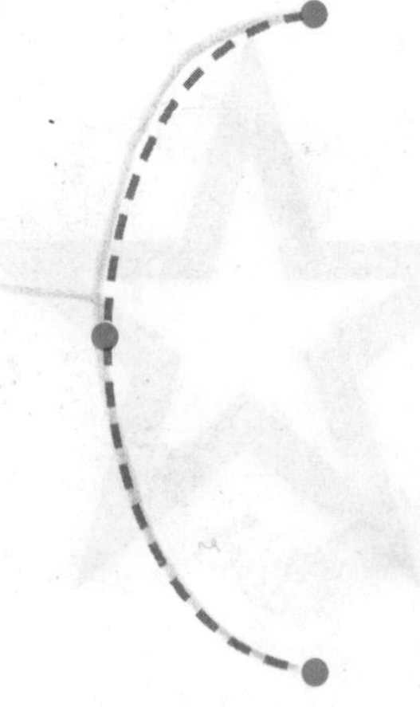

Parents: Read the rhyme. Then point to the oval and say, "This shape is called an oval. It looks like an egg." Have your child color the row of ovals. Then have him or her use a finger to trace the first oval in the bottom row and a pencil to trace and draw the others.

Heart

Heart Tarts

The Queen of Hearts made some tarts,
All on a summer's day.
The Jack of Hearts ate the tarts,
Then put away the tray.

Parents: Read the rhyme. Then point to the heart and ask, "What's this? It's a heart." Have your child color the row of hearts. Then have him or her use a finger to trace the first heart in the bottom row and a pencil to trace and draw the next two hearts.

Next Shape?

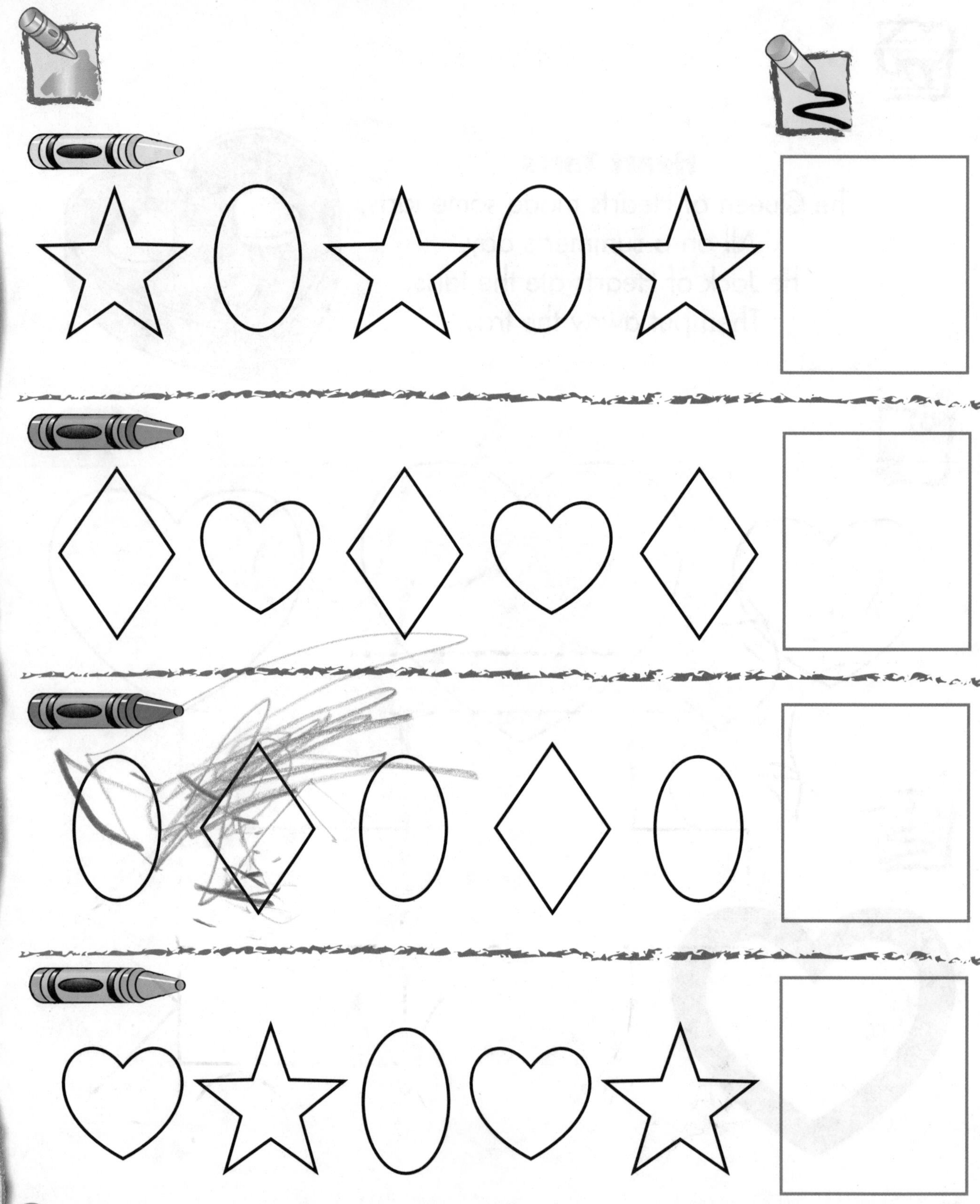

Parents: Have your child name the shapes in the first row. Then ask, "Which shape comes next?" Have your child color the shapes as indicated by the crayon, and draw the next shape in the empty box. Repeat for each row.

Practicing prewriting skills; recognizing and continuing patterns

Color Choo-Choo

Color Key

blue red yellow green

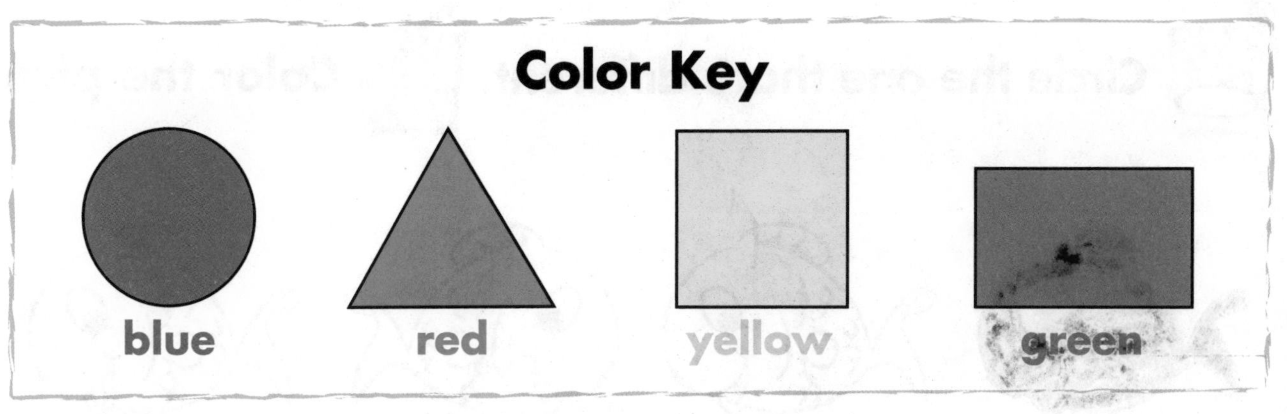

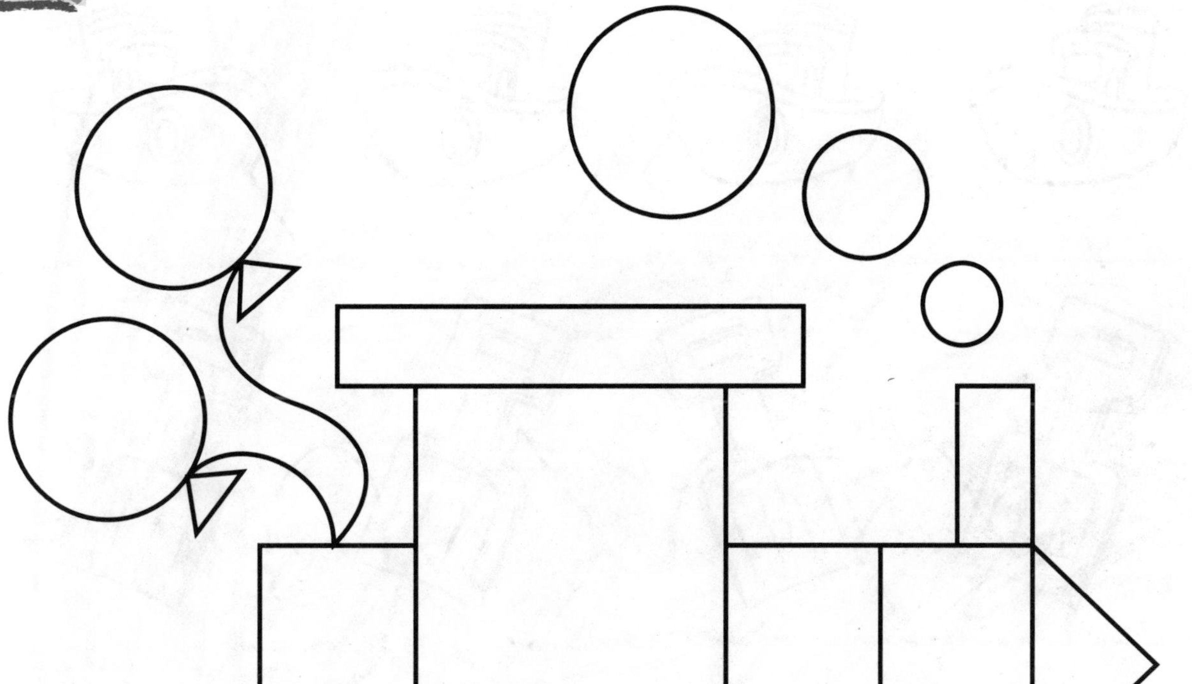

Parents: Ask your child to name each color and shape in the key at the top of the page. Then have him or her follow the key to color the choo-choo.

PREREADING

Wrong Way at the Beach

Circle the one that's different.

Color the picture

Parents: Ask your child to look carefully at the things in each row and circle the one that faces a different direction. Then have your child color the pictures.

Toy Turn-Around

Circle the one that's different.

Color the picture.

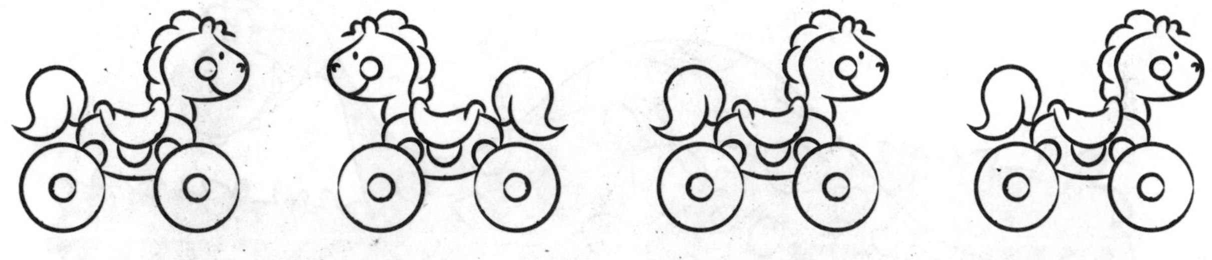

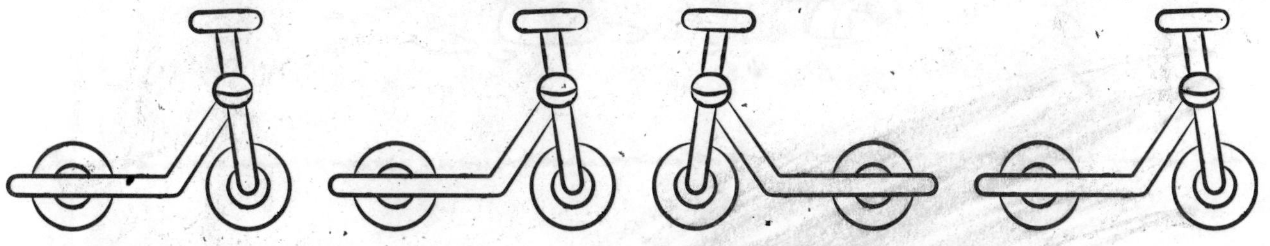

Parents: **Ask your child to look carefully at the things in each row and circle the one that faces a different direction. Then have your child color the pictures.**

MATH

Counting to 1

1 **one**

Circle 1  **.**

Parents: (Top) Ask your child to say *one* as he or she points to the numeral and number word, and then counts the one dinosaur. (Bottom) Then say, "Count the number of dinosaurs in each group and circle the picture with one."

Showing 1

Color 1  .

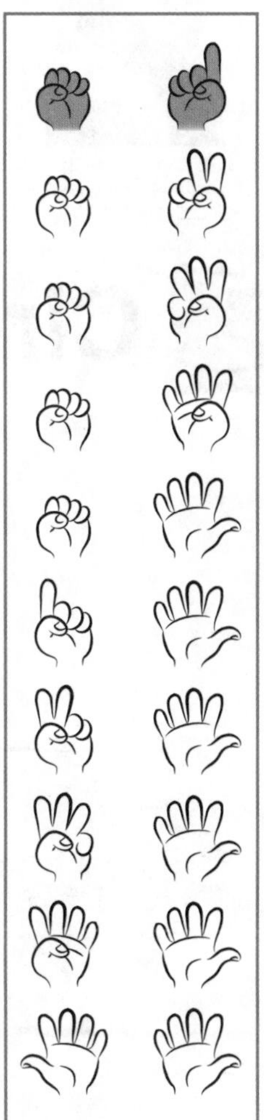

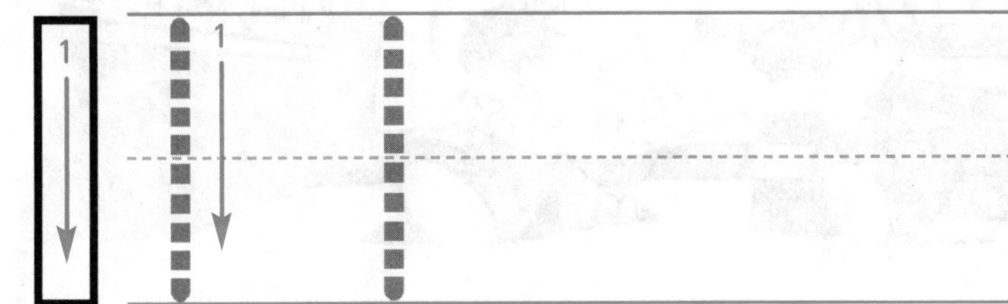

Parents: Ask your child to say *one* as he or she shows *one* finger. Help your child read the direction. Then have him or her color the correct number of dishes, and use a finger to trace the hollow numeral and a pencil or crayon to trace and write more 1s.

Counting to 2

2 two

Circle 2 .

Parents: (Top) Ask your child to say *two* as he or she points to the numeral and number word, and then counts the two bears. (Bottom) Then say, "Count the number of bears in each group and circle the picture with two."

Showing 2

Color 2  .

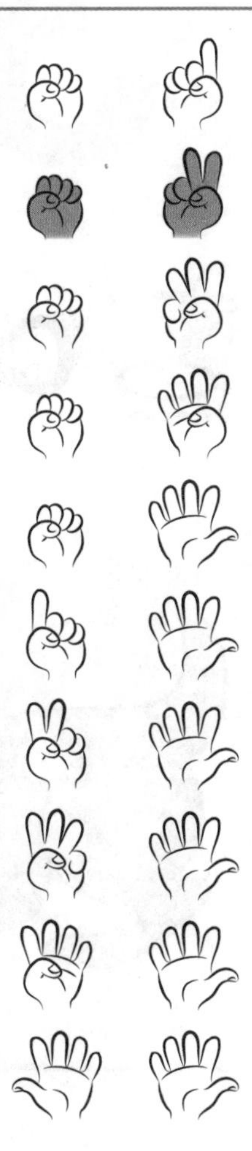

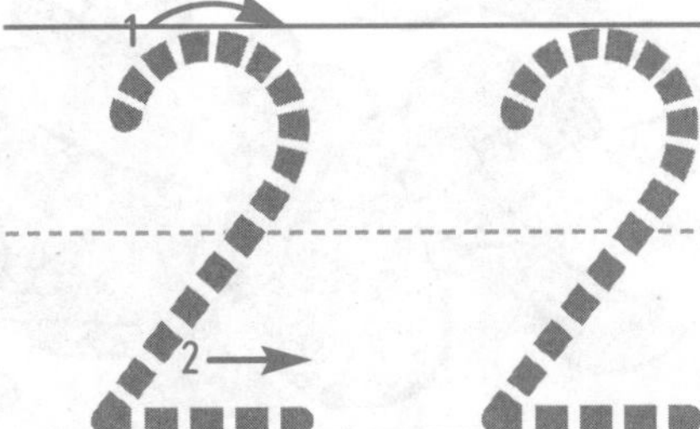

Parents: Ask your child to say *two* as he or she shows *two* fingers. Help your child read the direction. Then have him or her color the correct number of honey jars, and use a finger to trace the hollow numeral and a pencil or crayon to trace and write more 2s.

Understanding numbers: using fingers to show amounts; printing

Counting to 3

3 **three**

Circle 3  .

Parents: (Top) Ask your child to say *three* as he or she points to the numeral and number word, and then counts the three dogs. (Bottom) Then say, "Count the number of dogs in each group and circle the picture with three."

Showing 3

Color 3 .

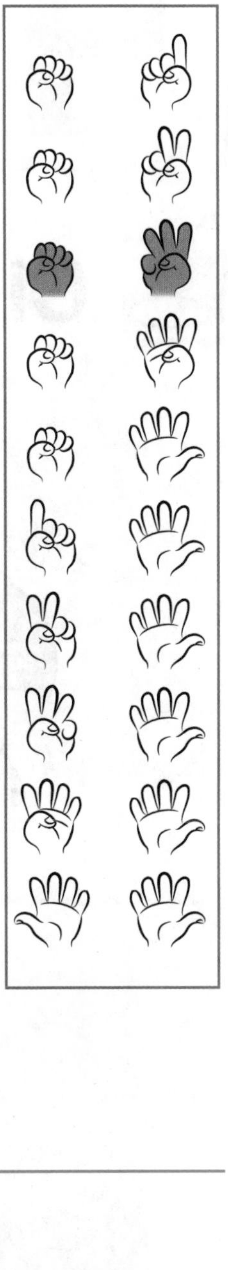

1 2

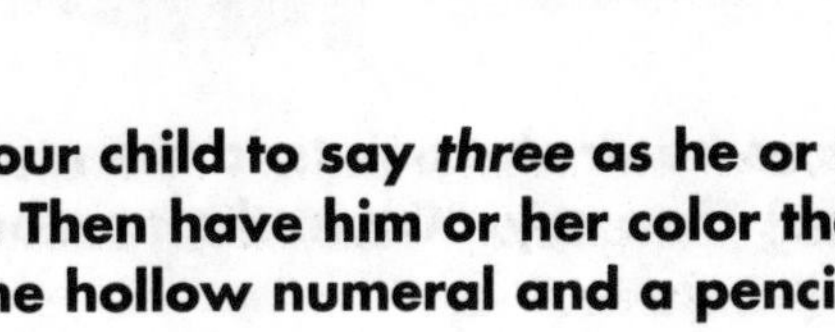

Parents: Ask your child to say *three* as he or she shows *three* fingers. Help your child read the direction. Then have him or her color the correct number of dog houses, and use a finger to trace the hollow numeral and a pencil or crayon to trace and write more 3s.

Counting to 4

4 four

Circle 4 .

Parents: (Top) Ask your child to say *four* as he or she points to the numeral and number word, and then counts the four girls. (Bottom) Then say, "Count the number of girls in each group and circle the picture with four."

Showing 4

Color 4  .

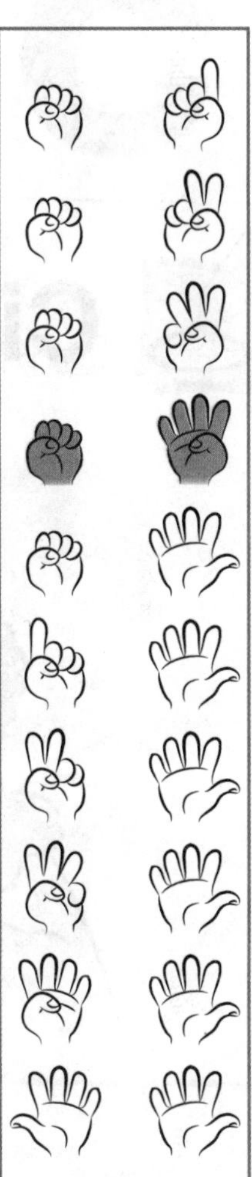

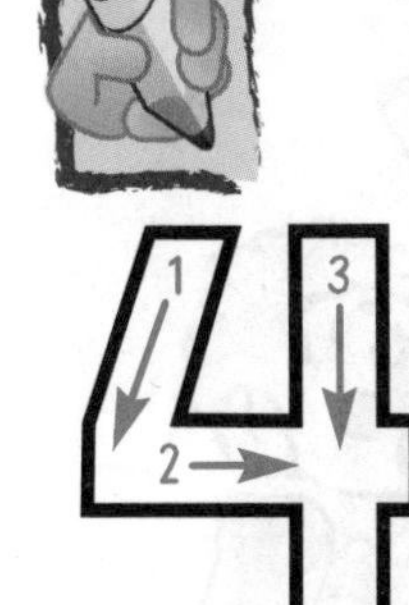

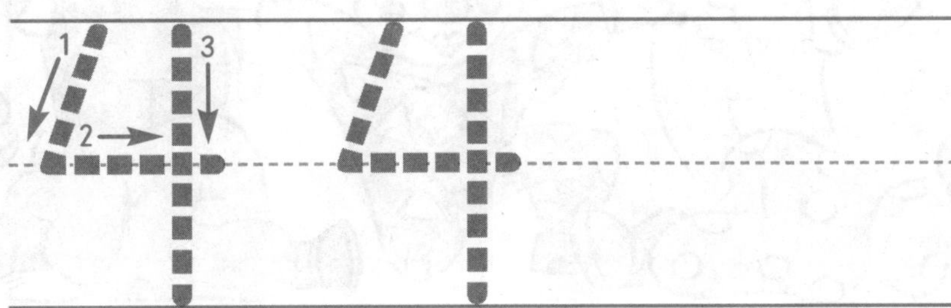

Parents: Ask your child to say *four* as he or she shows *four* fingers. Help your child read the direction. Then have him or her color the correct number of cakes, and use a finger to trace the hollow numeral and a pencil or crayon to trace and write more 4s.

Counting to 5

5 **five**

Circle 5 .

Parents: (Top) Ask your child to say *five* as he or she points to the numeral and number word, and then counts the five clowns. (Bottom) Then say, "Count the number of clowns in each group and circle the picture with five."

Showing 5

Color 5  .

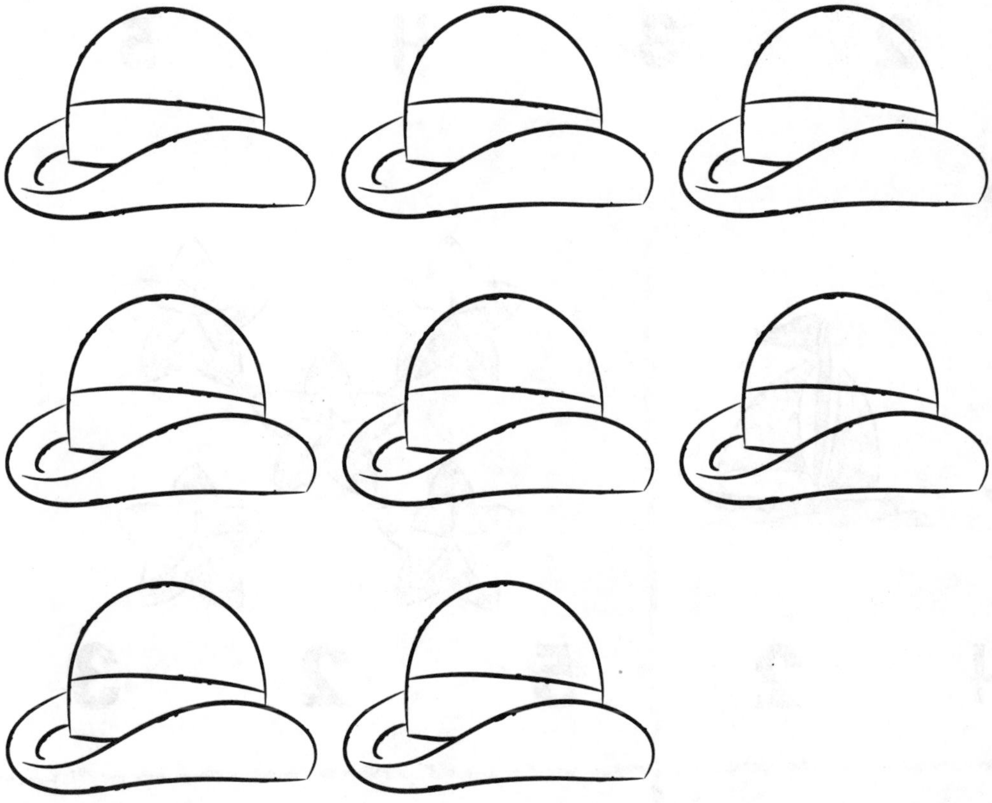

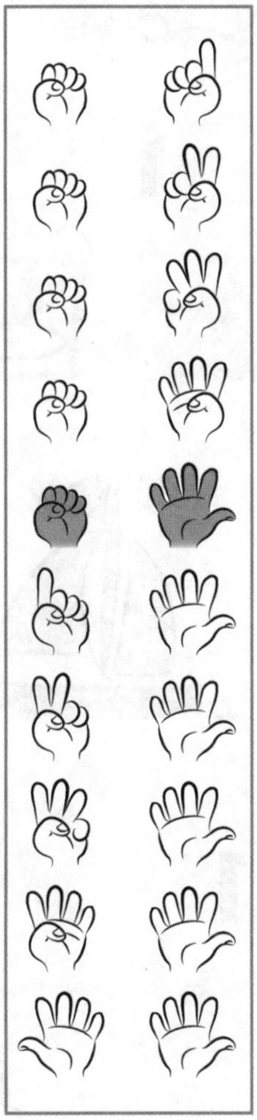

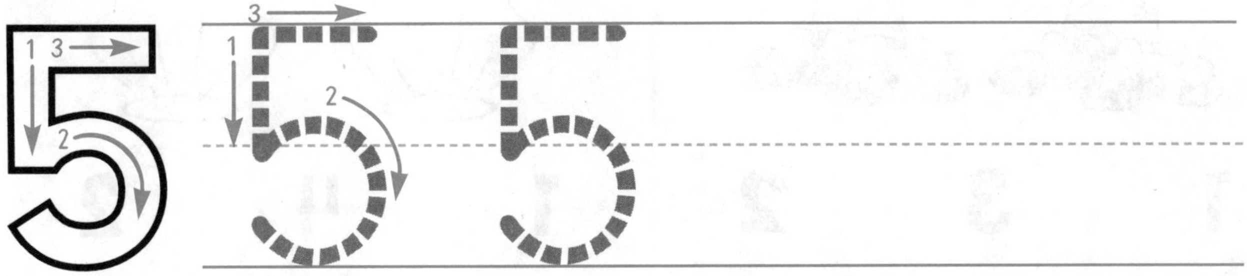

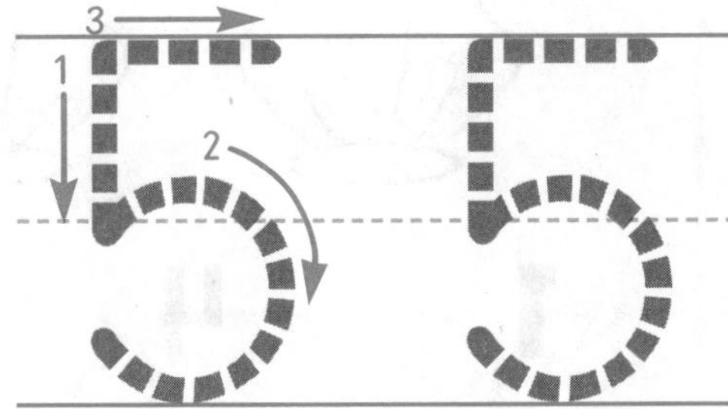

Parents: Ask your child to say *five* as he or she shows *five* fingers. Help your child read the direction. Then have him or her color the correct number of hats, and use a finger to trace the hollow numeral and a pencil or crayon to trace and write more 5s.

Counting 1 to 5

1, 2, 3, 4, 5. Little fishes learn to dive.

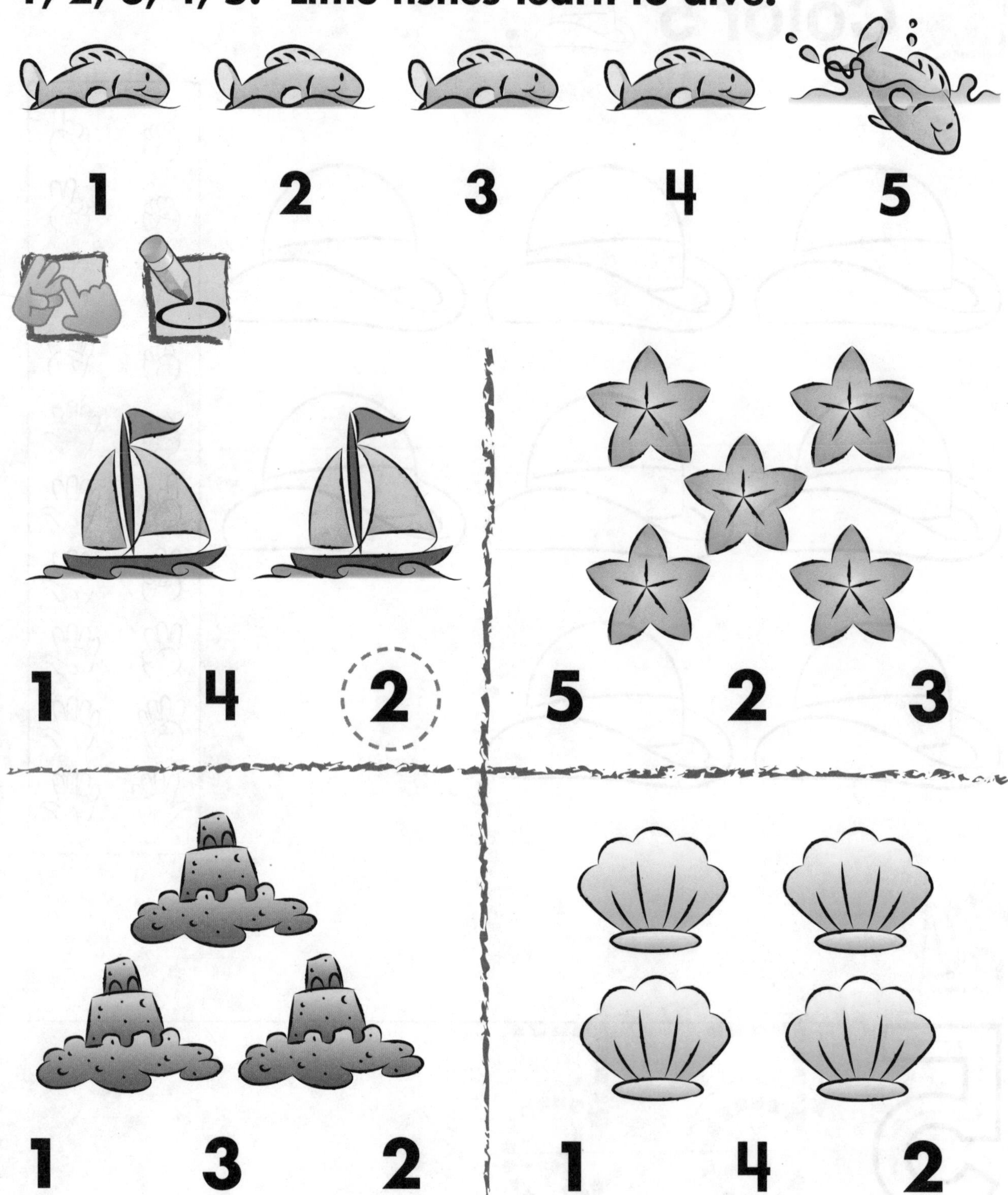

Parents: As you read the numbers in the counting rhyme at the top of the page, have your child point to each fish. Then have him or her count the objects in each box and circle the number that shows the correct amount.

Writing 1 to 5

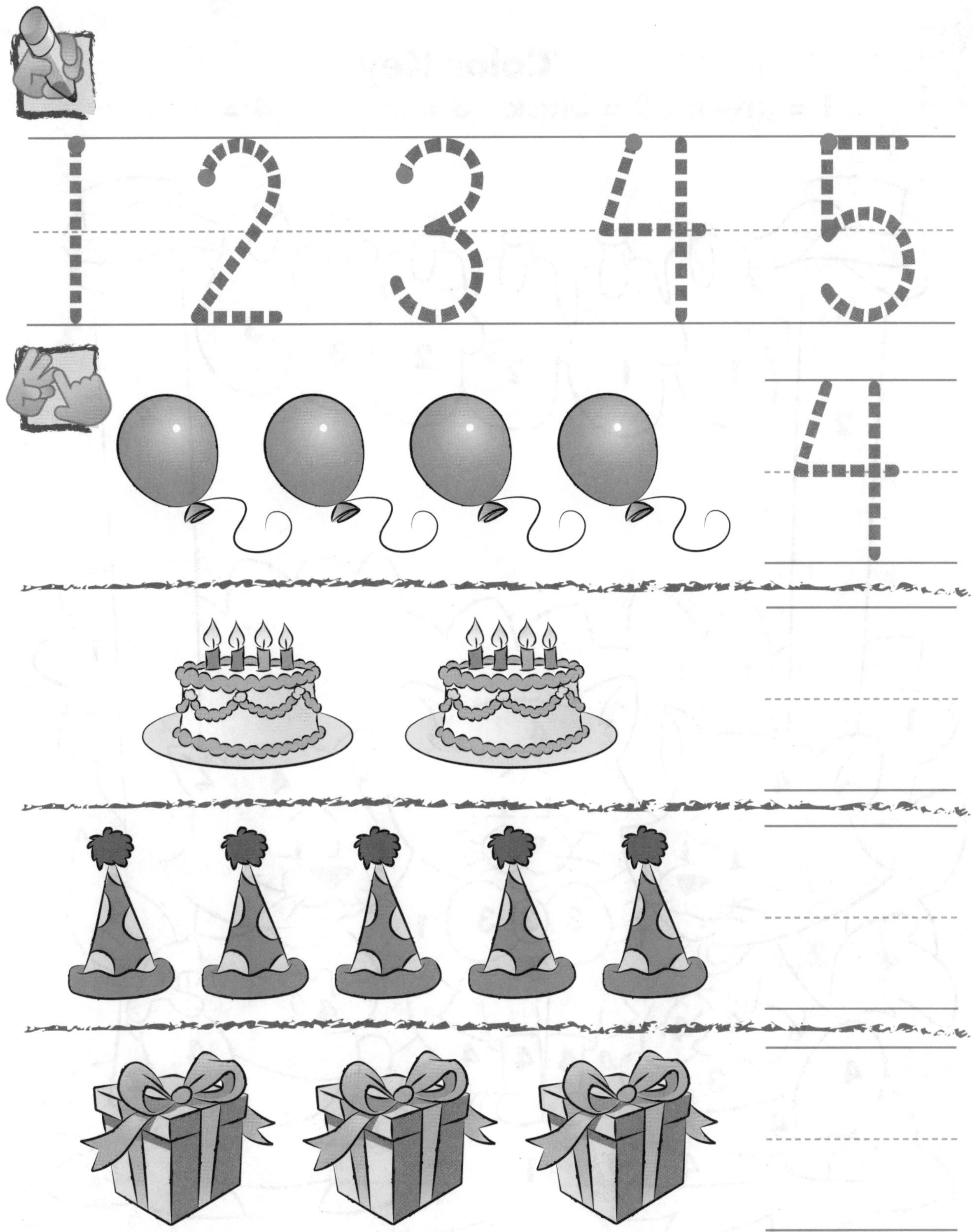

Parents: Have your child recite the numbers from 1 to 5 and use a pencil or crayon to trace each of the numbers at the top of the page. Then have him or her count the items in each row and write the correct numeral on the line.

Color Kittens

Color Key

1 = green 2 = black 3 = purple 4 = orange

Parents: Explain how to use the key as a coloring guide. Then have your child follow the key as he or she colors the kittens.

Get Up, Goldilocks!

Draw a path.

Parents: Ask your child to use a finger to trace the path between the bears and Goldilocks before drawing the path the bears should take with a crayon.

PREWRITING

Helping Hansel and Gretel

Draw a path.

Parents: Ask your child to use his or her finger to follow the path between the children and the witch's gingerbread house before drawing the path the children should take with a crayon.

Month 6 Checklist

Hands-on activities to help prepare your child for school!

SELF-CONCEPT

Address & Phone Number: pages 163-165

The self-awareness activities this month are very practical—mastering phone number and address and learning about community workers.

- ❑ Complete the worksheets.
- ❑ Take your child for a walk through the neighborhood and point out street addresses. Read the numbers together.
- ❑ Although your preschooler may not have the fine motor skills required to write addresses yet, give him or her as much practice as desired (only so long as it's fun!) tracing over your home address that you have printed out in large, clear letters and numbers.
- ❑ When you and your child are away from home, let him or her dial the home phone number for practice.

LANGUAGE

Opposites: pages 166-172; 189-192

Understanding opposites is a prerequisite for many academic tasks—following directions, thinking, reading. The activities here will help you make opposites more tangible for your child.

- ❑ Complete the worksheets.
- ❑ Play a game of opposites charades. To play, say a word, such as *sad*, and ask the other player to pantomime its opposite (*happy*).
- ❑ After your child completes each worksheet on opposites, find hands-on ways to reinforce the meaning of the words—e.g., help your child pour a full glass of water and tell what the opposite of full is.

PREREADING AND PREWRITING

Motor Control: pages 181-182

Sequence: pages 187-188

Use any of the activities from past months as well as the ones below to help your child work on fine motor skills and the important prereading skill of putting events in correct order (sequencing):

❑ Complete the worksheets.

❑ Have your child lie down on a large sheet of paper so that you can draw his or her outline. Then let the child use colored markers to fill in features and add color. Encourage the child to stay within the lines.

❑ Tell or read a story, such as "The Three Bears." Then ask your child to retell part of the story in correct order. For example, "Tell about how the story begins."

WRITING

Uppercase Letters A to H: pages 173-180

Learning the ABCs is a challenging process, but it's the first academic step in helping your child learn to read and write. The worksheets in this section will help him or her learn to recognize and write the letters A through H and begin to understand the sound associated with each.

❑ Complete the worksheets.

❑ Sing the ABC song with your child to help him or her learn alphabetic order.

❑ When making a connection between a letter and sound, say a word that begins with the letter and emphasize the beginning sound—e.g., AAA-Apple.

❑ Make letter shapes from clay. Talk about how some letter shapes are like others (e.g., E and F) and how some are very different (e.g., X and O).

READING

Rhyming Words: pages 183-186, 189-192

All of the worksheets for this month focus on word families—rhyming words that have the same ending sound, such as *-at* and *-ock*. Learning word families is very helpful for beginning readers who are struggling to make the connection between letter sounds and letter symbols.

❑ Brainstorm with your child as many words as you can for each word family—e.g., for *-an*: *man, can, fan, ran, Jan, ban, Dan, Nan, pan, tan, van,* etc. You can turn this into a game by saying, "I'll say a word. Then you say one that rhymes." Write each word so your child can see its written form.

❑ After singing a song together, say a word from the song and ask for a rhyming word. For example, after singing "Twinkle, Twinkle, Little Star," ask, "What word rhymed with *star*?"

My House

My address is

Parents: Let your child complete the dot-to-dot. Then explain, "Every house has an address that tells people where the house is located." Help your child write his or her address in the sentence and then read it together.

My Phone Number

My phone number is

____.

Parents: Let your child complete the dot-to-dot. Then explain, "Every phone has a number so people can call it from other phones." Help your child write his or her phone number in the sentence and then read it together.

What Do They Use?

Parents: Talk about the work of each person in the left column. Then ask your child to draw a line from the person to the item in the right column that he or she needs for the job.

LANGUAGE

Why Happy?

sad

happy

Color the sad rabbit blue.

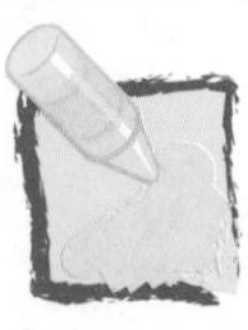

Color the happy rabbi yellow.

Parents: Point to the dog that is sad and ask, "Why is it sad?" Repeat for the happy dog. Explain that the words *sad* and *happy* are called opposites. Then ask your child to find the sad rabbit and color it blue. Color the happy rabbit yellow and discuss why it is happy.

Why Sad?

Color the clown who is not happy.

happy

sad

Color the rabbit that is not happy.

happy

sad

Parents: Discuss whether the colored clown is happy or sad. Then ask, "What's the opposite of *happy*? Color the clown picture that shows the opposite." Repeat for the tennis players. Point out the words *happy* and *sad* below each face.

In and Out

in **out**

Color the dog in the doghouse blue.

Color the dog out of the doghouse Brown.

Parents: Ask your child to point to the lion that's in his cage and then to the lion that's out of his cage. Point to the words *in* and *out*. Explain that they are called opposites. Then say, "Find the dog in the doghouse and color him blue. Color the dog that's out brown."

More In and Out

Color the dog that is not in bed.

Color the bear that is not in the tent.

Parents: **Discuss whether the colored dog is in or out of the bed. Ask, "What is the opposite of *in*? Color the dog picture that shows the opposite." Repeat for the bears. Point out the word *in* or *out* next to each picture.**

LANGUAGE

Full and Empty

full

empty

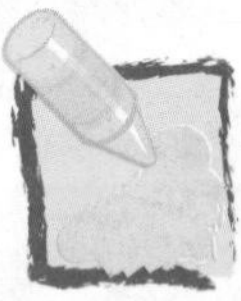

Color the full box yellow.

Color the empty box red.

Parents: Ask your child to point to the rabbit with a full glass and then to the rabbit with an empty glass. Point to the words *full* and *empty*. Explain that they are called opposites. Then say, "Color the full bag of popcorn yellow. Color the empty popcorn bag red."

The Letter A

Circle if its name begins like Ant.

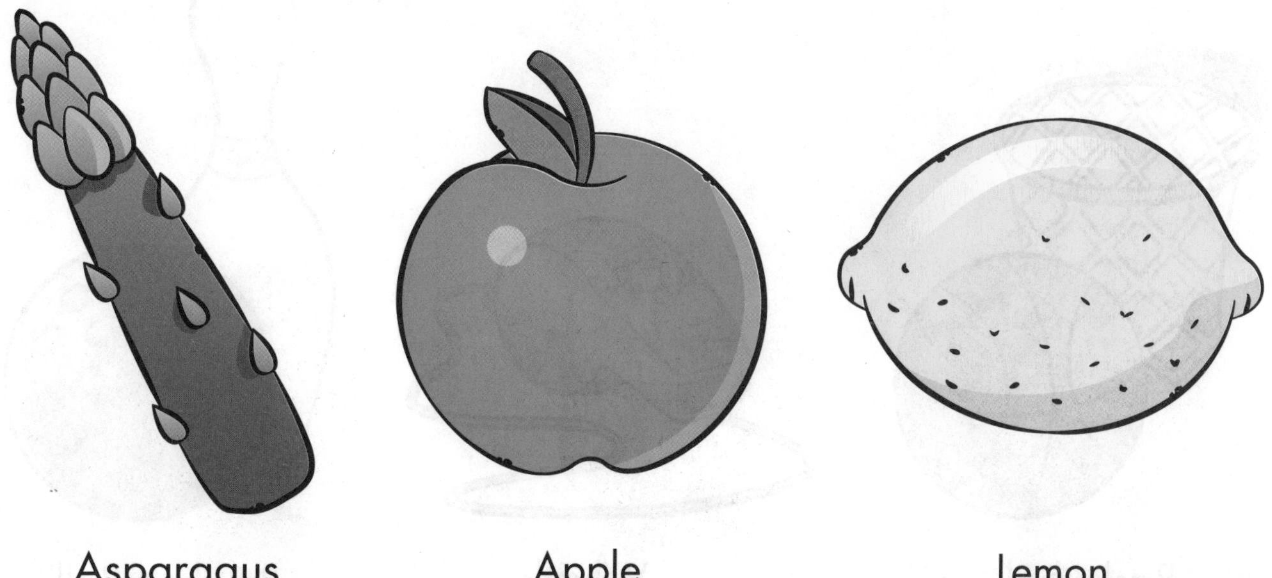

Asparagus Apple Lemon

Parents: Say, "*Ant* begins with the letter *A*. Listen for the sound *A* makes at the beginning of *aaa-ant*. Say it!" Show your child how to trace the hollow letter with a finger. Have him or her use a pencil or crayon to trace and write the letter. Then ask your child to circle the pictures that begin with A.

WRITING

The Letter B

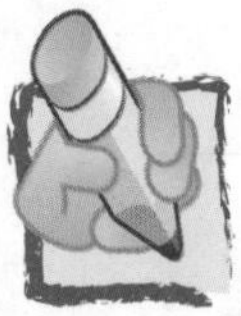

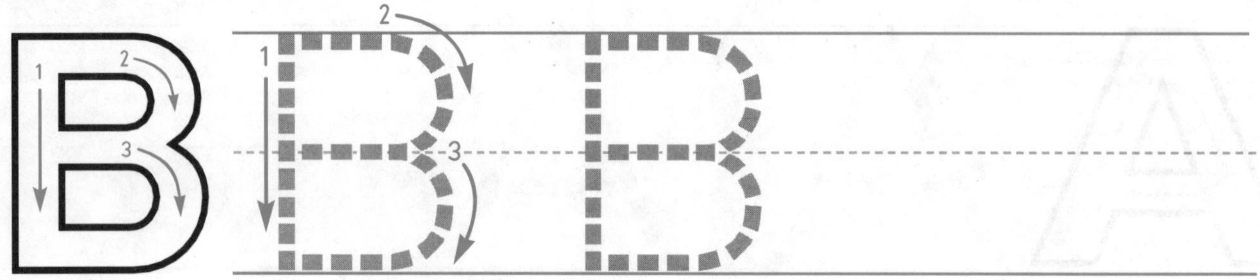

Circle if its name begins like Butterfly.

Basketball

Whistle

Bowling Ball

Parents: **Say, "*Butterfly* begins with the letter *B*. Listen for the sound *B* makes at the beginning of *buh-buh-butterfly*. Say it!" Show your child how to trace the hollow letter with a finger. Have him or her use a pencil or crayon to trace and write the letter. Then ask your child to circle the pictures that begin with B.**

Recognizing, tracing, and writing uppercase letters; recognizing letter sounds

The Letter C

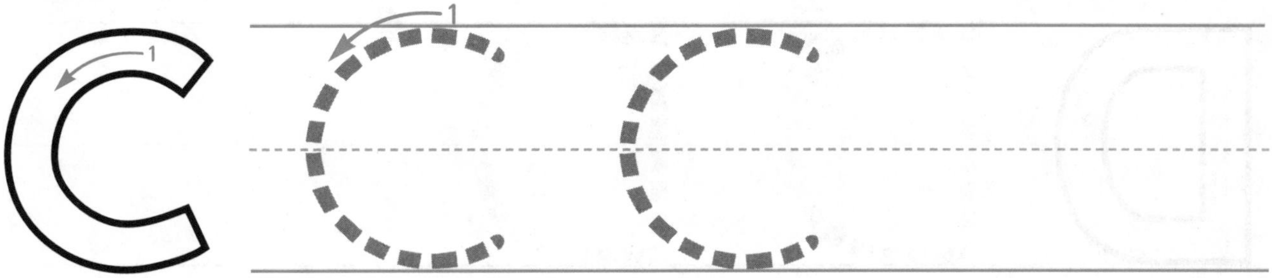

Circle if its name begins like Cat.

Sailboat Car Cart

Parents: Say, "*Cat* begins with the letter *C*. Listen for the sound *C* makes at the beginning of *ccc-cat*. Say it!" Show your child how to trace the hollow letter with a finger. Have him or her use a pencil or crayon to trace and write the letter. Then ask your child to circle the pictures that begin with C.

WRITING

The Letter D

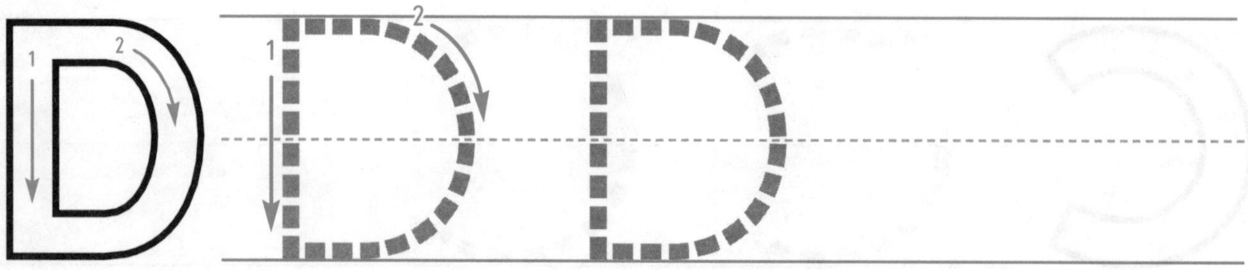

Circle if its name begins like Dinosaur.

Duck Lion Dog

Parents: Say, "*Dinosaur* begins with the letter *D*. Listen for the sound *D* makes at the beginning of *ddd-dinosaur*. Say it!" Show your child how to trace the hollow letter with a finger. Have him or her use a pencil or crayon to trace and write the letter. Then ask your child to circle the pictures that begin with D.

Recognizing, tracing, and writing uppercase letters; recognizing letter sounds

The Letter E

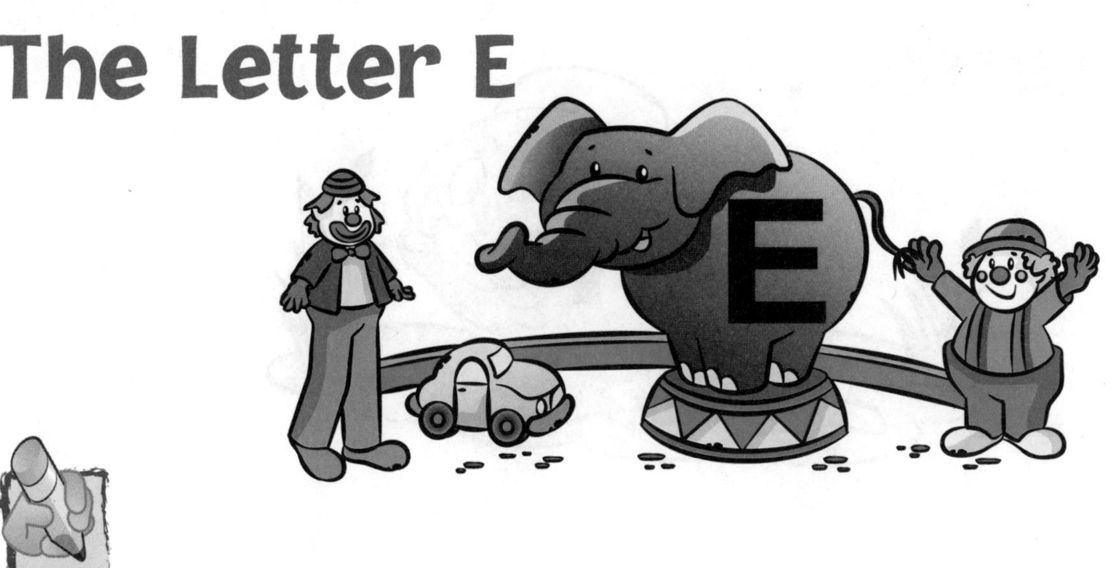

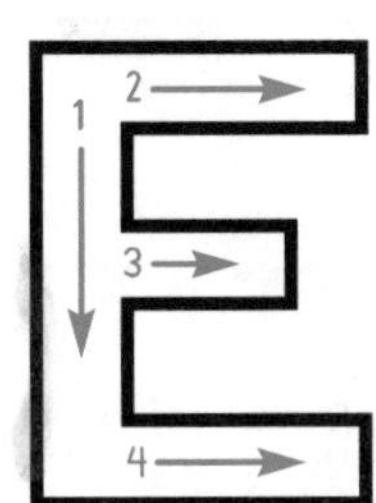

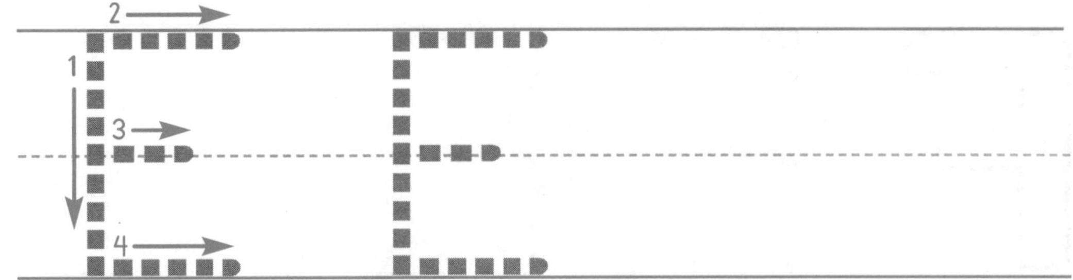

Circle if its name begins like Elephant.

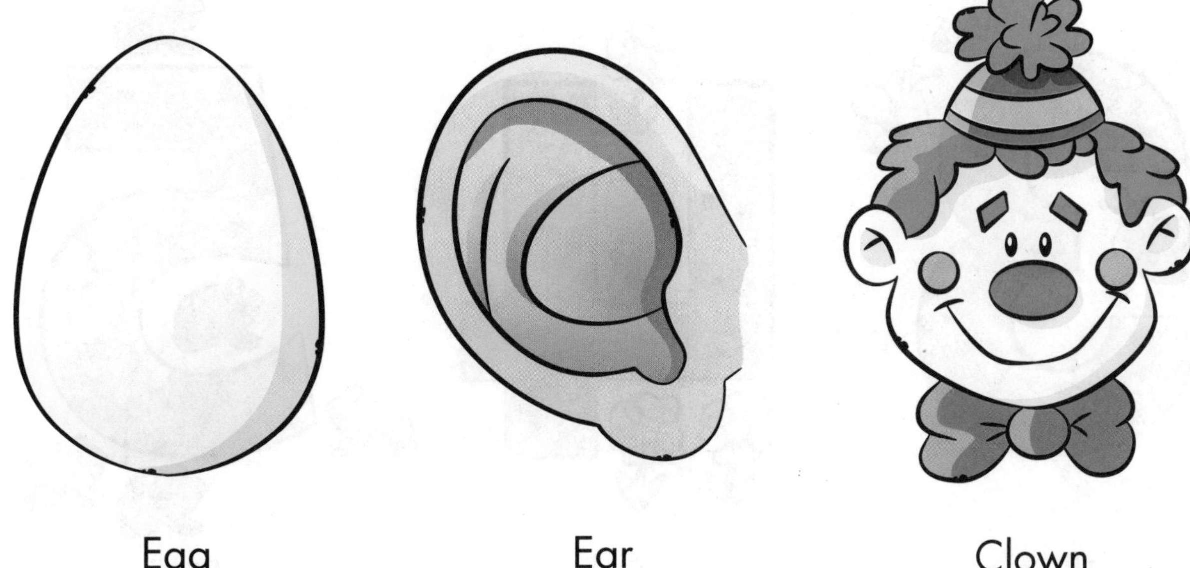

Egg   Ear   Clown

Parents: Say, "*Elephant* begins with the letter *E*. Listen for the sound *E* makes at the beginning of *eee-elephant*. Say it!" Show your child how to trace the hollow letter with a finger. Have him or her use a pencil or crayon to trace and write the letter. Then ask your child to circle the pictures that begin with E.

The Letter F

Circle if its name begins like Fish.

Three

Four

Five

Parents: Say, "*Fish* begins with the letter *F*. Listen for the sound *F* makes at the beginning of *fff-fish*. Say it!" Show your child how to trace the hollow letter with a finger. Have him or her use a pencil or crayon to trace and write the letter. Then ask your child to circle the pictures that begin with F.

The Letter G

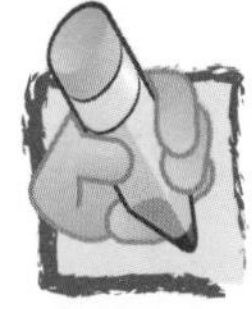

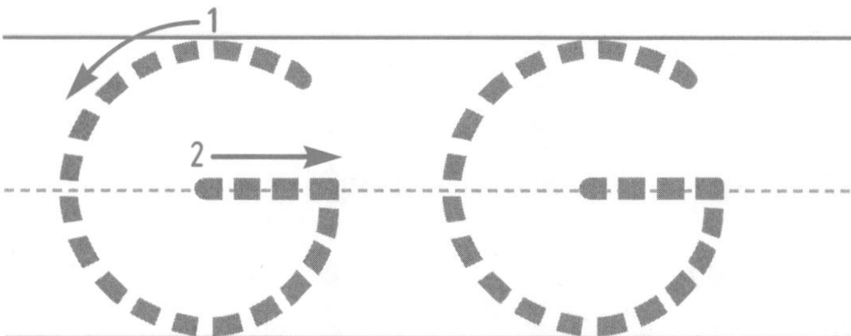

Circle if its name begins like Goat.

Guitar Corn Gate

Parents: Say, "*Goat* begins with the letter *G*. Listen for the sound *G* makes at the beginning of *ggg-goat*. Say it!" Show your child how to trace the hollow letter with a finger. Have him or her use a pencil or crayon to trace and write the letter. Then ask your child to circle the pictures that begin with G.

Recognizing, tracing, and writing uppercase letters; recognizing letter sounds

The Letter H

Circle if its name begins like House.

Horse Mouse Hen

Parents: **Say, "*House* begins with the letter *H*. Listen for the sound *H* makes at the beginning of *hhh-house*. Say it!" Show your child how to trace the hollow letter with a finger. Have him or her use a pencil or crayon to trace and write the letter. Then ask your child to circle the pictures that begin with H.**

Stop, Look, and Listen!

Parents: Help your child connect the letters in alphabetical order to complete the picture. Then let him or her color the picture.

PREWRITING

Batter Up!

Parents: Help your child connect the letters in alphabetical order to complete the picture. Then let him or her color the picture.

-at Rhymes

cat

hat

Color the one that rhymes with *cat*.

Color the ones with rhyming names.

Parents: Point to each picture at the top of the page and say its name. Have your child do the same. Explain that those names rhyme, because they both have the *-at* sound at the end. Then help your child complete the rest of the page.

-ock Rhymes

clock

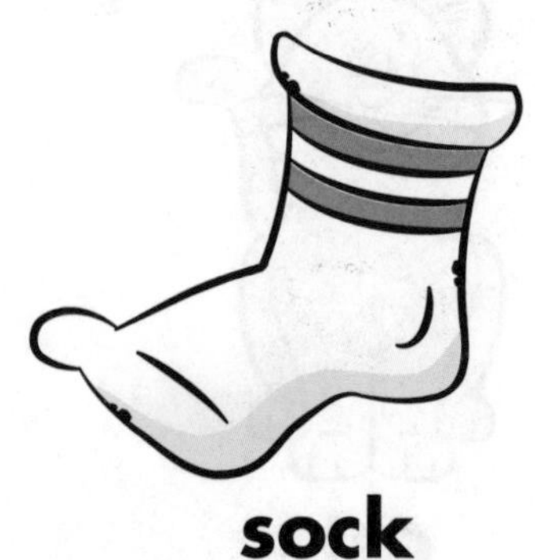

sock

Color the one that rhymes with *clock*.

Color the ones with rhyming names.

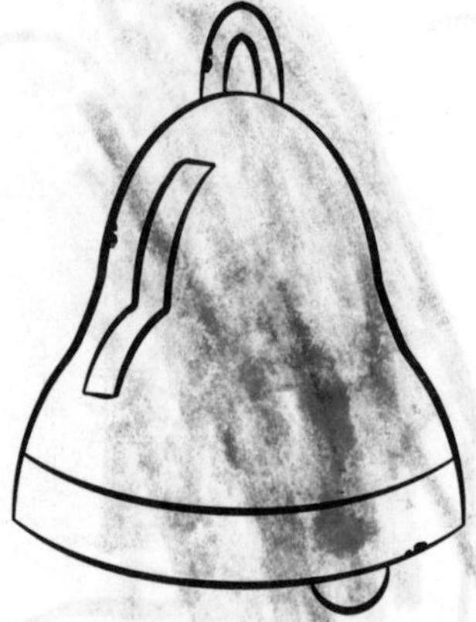

Parents: Point to each picture at the top of the page and say its name. Have your child do the same. Explain that those names rhyme, because they both have the *-ock* sound at the end. Then help your child complete the rest of the page.

-an Rhymes

man **can**

Color the one that rhymes with *can*.

Color the ones with rhyming names.

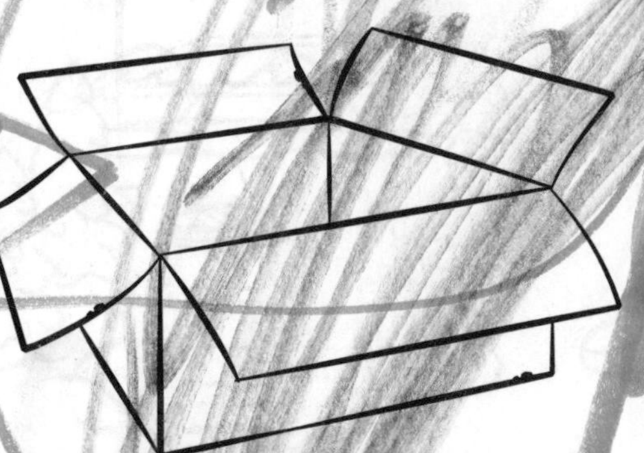

Parents: **Point to each picture at the top of the page and say its name. Have your child do the same. Explain that those names rhyme, because they both have the *-an* sound at the end. Then help your child complete the rest of the page.**

-ake Rhymes

cake

lake

Color the one that rhymes with *cake*.

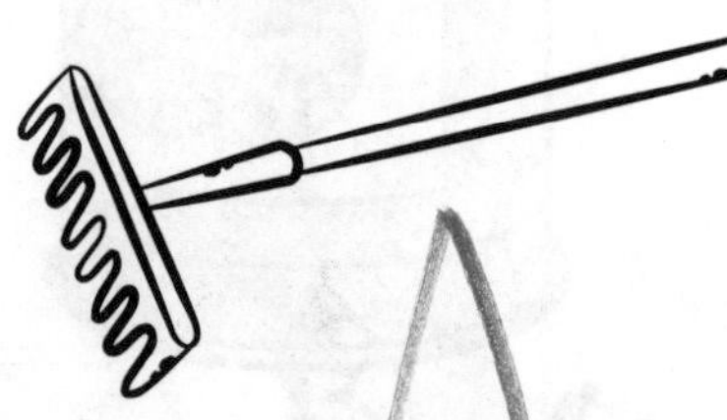

Color the ones that rhyme.

Parents: Point to each picture at the top of the page and say its name. Have your child do the same. Explain that those names rhyme, because they both have the *-ake* sound at the end. Then help your child complete the rest of the page.

First, Next I

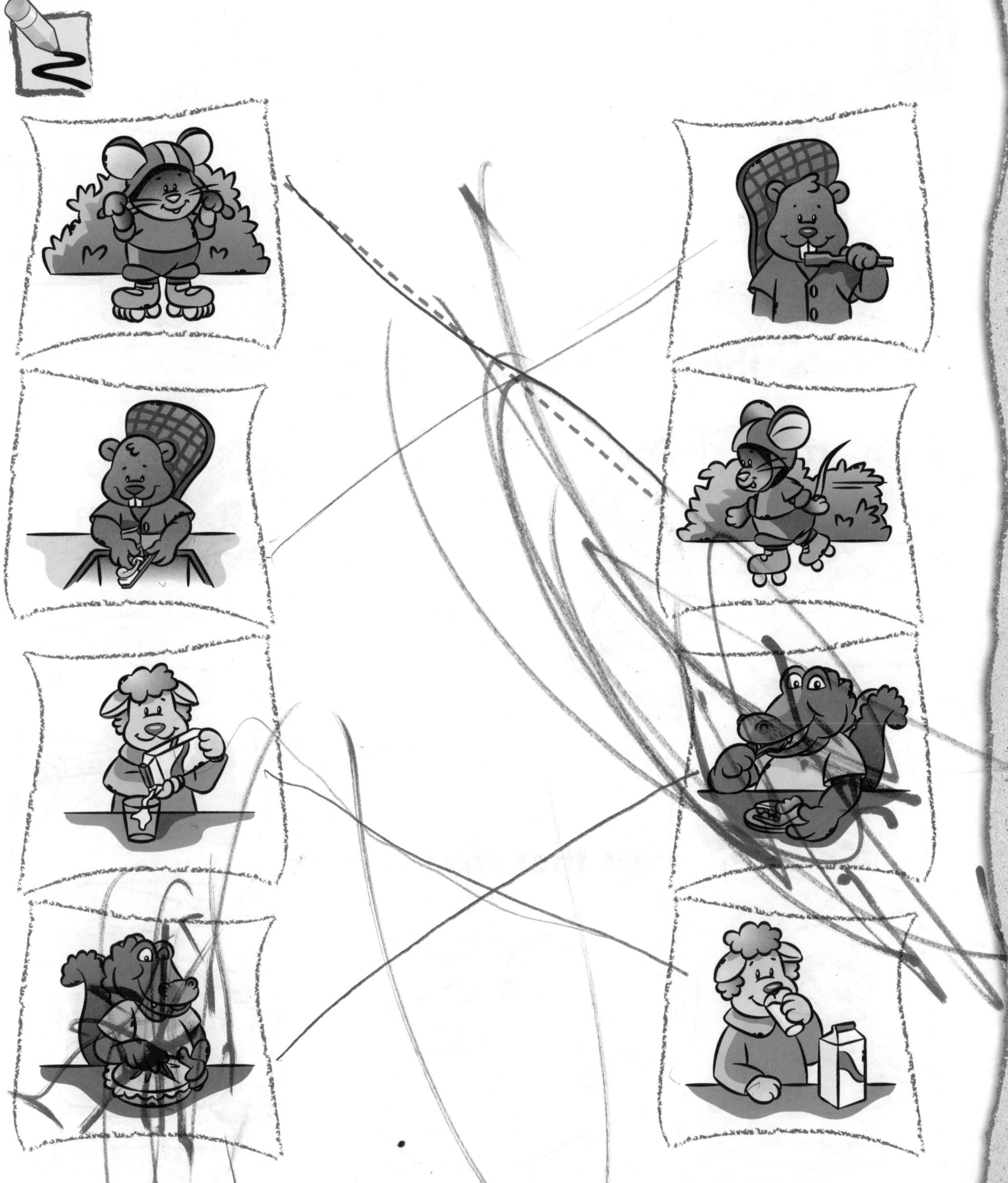

Parents: Point to the picture at the top left and ask, "What's happening here? Draw a line to the picture that shows what might happen next." Repeat for each picture. Encourage your child to tell a story about each set of pictures using the words *first* and *next.*

PREREADING

First, Next II

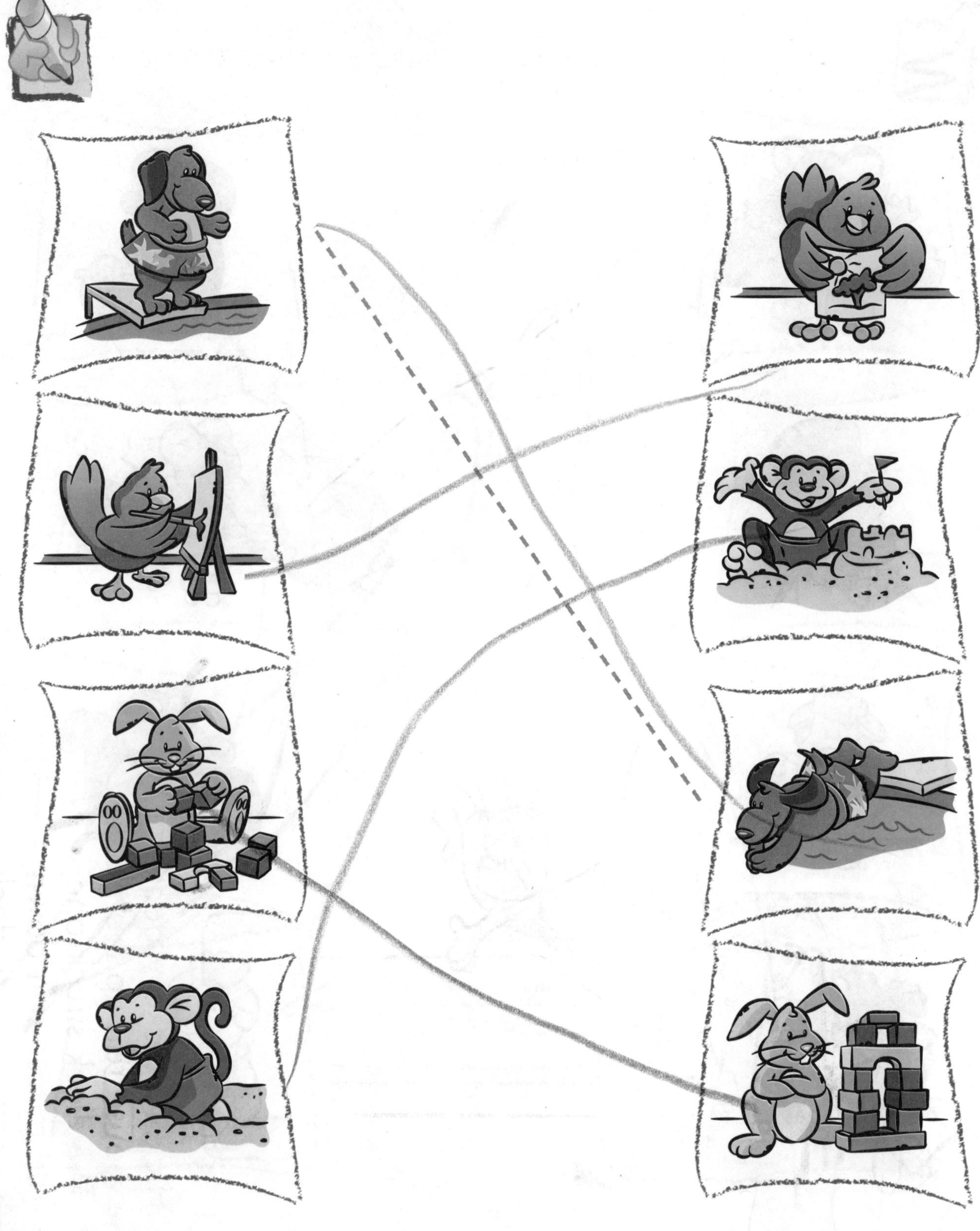

Parents: Point to the picture at the top left and ask, "What's happening here? Draw a line to the picture that shows what might happen next." Repeat for each picture. Encourage your child to tell a story about each set of pictures using the words *first* and *next*.

Opposite Rhymes

Hickory dickory dock,
The mouse ran up the clock.
The clock struck one,
The mouse ran down,
Hickory dickory dock.

Diddle, diddle, dumpling, my son John
Went to bed with his stockings on;

One shoe off and one shoe on,
Diddle, diddle dumpling, my son John.

Some like
it hot,

Some like
it cold,

Some like it in the pot,
Nine days old.

Pease
porridge
hot,

Pease
porridge
cold,

Pease porridge in a pot
Nine days old.

The Itsy Bitsy Spider
went up the water spout;
Down came the rain
and washed the spider out;

Up came the sun and
dried up all the rain,

And the Itsy Bitsy Spider
climbed up the spout again.

Month 7 Checklist

Hands-on activities to help prepare your child for school!

LANGUAGE

Opposites: pages 195-201

Use any of the activities for opposites suggested in previous checklists or try the ones below:

- ❑ Complete the worksheets.
- ❑ Help your child find pictures in old magazines that show opposites—for example, an open garage door, a closed garage door. Use one sheet of paper for each pair of pictures: paste one picture on one side of the paper and the other picture on the other side. Write the opposite word under each picture. Then ask your child to show you the opposite of a specific word.
- ❑ Make up riddles to help your child practice opposite words—for example, "I'm the opposite of up. What am I?"

MATH

Counting 6 to 10: pages 202-210

In addition to learning to recognize and write numerals, it's also important to learn early about the number properties listed in this section.

- ❑ Complete the worksheets.
- ❑ Make sure your child understands that each number describes "how many" and the "how many" can be anything. For example: 6 can refer to the number of dogs, pictures, pennies, polar bears, or anything else.
- ❑ Explain that the number of objects in a group does not change, even when arranged differently. For example: a row of 4 pennies and a row of 2 pennies is the same amount as a row of 6 pennies. Use coins or other counters to help your child grasp this fact.

PREREADING AND PREWRITING

Dot-to-Dot Picture: page 208

Mazes: pages 219-220

The worksheets in this month provide more prewriting practice. Use the activities below or ones from other months to help your child practice fine motor skills.

- ❑ Complete the worksheets.
- ❑ Spray shaving foam on a bathtub wall during bath time. Let your child draw letters, numbers, or shapes in the foam with his or her fingers.
- ❑ A couple of times each week, let your child trace over the letters in his or her name with a pencil or crayon. Continue this practice until the child can print the name without tracing.

WRITING

Uppercase Letters I to P: pages 211-218

While the focus of the worksheets this month is on how to form letters, it is always helpful to also practice letter recognition skills. Use any of the activities below or ones from previous months.

- ❑ Complete the worksheets.
- ❑ Say a letter name to your child and ask him or her to find it among a group of magnetic letters or alphabet blocks.
- ❑ Help your child make letter shapes from clay. Then play a game. Blindfold the child, mix up the letters, and ask your child to touch one of the letters and guess its name. Only include letters that the child has already been exposed to.

READING

Rhyming Words: pages 221-224

More word families are presented for this month. In addition to the activities below, regularly read rhyming stories to your child and ask which words rhyme.

- ❑ Complete the worksheets.
- ❑ Write two rhyming words on the same side of an index card, then cut apart the card so that each word is on a separate piece. It's best to also include a picture for each word. Use ones from the worksheets or from other sources. Make several of these two-piece rhyming word puzzles. Then let your child practice matching the pieces that go together. As he or she plays, encourage the child to say the name of each picture, listening for the rhyme.
- ❑ Build a collection of pictures with rhyming names. Paste each picture on its own index card. Let your child match pictures of words that rhyme.

Open and Closed

open

closed

Color the open lunch box green.

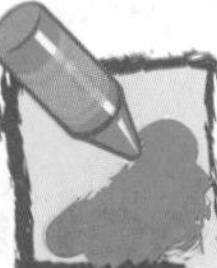

Color the closed lunch box red.

Parents: Ask your child to point to the turtle's box that is open and then to the box that is closed. Point to the words *open* and *closed*. Explain that they are called opposites. Then say, "Color the open lunchbox green. Color the closed lunchbox red."

More Open and Closed

Color the book that is not closed.

Color the door that is not open.

Parents: Discuss whether the colored book is open or closed. Ask, "What is the opposite of *closed*? Color the picture that shows the opposite." Repeat for the doors. Point out the words *open* and *closed* next to the pictures.

Up and Down

Color the balloon that is up yellow.

Color the balloon that is down blue.

Parents: Ask your child to point to the bear that is *up* and then to the bear that is *down*. Point to the words *up* and *down*. Explain that they are called opposites. Then say, "Color the balloon that is up yellow. Color the balloon that is down blue."

LANGUAGE

More Up and Down

Color the bird that is not up.

up

up

down

Color the plane that is not up.

up

up

down

Parents: **Discuss whether the bird is up or down. Ask, "What is the opposite of *up*? Color the picture that shows the opposite." Repeat for the planes. Point out the words *up* and *down* next to the pictures.**

Front and Back

front

back

Color the toy soldier facing frontward blue.

Color the toy soldier facing backward red.

Parents: Ask your child to point to the front of the car and then to the back. Point to the words *front* and *back*. Explain that they are called opposites. Then say, "Color the toy soldier with its front to us blue. Color the toy soldier with its back to us red.

More Front and Back

Color the bunny that is not facing front.

front

front

back

Color the kangaroo that is not facing front.

front

back

front

Parents: Discuss whether you can see the front or the back of the rabbit on the left. Then ask, "What is the opposite of *front*? Find the picture that shows the opposite." Repeat for the kangaroos. Point out the words *front* and *back* below the pictures.

Opposites Review II

Circle the picture that shows the opposite.

closed

up

back

Parents: Have your child tell about the first picture in each row. Point out and read the word under the picture. Then have your child circle the picture that shows its opposite.

MATH

Bird Counting

1, 2, 3, 4, 5. Little birdies learn to fly.

1 2 3 4 5

Circle the correct number.

1 2 4

2 3 5

1 3 5

2 3 4

Parents: Read the verse to your child. Have him or her touch each bird as you count. Then ask your child to circle the number under each group of items that shows how many.

Six

Parents: (Top) Ask your child to say *six* as he or she points to the numeral and number word, and then counts the six dog dishes. (Middle) Ask your child to count and color six dogs. (Bottom) Have your child trace and write more 6s.

MATH

Seven

7

seven

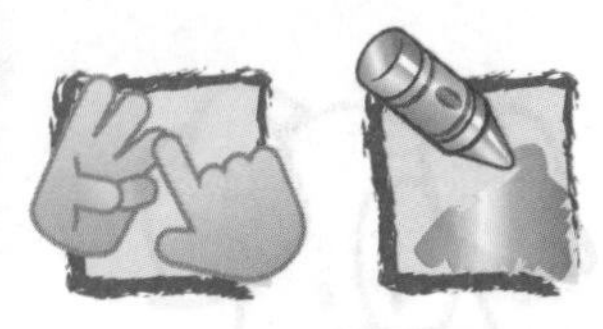

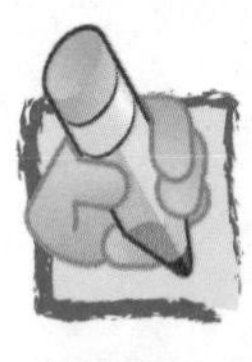

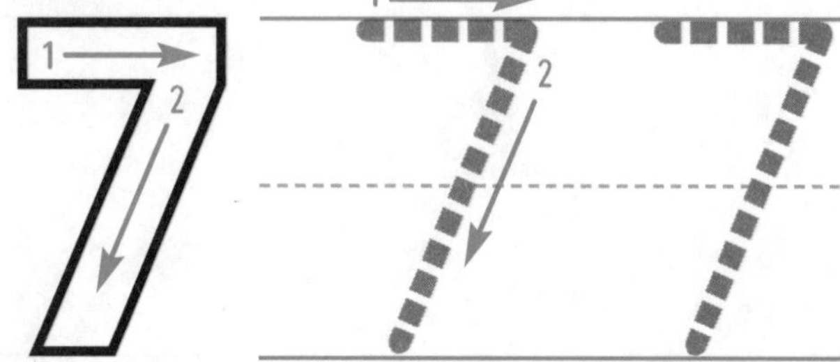

Parents: **(Top) Ask your child to say *seven* as he or she points to the numeral and number word, and then counts the seven insects. (Middle) Ask your child to count and color seven grasshoppers. (Bottom) Have your child trace and write more 7s.**

Eight

8 eight

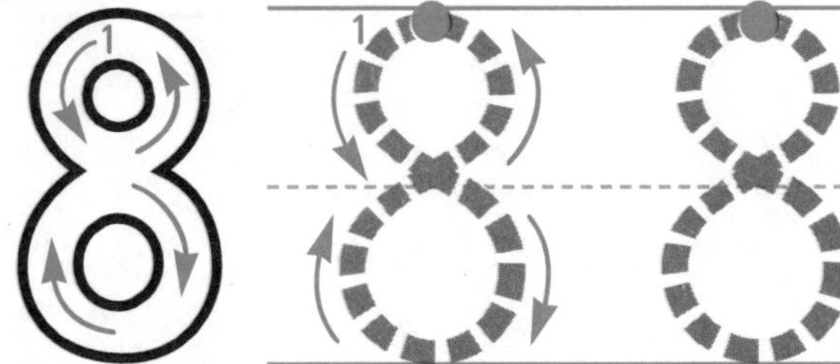

Parents: (Top) Ask your child to say *eight* as he or she points to the numeral and number word, and then counts the eight cherries. (Middle) Ask your child to count and color eight strawberries. (Bottom) Have your child trace and write more 8s.

MATH

nine

9 nine

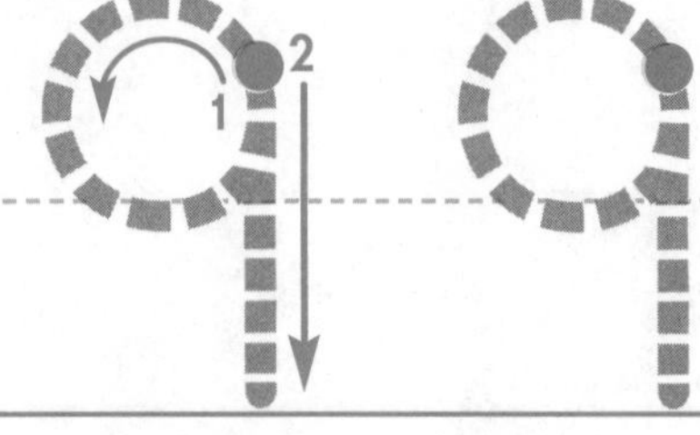

Parents: (Top) Ask your child to say *nine* as he or she points to the numeral and number word, and then counts the nine flowers. (Middle) Ask your child to count and color nine butterflies. (Bottom) Have your child trace and write more 9s.

Ten

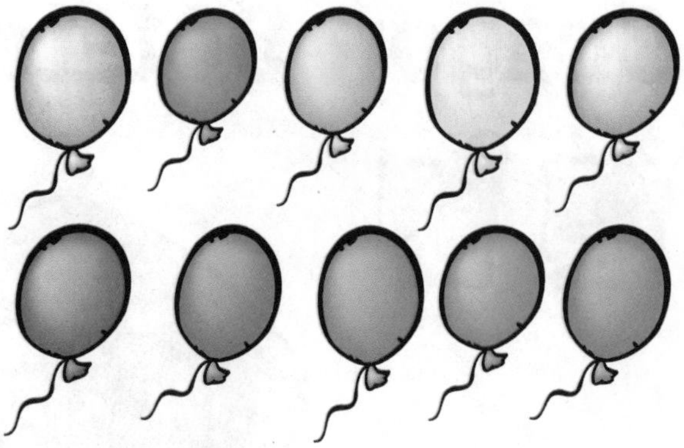

10 **ten**

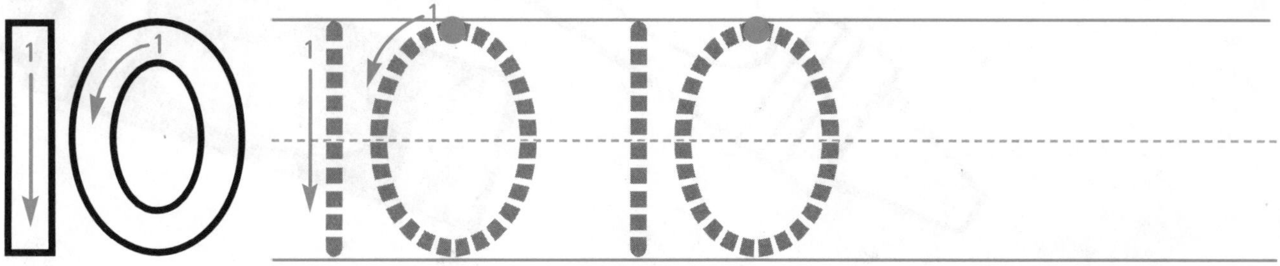

Parents: (Top) Ask your child to say *ten* as he or she points to the numeral and number word, and then counts the ten balloons. (Middle) Ask your child to count and color ten cupcakes. (Bottom) Have your child trace and write more 10s.

PREWRITING

Crayon Dot-to-Dot

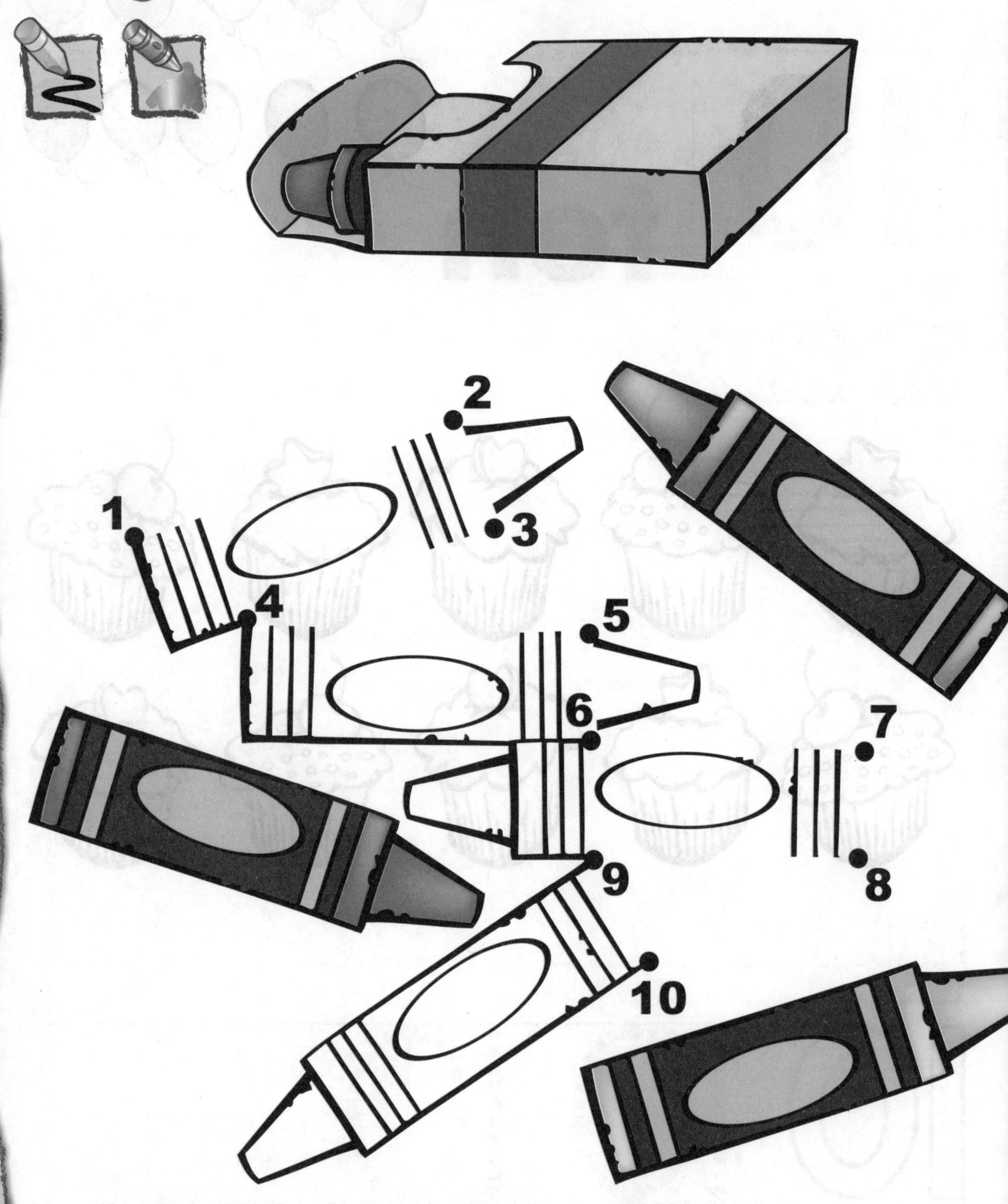

Parents: First, ask your child to predict what the dot-to-dot picture will show. Then have him or her point to the numerals in order from 1 to 10 before connecting them with a pencil or crayon in numeric order. Let your child color the completed picture.

 Understanding numerical order; developing fine motor control

1 one

2 two

3 three

4 four

5 five

Parents: Ask your child to name each numeral and number word and count the corresponding objects. Then help him or her cut apart and shuffle the cards. Have your child match each numeral card to the card showing the same number of objects.

6 six	
7 seven	
8 eight	
9 nine	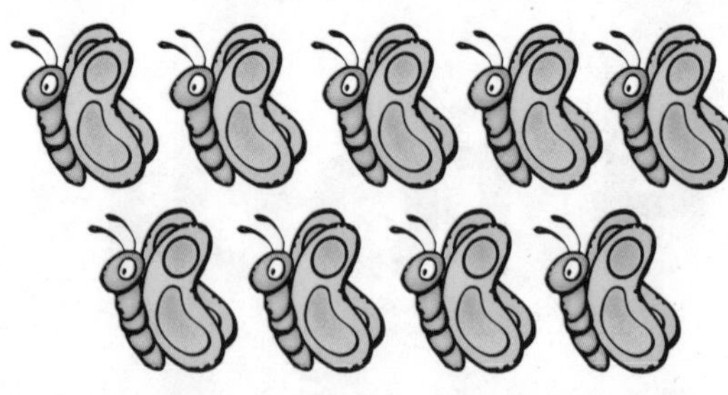
10 ten	

Parents: Ask your child to name each numeral and number word and count the corresponding objects. Then help him or her cut apart and shuffle the cards. Have your child match each numeral card to the card showing the same number of objects.

The Letter I

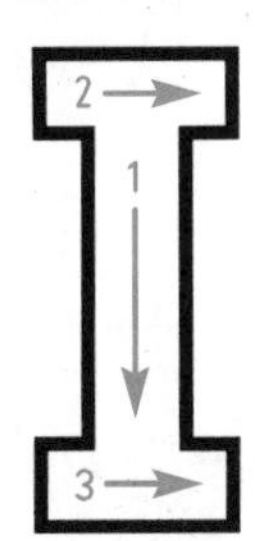

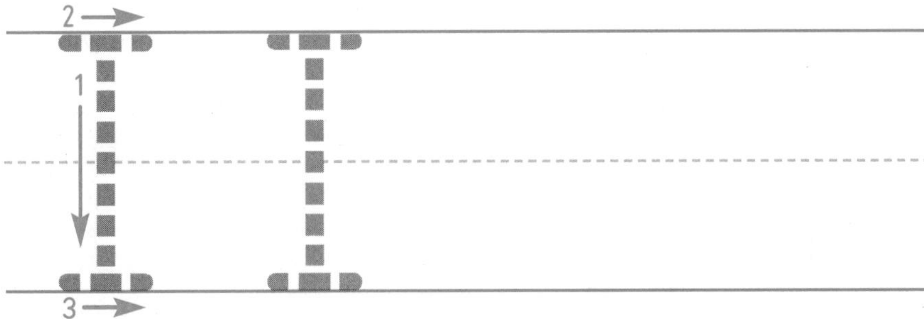

Circle if its name begins like Igloo.

Indian

Squirrel

Iguana

Parents: Say, "*Igloo* begins with the letter *I*. Listen for the sound *I* makes at the beginning of *iii-igloo*. Say it!" Show your child how to trace the hollow letter with a finger. Have him or her use a pencil or crayon to trace and write the letter. Then ask your child to circle the pictures that begin with I.

WRITING

The Letter J

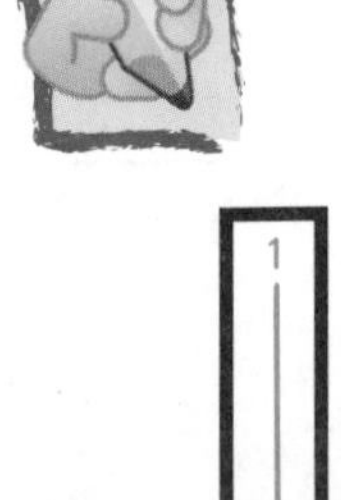

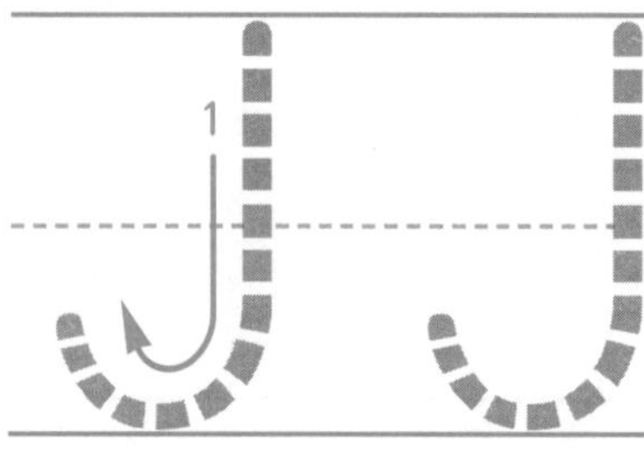

Circle if its name begins like Jug.

Milk

Jam

Juice

Parents: Say, "*Jug* begins with the letter *J*. Listen for the sound *J* makes at the beginning of jjj-*jug*. Say it!" Then show your child how to trace the hollow letter with a finger. Have him or her use a pencil or crayon to trace and write the letter. Then ask your child to circle the pictures that begin with J.

Recognizing, tracing, and writing uppercase letters; recognizing letter sounds

The Letter K

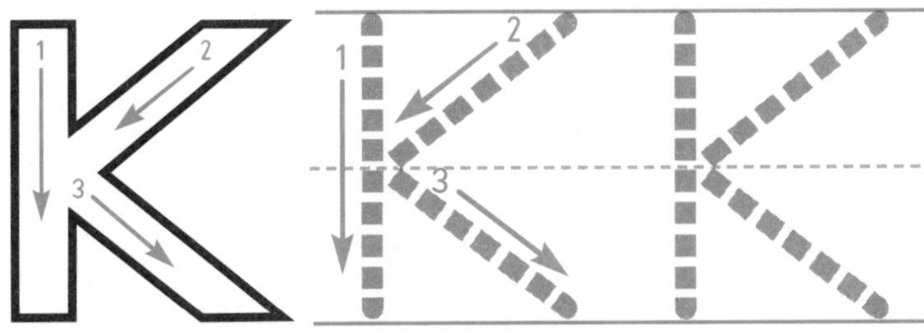

Circle if its name begins like Kangaroo.

Snail Kitten Koala

Parents: Say, "*Kangaroo* begins with the letter *K*. Listen for the sound *K* makes at the beginning of *kkk-kangaroo*. Say it!" Show your child how to trace the hollow letter with a finger. Have him or her use a pencil or crayon to trace and write the letter. Then ask your child to circle the pictures that begin with K.

Recognizing, tracing, and writing uppercase letters; recognizing letter sounds

WRITING

The Letter L

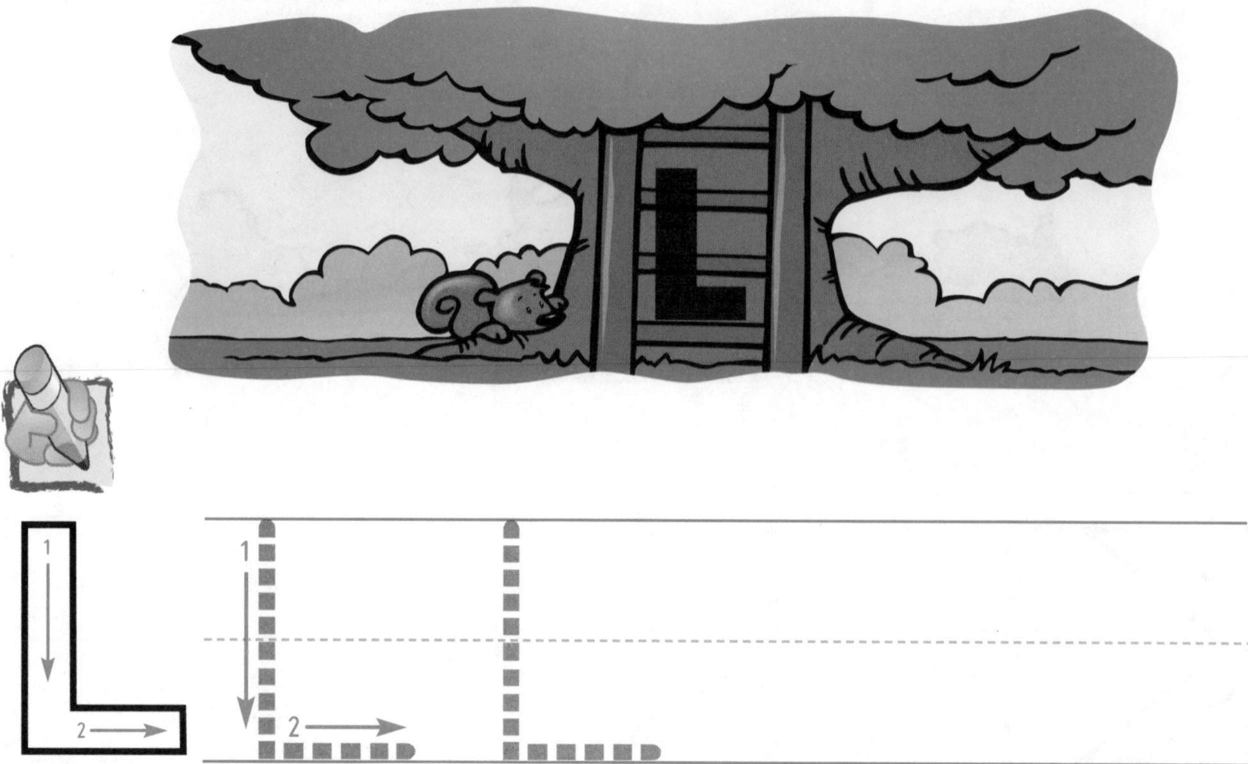

Circle if its name begins like Ladder.

Lamb

Lion

Grasshopper

Parents: Say, "*Ladder* begins with the letter *L*. Listen for the sound *L* makes at the beginning of *lll-ladder*. Say it!" Show your child how to trace the hollow letter with a finger. Have him or her use a pencil or crayon to trace and write the letter. Then ask your child to circle the pictures that begin with L.

Recognizing, tracing, and writing uppercase letters; recognizing letter sounds

The Letter M

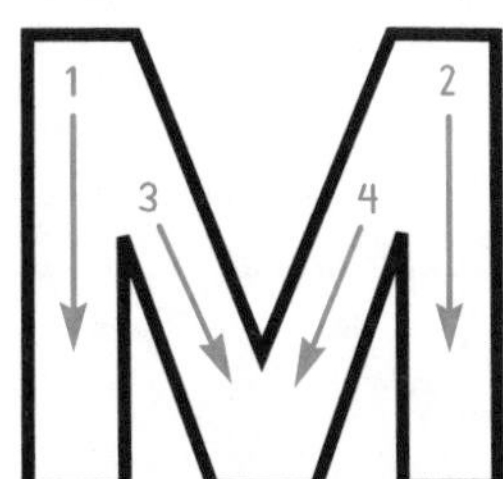

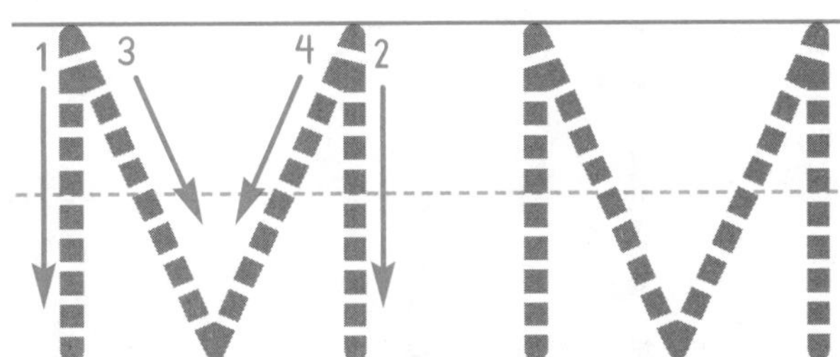

Circle if its name begins like Mountain.

Giraffe

Mouse

Monkey

Parents: Say, "*Mountain* begins with the letter *M*. Listen for the sound *M* makes at the beginning of *mmm-mountain*. Say it!" Show your child how to trace the hollow letter with a finger. Have him or her use a pencil or crayon to trace and write the letter. Then ask your child to circle the pictures that begin with M.

The Letter N

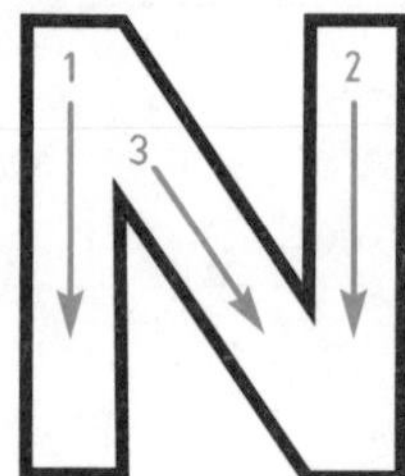

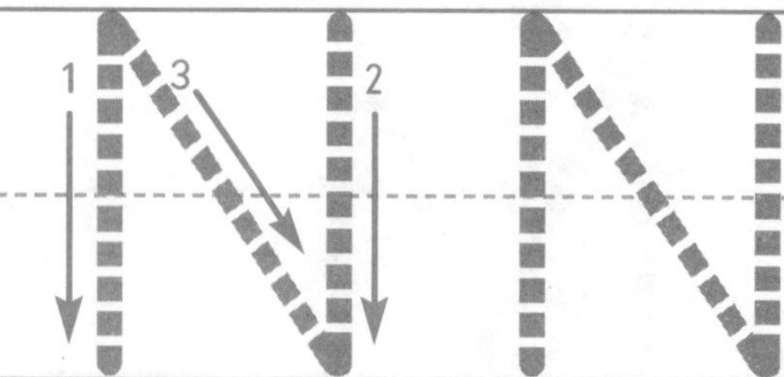

Circle if its name begins like Nest.

Notebook

Nurse

Chick

Parents: Say, "*Nest* begins with the letter *N*. Listen for the sound *N* makes at the beginning of *nnn-nest*. Say it!" Show your child how to trace the hollow letter with a finger. Have him or her use a pencil or crayon to trace and write the letter. Then ask your child to circle the pictures that begin with N.

The Letter O

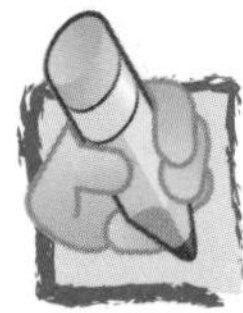

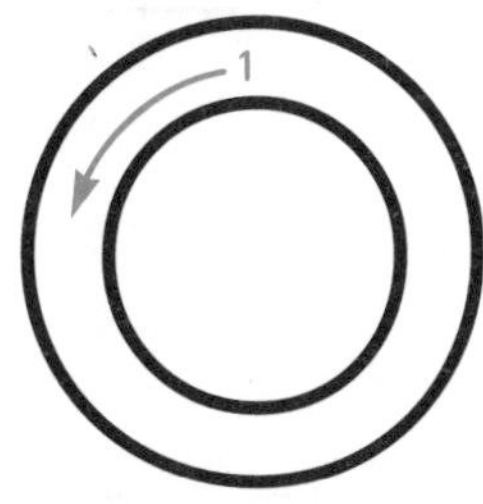

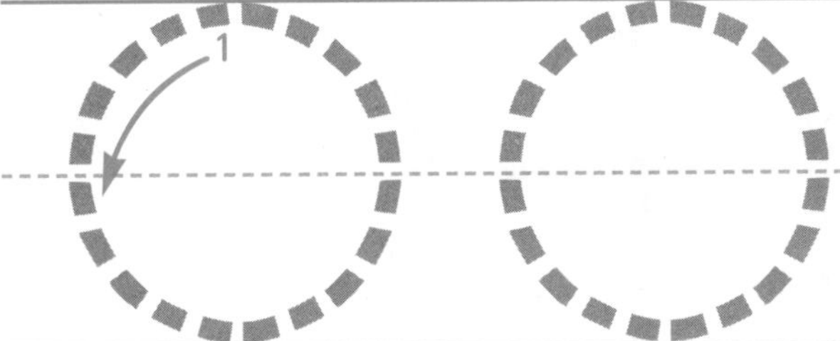

Circle if its name begins like Octopus.

Otter

Squirrel

Owl

Parents: Say, "*Octopus* begins with the letter *O*. Listen for the sound *O* makes at the beginning of *ooo-octopus*. Say it!" Show your child how to trace the hollow letter with a finger. Have him or her use a pencil or crayon to trace and write the letter. Then ask your child to circle the pictures that begin with O.

The Letter P

Circle if its name begins like Parrot.

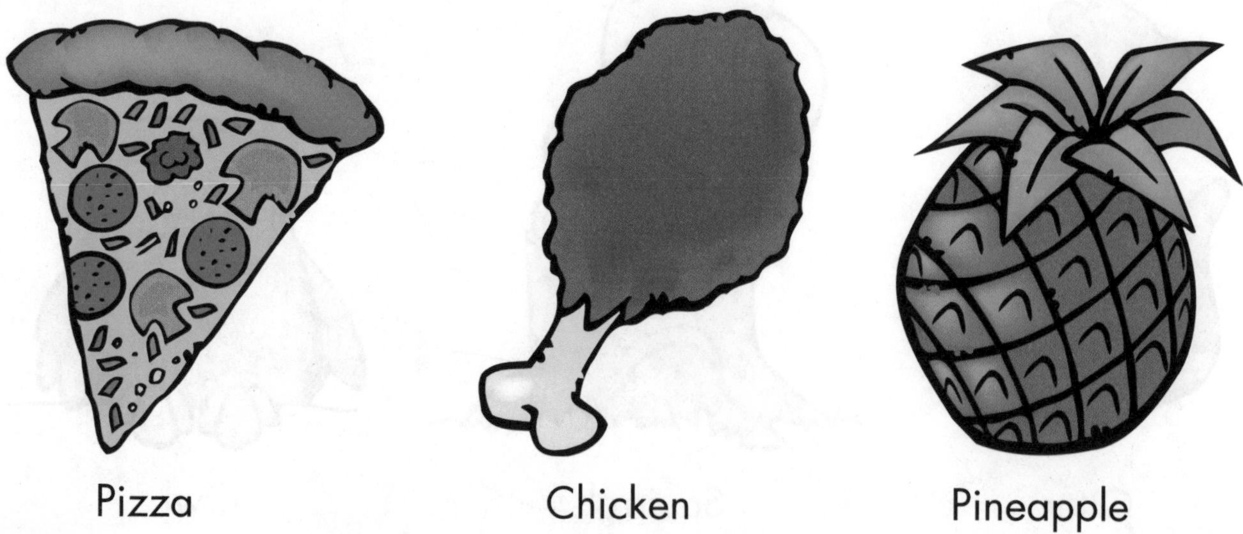

Pizza Chicken Pineapple

Parents: Say, "*Parrot* begins with the letter *P*. Listen for the sound *P* makes at the beginning of *ppp-parrot*. Say it!" Show your child how to trace the hollow letter with a finger. Have him or her use a pencil or crayon to trace and write the letter. Then ask your child to circle the pictures that begin with P.

Recognizing, tracing, and writing uppercase letters; recognizing letter sounds

Pot of Gold

Parents: Ask your child to use a finger to follow the path of letters in alphabetical order from I to P before using a pencil or crayon to draw a path that leads the leprechaun to the pot of gold.

Autumn Leaves

Parents: Ask your child to use a finger to follow the path of letters in alphabetical order from I to P before using a pencil or crayon to draw a path that leads the farmer home.

-am Rhymes

ram

jam

Color the one that rhymes with ram.

Color the ones with rhyming names.

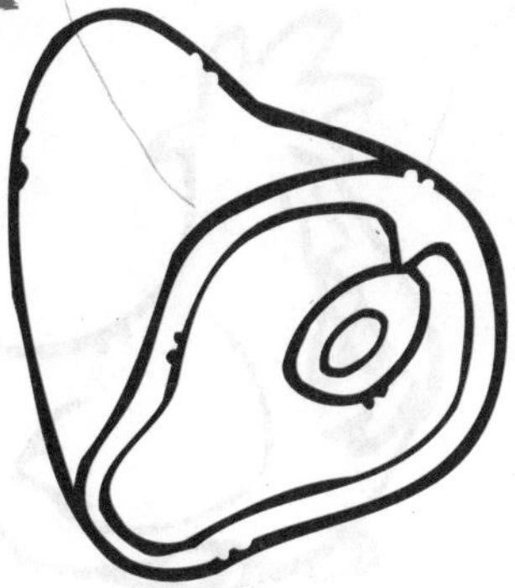

Parents: Point to each picture at the top of the page and say its name. Have your child do the same. Explain that those names rhyme because they both have the *-am* sound at the end. Then help your child complete the rest of the page.

-en Rhymes

pen

ten

Color the one that rhymes with pen.

Color the ones with rhyming names.

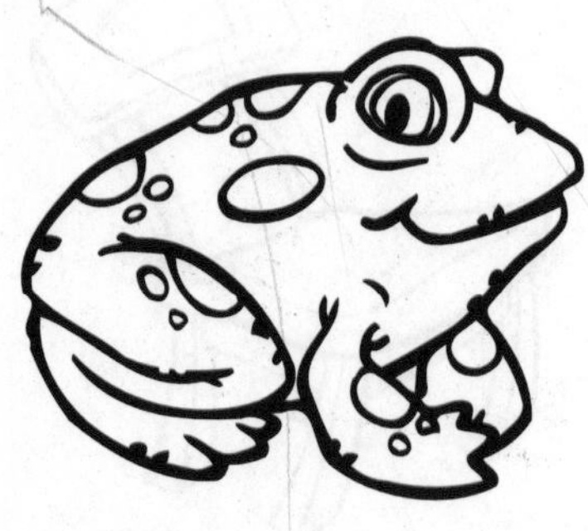

Parents: Point to each picture at the top of the page and say its name. Have your child do the same. Explain that those names rhyme because they both have the *-en* sound at the end. Then help your child complete the rest of the page.

Long E Rhymes

tree

bee

Color the one that rhymes with bee.

Color the ones with rhyming names.

Parents: Point to each picture at the top of the page and say its name. Have your child do the same. Explain that those names rhyme because they both have the *-ee* sound at the end. Then help your child complete the rest of the page.

READING

-um Rhymes

drum

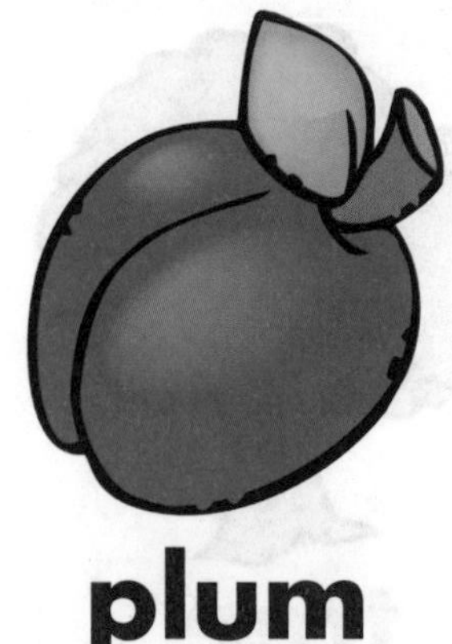

plum

Color the one that rhymes with drum.

Color the ones with rhyming names.

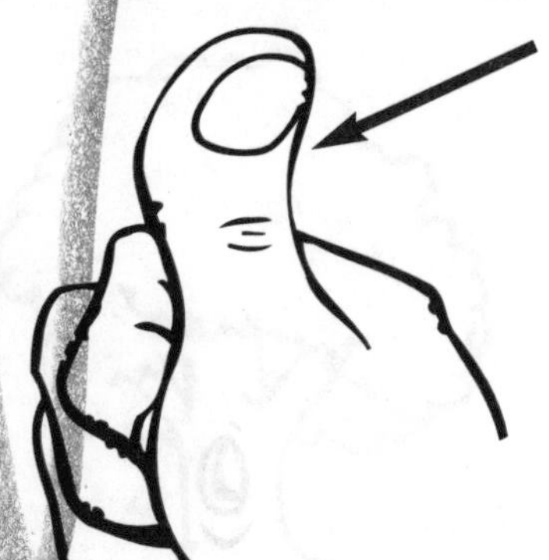

Parents: Point to each picture at the top of the page and say its name. Have your child do the same. Explain that those names rhyme because they both have the *-um* sound at the end. Then help your child complete the rest of the page.

Month 8 Checklist

Hands-on activities to help prepare your child for school!

MATH

Writing Numerals and Counting 6 to 8: pages 227-233
Matching Numerals with Amounts: pages 234, 254-258

Learning is always easiest when its purpose is clear. The activities in this section include ideas that will help your child see the value of numbers in everyday life:

- ❑ Complete the worksheets.
- ❑ To help your child understand the idea of one-to-one correspondence, let him or her help you set the table. First, talk about the number of people dining. Then say, "We need a plate, silverware, and glass for each person. Can you make sure that each place has those things?"
- ❑ If you have number cards, shuffle them and have your child practice putting them in correct numeric order.
- ❑ Apply counting to physical activities by asking your child to do six jumping jacks, to hop on one foot eight times, to touch his or her toes seven times, and so on.
- ❑ Post page 254 at your child's level and use it to review numbers 1 to 10. Then read "Counting Rhymes," pages 255-258, together.

PREREADING AND PREWRITING

Following Directions: pages 236-237, 243-244
Fine Motor Control: pages 235, 252

Learning to follow spoken directions is a very important school skill—perhaps one of the most important of all. Use the ideas below to help your child learn to follow simple directions as he or she also practices fine motor skills:

- ❑ Complete the worksheets.
- ❑ To help your child practice listening skills, play "Simon Says" often. Remind the child to listen for the words *Simon Says* before acting on any command.
- ❑ To practice fine motor skills, color pasta pieces with markers or water paints and then string them.

WRITING

Uppercase Letters Q to Z: pages 238-242, 245-249
Alphabet: pages 250-251

As you continue to work on ABCs with your child, remember to let him or her practice drawing each letter shape with a finger in sand or flour before trying to draw it with a crayon or pencil.

- ❑ Complete the worksheets.
- ❑ Make letter sacks or boxes. On each one, write one capital letter. Ask your child to find objects with names that begin with the letter and put them in the sack or box. For example, in the S sack might go a sock, a picture of a swan, and so on. When working with initial vowel sounds, make sure that items going into the sack have names with the appropriate long or short sound—e.g., apple (short a) versus apron (long a).
- ❑ Sing the ABC song with your child as he or she points to the letters on pages 250-251. Depending on your child's attention span and motor control, you may wish to have him or her trace the letters on these pages in several short sessions.

READING

Alphabet: page 253

By the end of this month, you will have presented all uppercase letters to your child. The chart on page 253 can be used to review the letters.

- ❑ Post page 253 on the refrigerator or another spot frequented by your child.
- ❑ Periodically quiz your child with questions such as: "What letter comes before M?" "What letter comes after M?" "What's the last letter?" "The first letter?" "The letter between C and E?"

Birthdays Count!

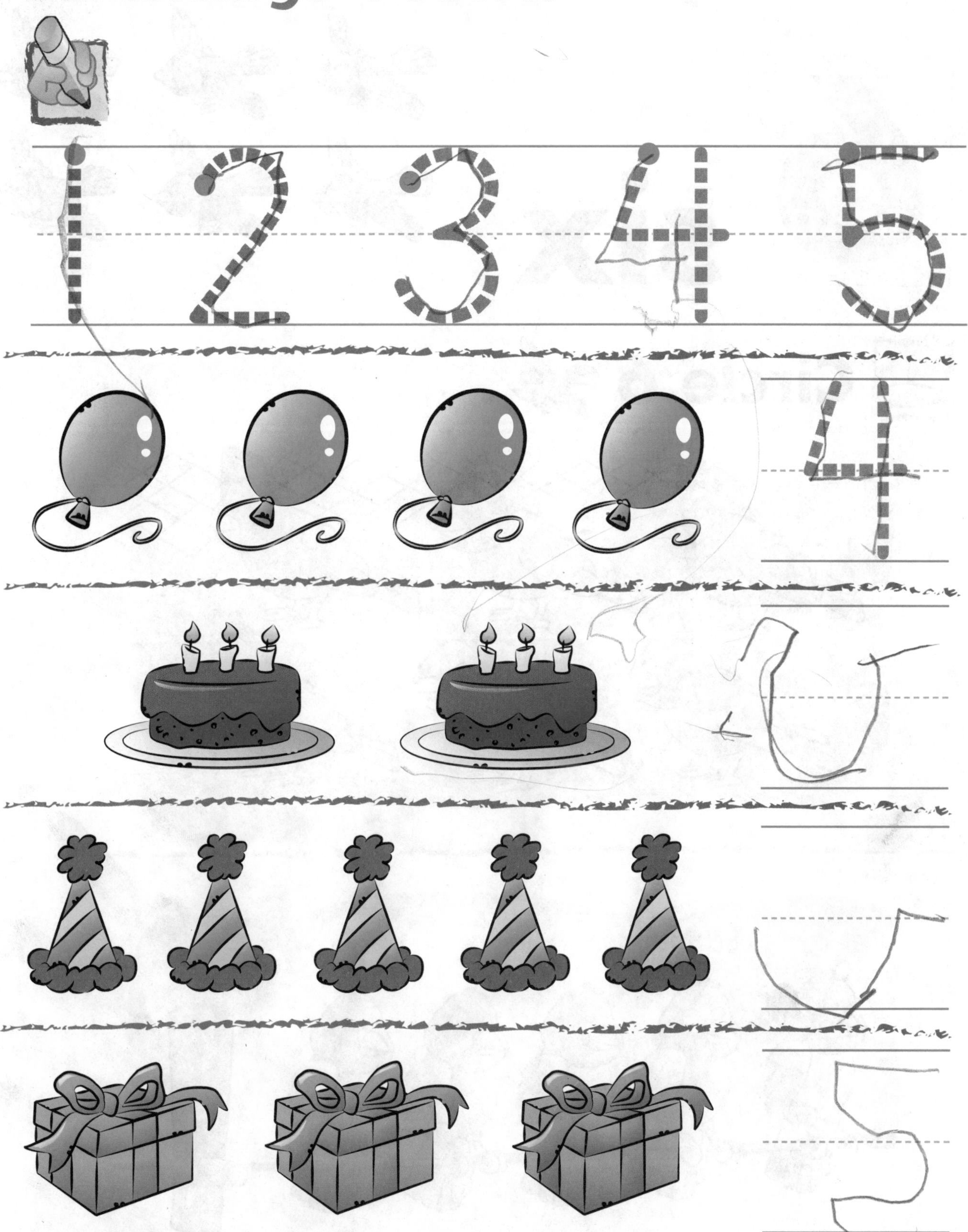

Parents: **Have your child trace over the numbers. Then ask him or her to count the items in each row and write the number on the write-on line.**

Counting to 6

6 six

Circle 6 .

Parents: (Top) Ask your child to say *six* as he or she points to the numeral and to the number word and counts the six birds in flight. (Bottom) Then say, "Count the number of birds in each group and circle the picture with six."

Showing 6

Color 6 .

6 6 6

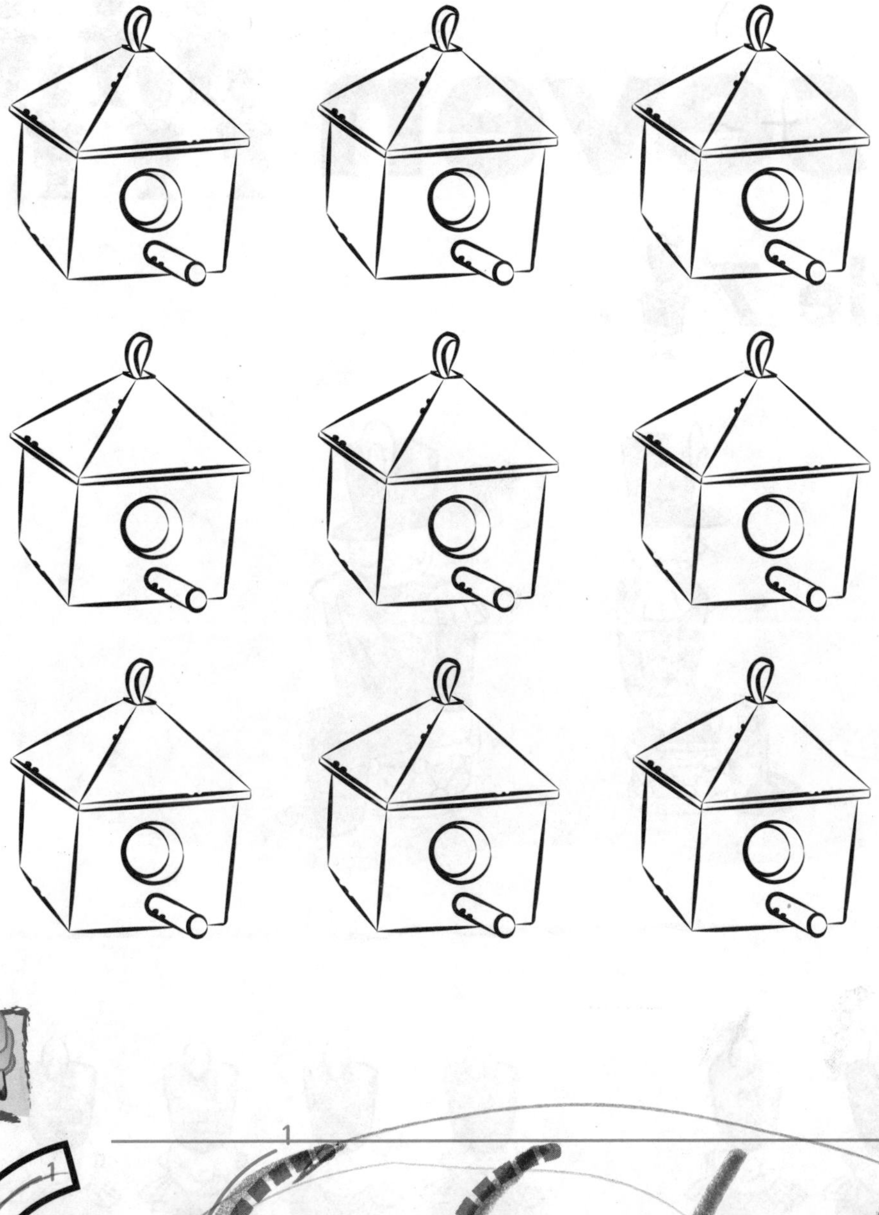

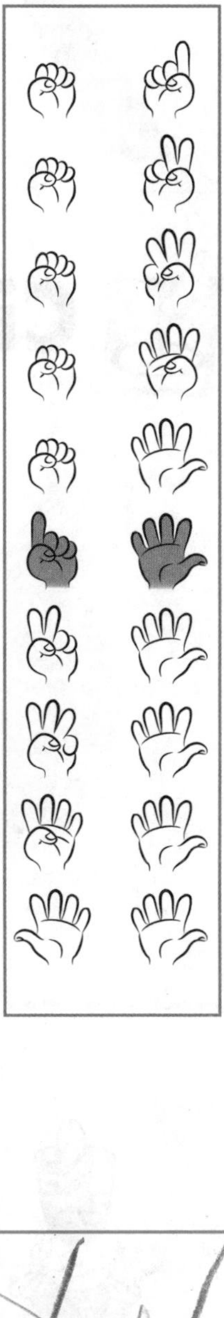

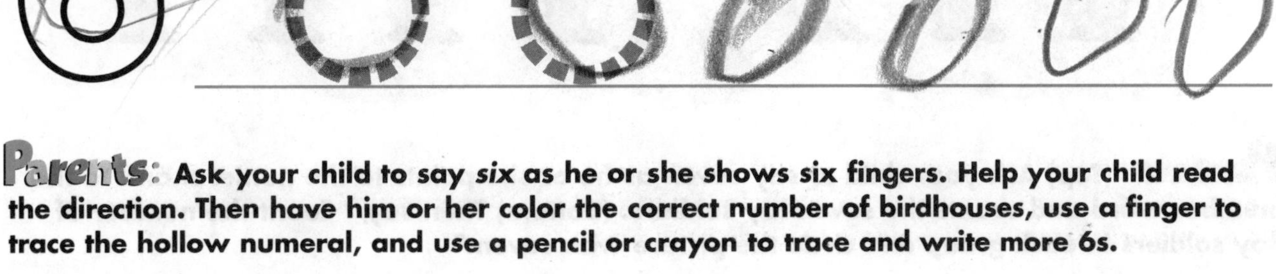

Parents: **Ask your child to say *six* as he or she shows six fingers. Help your child read the direction. Then have him or her color the correct number of birdhouses, use a finger to trace the hollow numeral, and use a pencil or crayon to trace and write more 6s.**

Counting to 7

7 seven

Circle 7 .

Parents: (Top) Ask your child to say *seven* as he or she points to the numeral and to the number word and counts the seven toy soldiers. (Bottom) Then say, "Count the number of toy soldiers in each group and circle the picture with seven."

Showing 7

Color 7 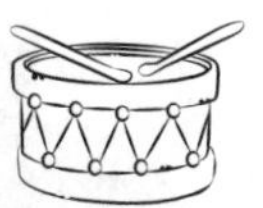 .

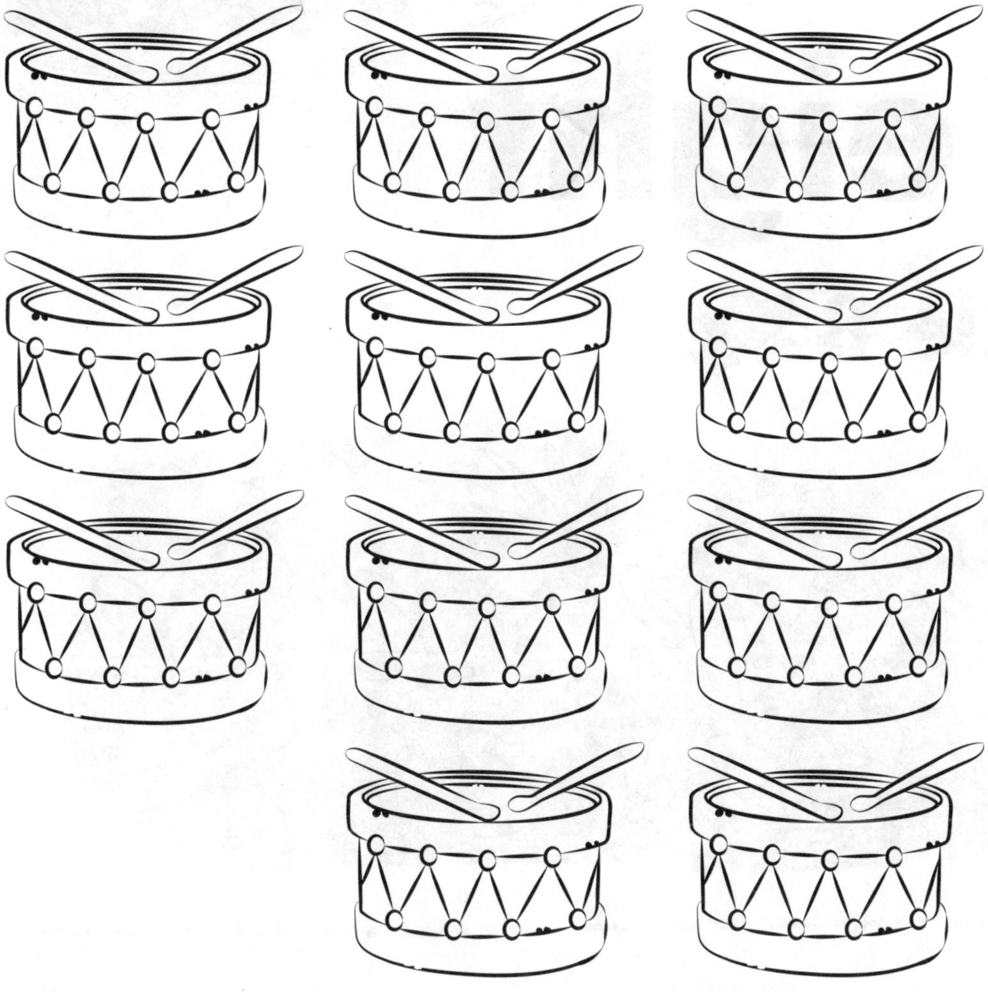

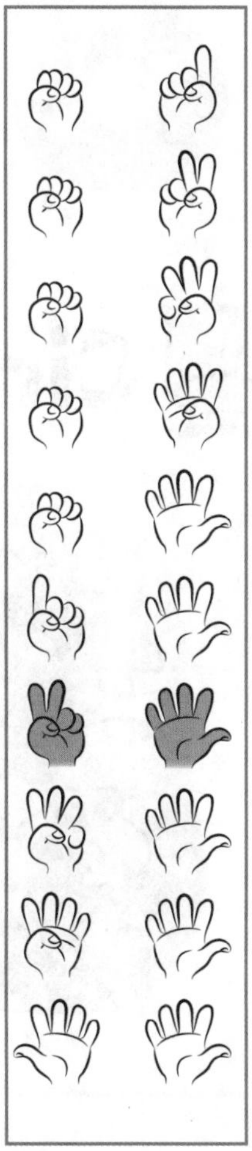

Parents: Ask your child to say *seven* as he or she shows seven fingers. Help your child read the direction. Then have him or her color the correct number of drums, use a finger to trace the hollow numeral, and use a pencil or crayon to trace and write more 7s.

Counting to 8

8 eight

Circle 8 .

Parents: (Top) Ask your child to say *eight* as he or she points to the numeral and to the number word and counts the eight frogs. (Bottom) Then say, "Count the number of frogs in each group and circle the picture with eight."

Showing 8

Color 8 .

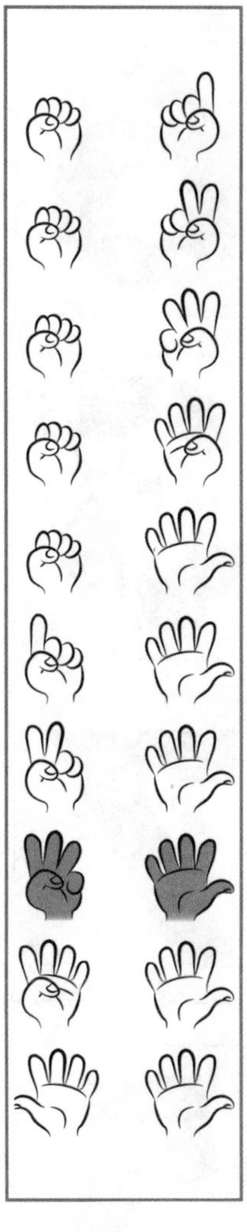

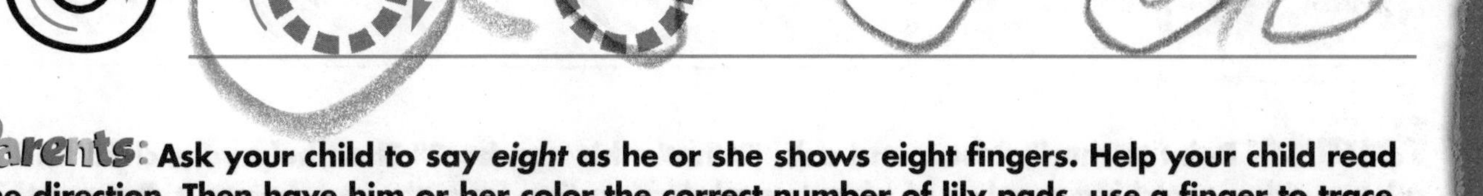

Parents: Ask your child to say *eight* as he or she shows eight fingers. Help your child read the direction. Then have him or her color the correct number of lily pads, use a finger to trace the hollow numeral, and use a pencil or crayon to trace and write more 8s.

MATH

Garden Counting

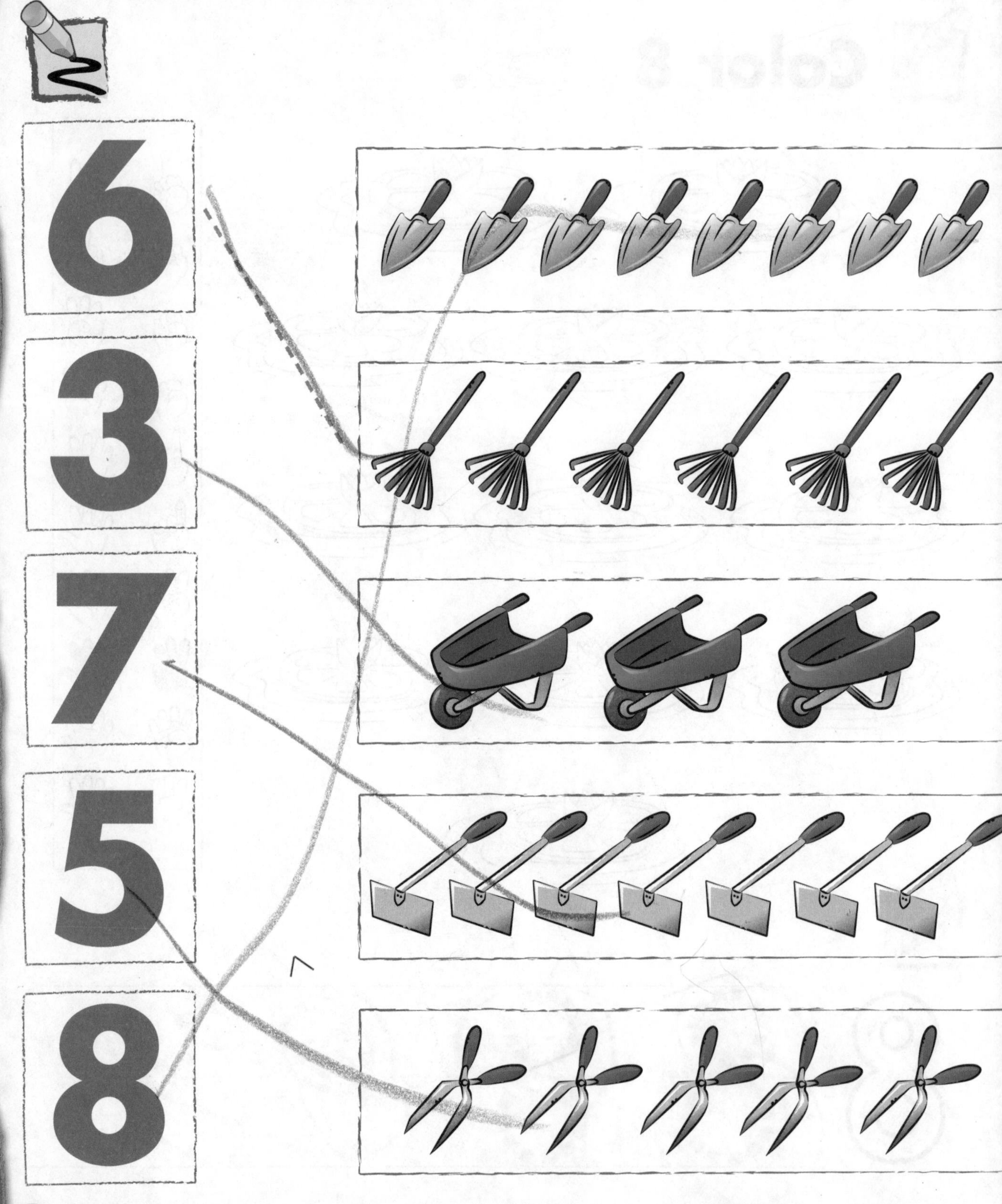

Parents: Point to the first box and ask, "What's this number?" Then help your child find a box with a matching number of objects and draw a line from the number to it. Repeat this process for the rest of the page.

Bus Dot-to-Dot

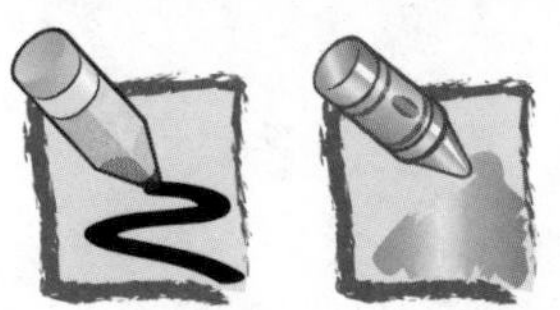

Parents: Have your child read aloud and point to the numerals in order from 1 to 8. Then have him or her use a crayon to connect the numerals in order and color the completed picture.

Clowning Around

Parents: Ask your child to follow these directions: (1) Draw a nose on the clown. (2) Draw buttons on the clown's shirt. (3) Draw a hat on the clown. (4) Color the picture.

Here, Kitty!

Parents: Point to the faceless cat and ask your child to follow these directions: (1) Draw eyes on the cat. (2) Draw a nose on the cat. (3) Draw whiskers on the cat. (4) Draw a tail on the cat.

Following directions; adding details to complete a picture

The Letter Q

Circle if its name begins like Queen.

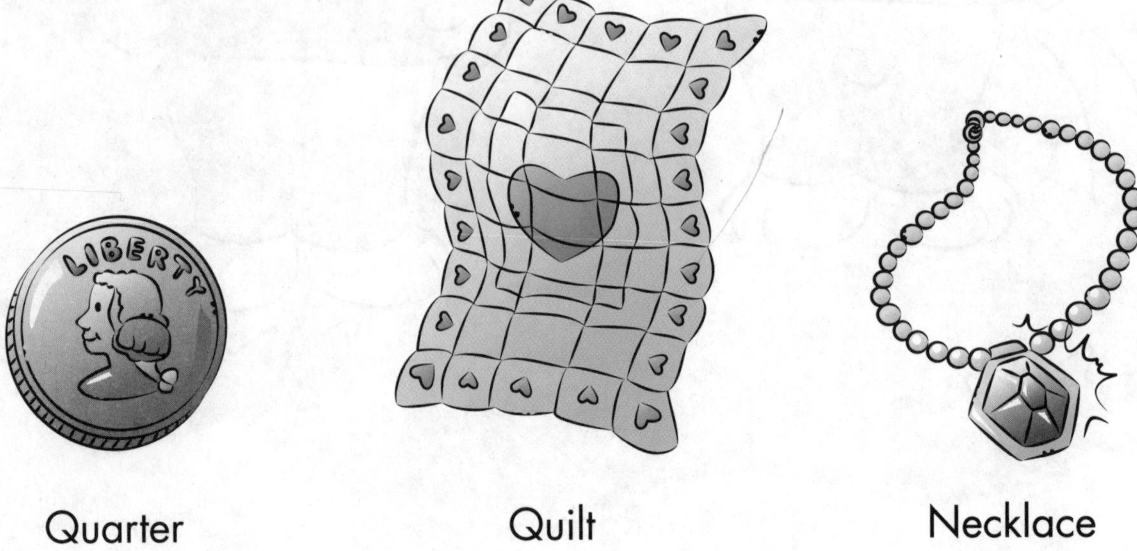

Quarter Quilt Necklace

Parents: Say, "*Queen* begins with the letter Q. Listen for the sound Q makes at the beginning of *qqq-queen*. Say it!" Show your child how to trace the hollow letter with a finger. Have him or her use a pencil or crayon to trace and write the letter. Then ask your child to circle the pictures that begin with Q.

The Letter R

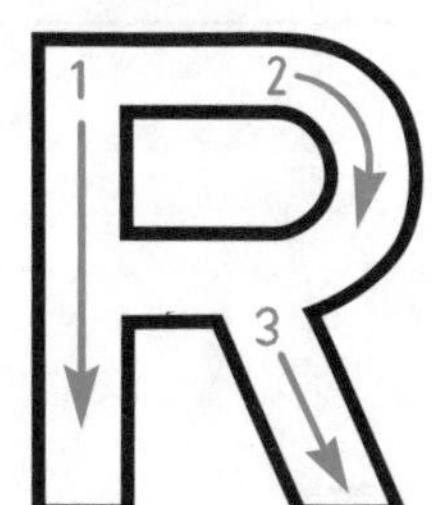

Circle if its name begins like Robot.

Rake

Rocket

Plane

Parents: Say, "*Robot* begins with the letter *R*. Listen for the sound *R* makes at the beginning of *rrr-robot*. Say it!" Show your child how to trace the hollow letter with a finger. Have him or her use a pencil or crayon to trace and write the letter. Then ask your child to circle the pictures that begin with R.

Recognizing, tracing, and writing uppercase letters; recognizing letter sounds

WRITING

The Letter S

Circle if its name begins like Seahorse.

Sailor

Seal

Crab

Parents: Say, "*Seahorse* begins with the letter *S*. Listen for the sound *S* makes at the beginning of *sss-seahorse*. Say it!" Show your child how to trace the hollow letter with a finger. Have him or her use a pencil or crayon to trace and write the letter. Then ask your child to circle the pictures that begin with S.

Recognizing, tracing, and writing uppercase letters; recognizing letter sounds

The Letter T

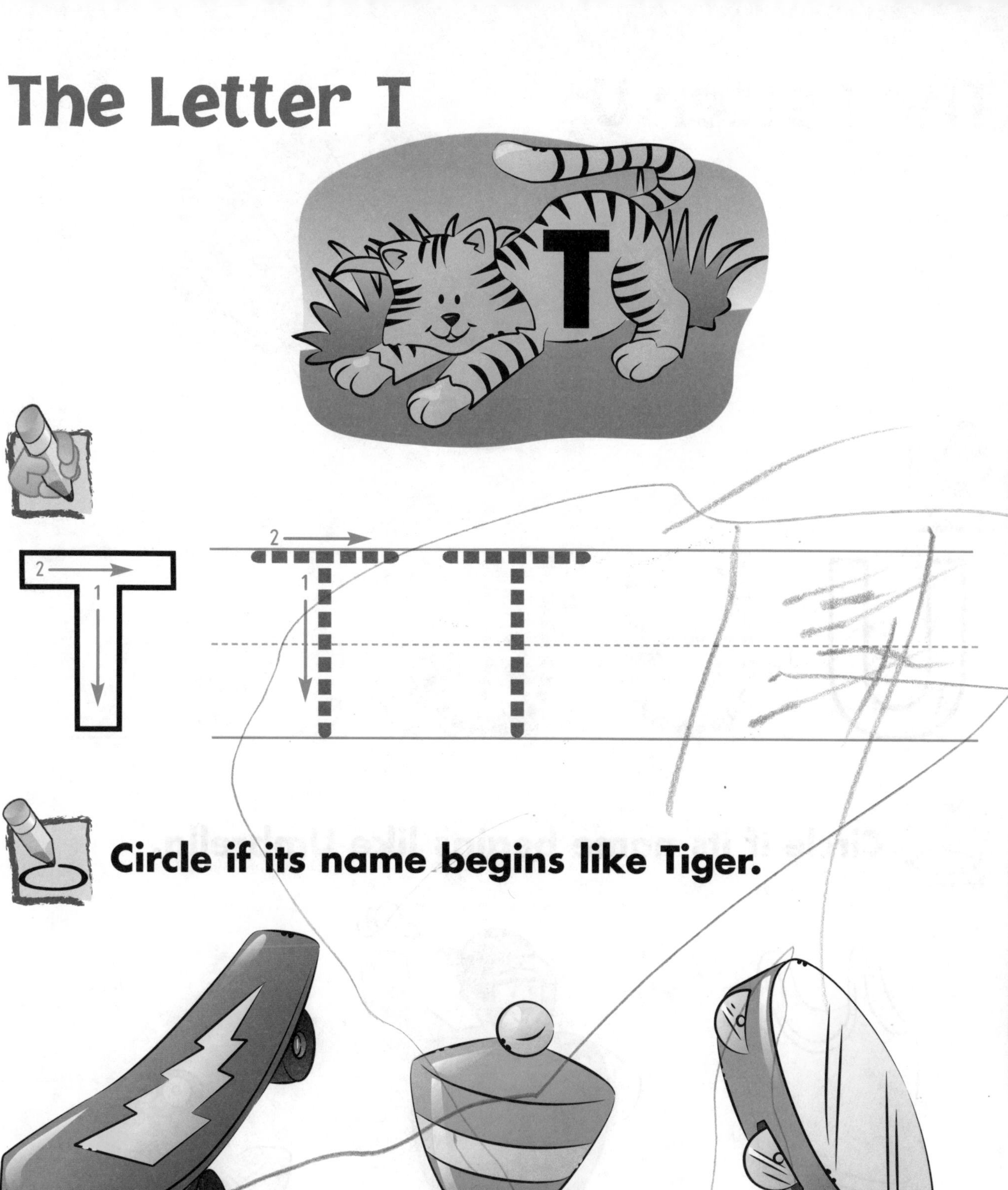

Circle if its name begins like Tiger.

Skateboard

Top

Tambourine

Parents: Say, "*Tiger* begins with the letter *T*. Listen for the sound *T* makes at the beginning of *ttt-tiger*. Say it!" Show your child how to trace the hollow letter with a finger. Have him or her use a pencil or crayon to trace and write the letter. Then ask your child to circle the pictures that begin with T.

Recognizing, tracing, and writing uppercase letters; recognizing letter sounds

WRITING

The Letter U

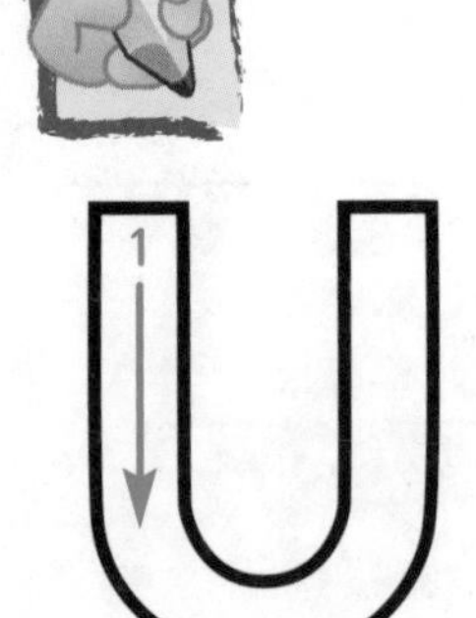

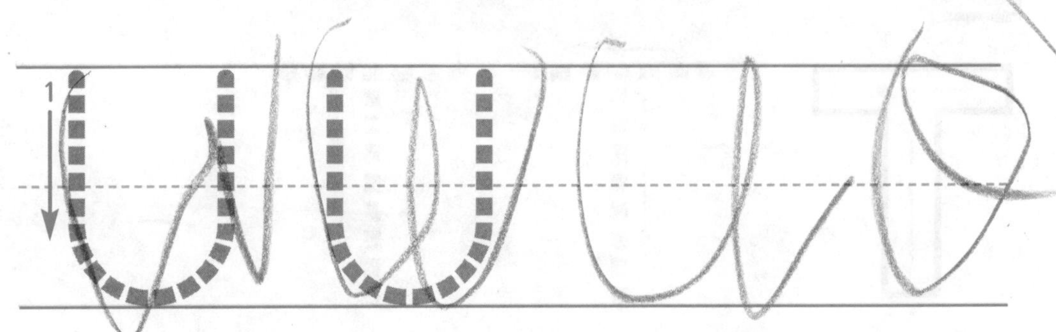

Circle if its name begins like Umbrella.

Underwear

Umpire

Frog

Parents: Say, "*Umbrella* begins with the letter *U*. Listen for the sound *U* makes at the beginning of *uuu-umbrella*. Say it!" Show your child how to trace the hollow letter with a finger. Have him or her use a pencil or crayon to trace and write the letter. Then ask your child to circle the pictures that begin with U.

Recognizing, tracing, and writing uppercase letters; recognizing letter sounds

On the Beach

Parents: Ask your child to follow these directions: (1) Draw a ball for the girl bunny. (2) Draw the sun in the sky. (3) Draw a flag on a flagpole on top of the sand castle. (4) Draw waves in the water.

Winter Fun

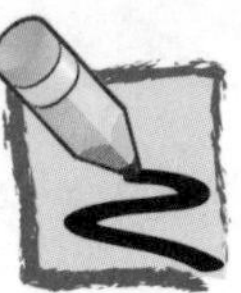

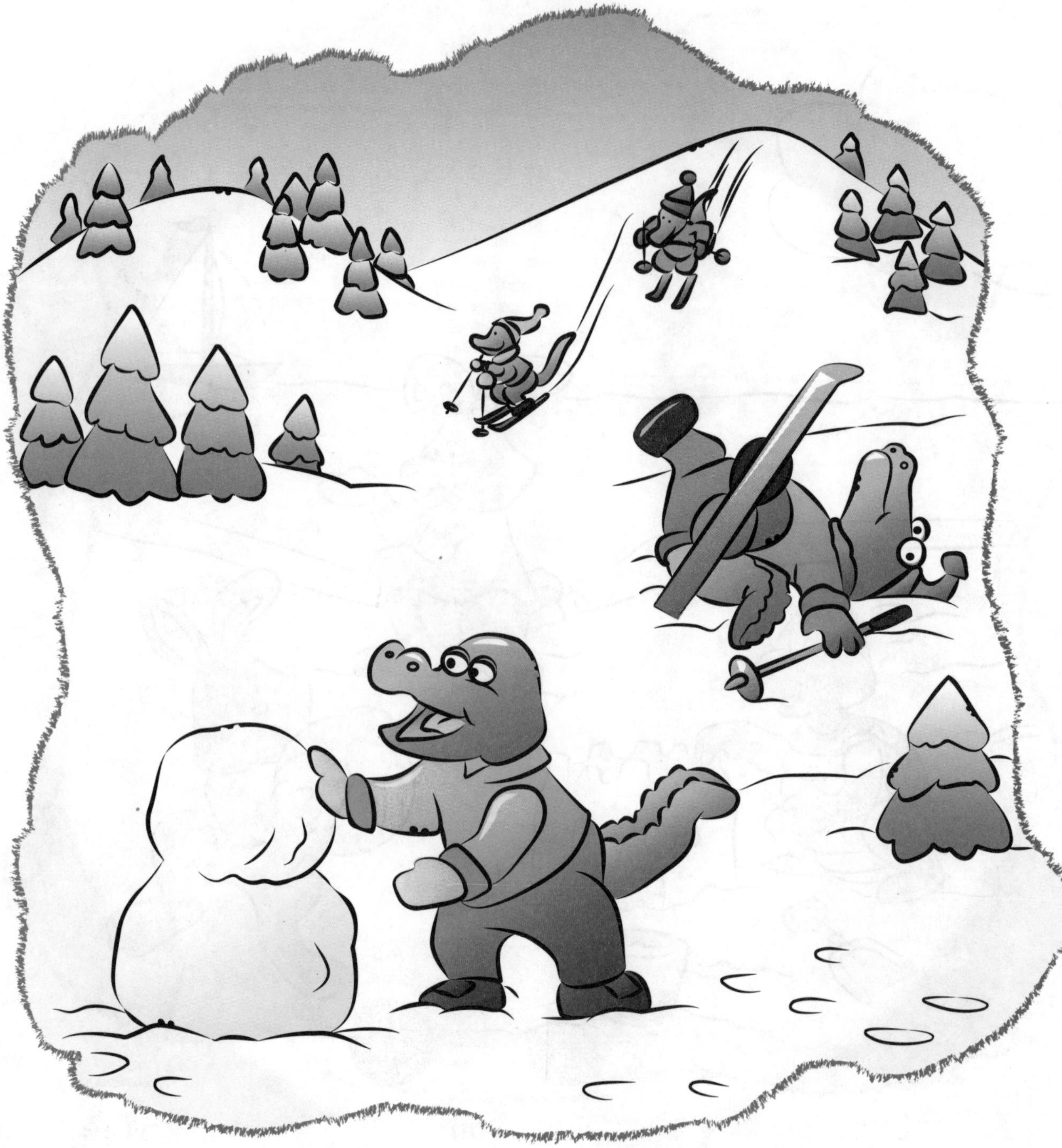

Parents: Ask your child to follow these directions: (1) Draw the missing ski for the alligator that fell. (2) Draw a head on the snowman. (3) Draw eyes and a nose on the snowman. (4) Draw a hat on the alligator that isn't wearing a hat.

Following directions; adding details to complete a picture

The Letter V

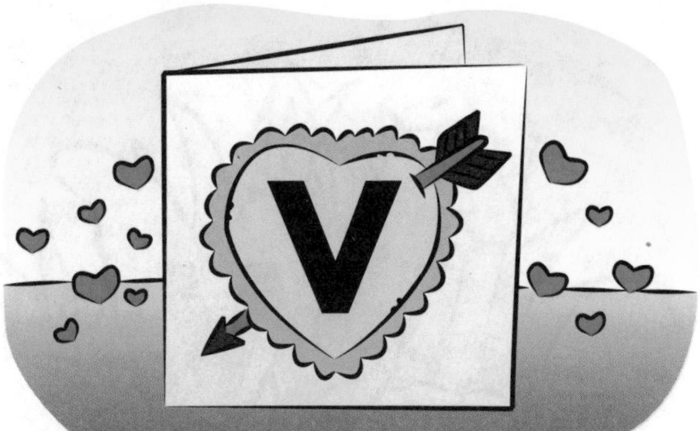

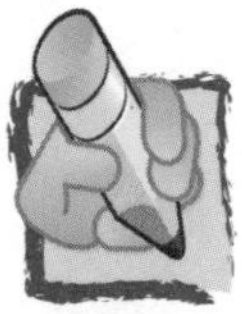

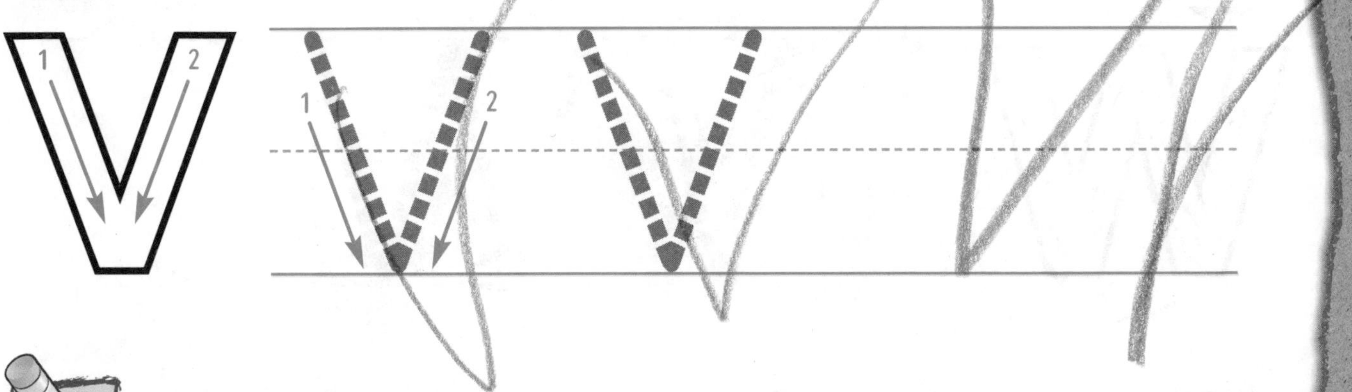

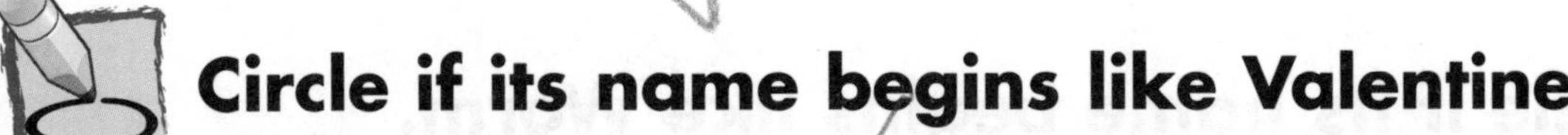

Circle if its name begins like Valentine.

Parents: **Say, "*Valentine* begins with the letter *V*. Listen for the sound *V* makes at the beginning of *vvv-valentine*. Say it!" Show your child how to trace the hollow letter with a finger. Have him or her use a pencil or crayon to trace and write the letter. Then ask your child to circle the pictures that begin with V.**

The Letter W

Circle if its name begins like Worm.

Parents: Say, "*Worm* begins with the letter *W*. Listen for the sound *W* makes at the beginning of *www-worm*. Say it!" Show your child how to trace the hollow letter with a finger. Have him or her use a pencil or crayon to trace and write the letter. Then ask your child to circle the pictures that begin with W.

Recognizing, tracing, and writing uppercase letters; recognizing letter sounds

The Letter X

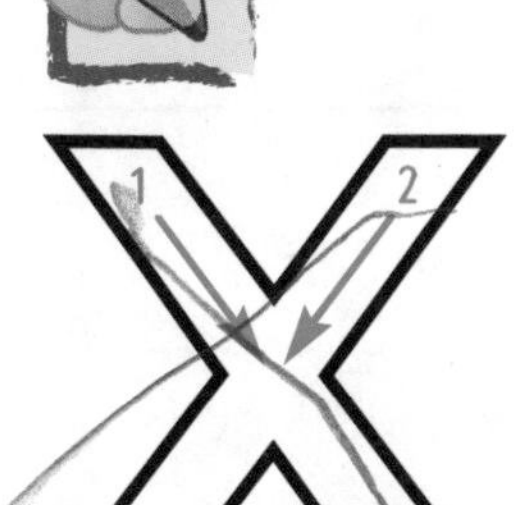

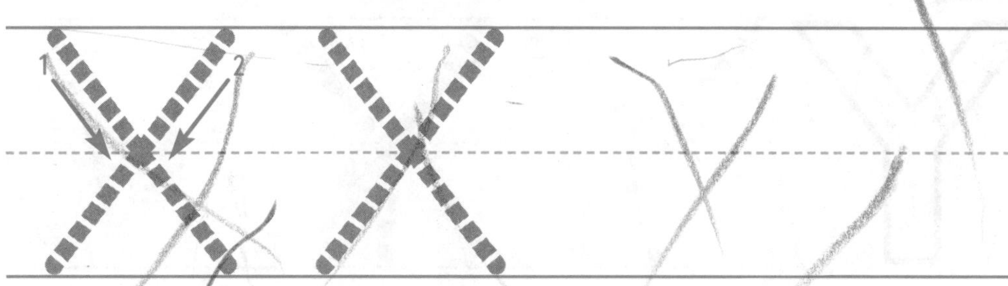

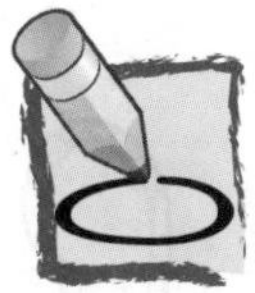

Circle if its name begins like X-ray.

X-ray

Elf

Parents: Say, "*X-ray* begins with the letter *X*. Listen for the sound *X* makes at the beginning of *xxx-x-ray*. Say it!" Show your child how to trace the hollow letter with a finger. Have him or her use a pencil or crayon to trace and write the letter. Then ask your child to circle the pictures that begin with X.

The Letter Y

Circle if its name begins like Yellow.

Parents: Say, "*Yellow* begins with the letter *Y*. Listen for the sound *Y* makes at the beginning of *yyy-yellow*. Say it!" Show your child how to trace the hollow letter with a finger. Have him or her use a pencil or crayon to trace and write the letter. Then ask your child to circle the pictures that begin with Y.

The Letter Z

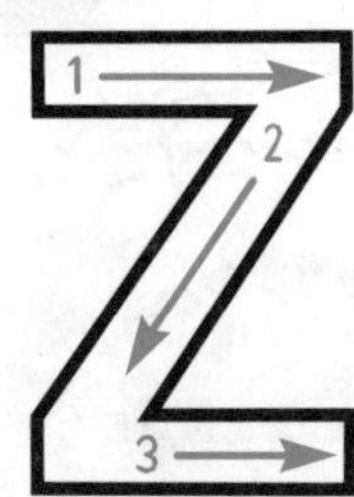

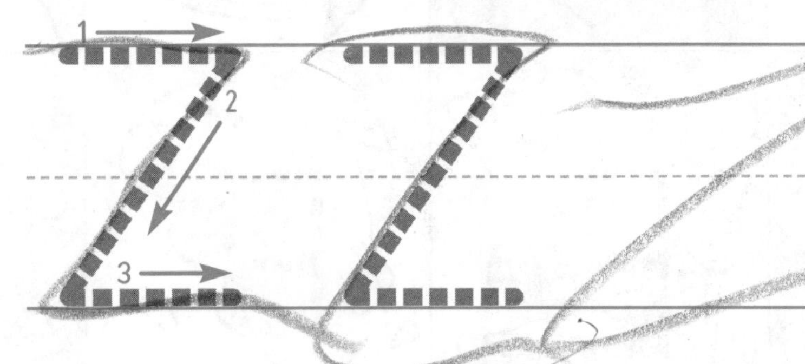

Circle if its name begins like Zebra.

Zoo

Supermarket

Parents: Say, "*Zebra* begins with the letter *Z*. Listen for the sound *Z* makes at the beginning of *zzz-zebra*. Say it!" Show your child how to trace the hollow letter with a finger. Have him or her use a pencil or crayon to trace and write the letter. Then ask your child to circle the pictures that begin with Z.

Recognizing, tracing, and writing uppercase letters; recognizing letter sounds

WRITING

Uppercase ABCs

A B C D E F G H I J K L M N O

Parents: **Ask your child to point to each animal or object pictured on pages 250 and 251, say its name, tell what letter the name begins with, and then trace over the letter with a black crayon or marker.**

Recognizing, tracing, and writing uppercase letters; recognizing letter sounds

Uppercase ABCs

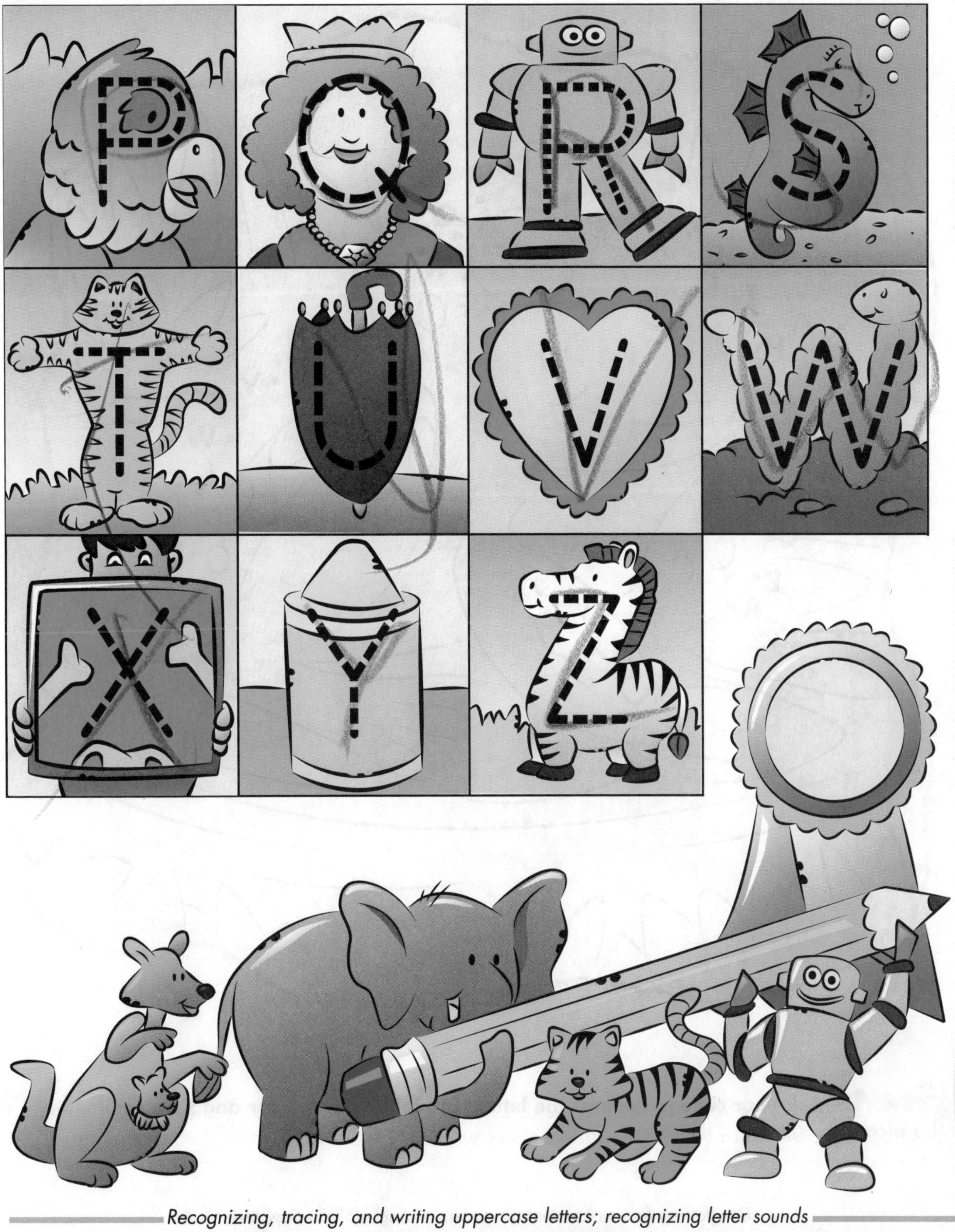

P Q R S T U V W X Y Z

Frog Dot-to-Dot

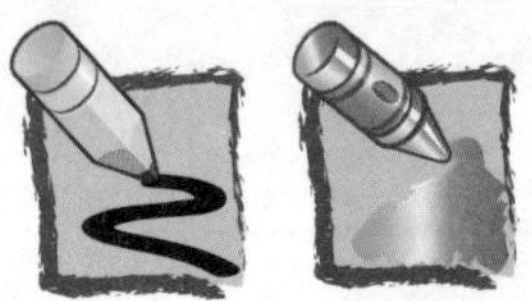

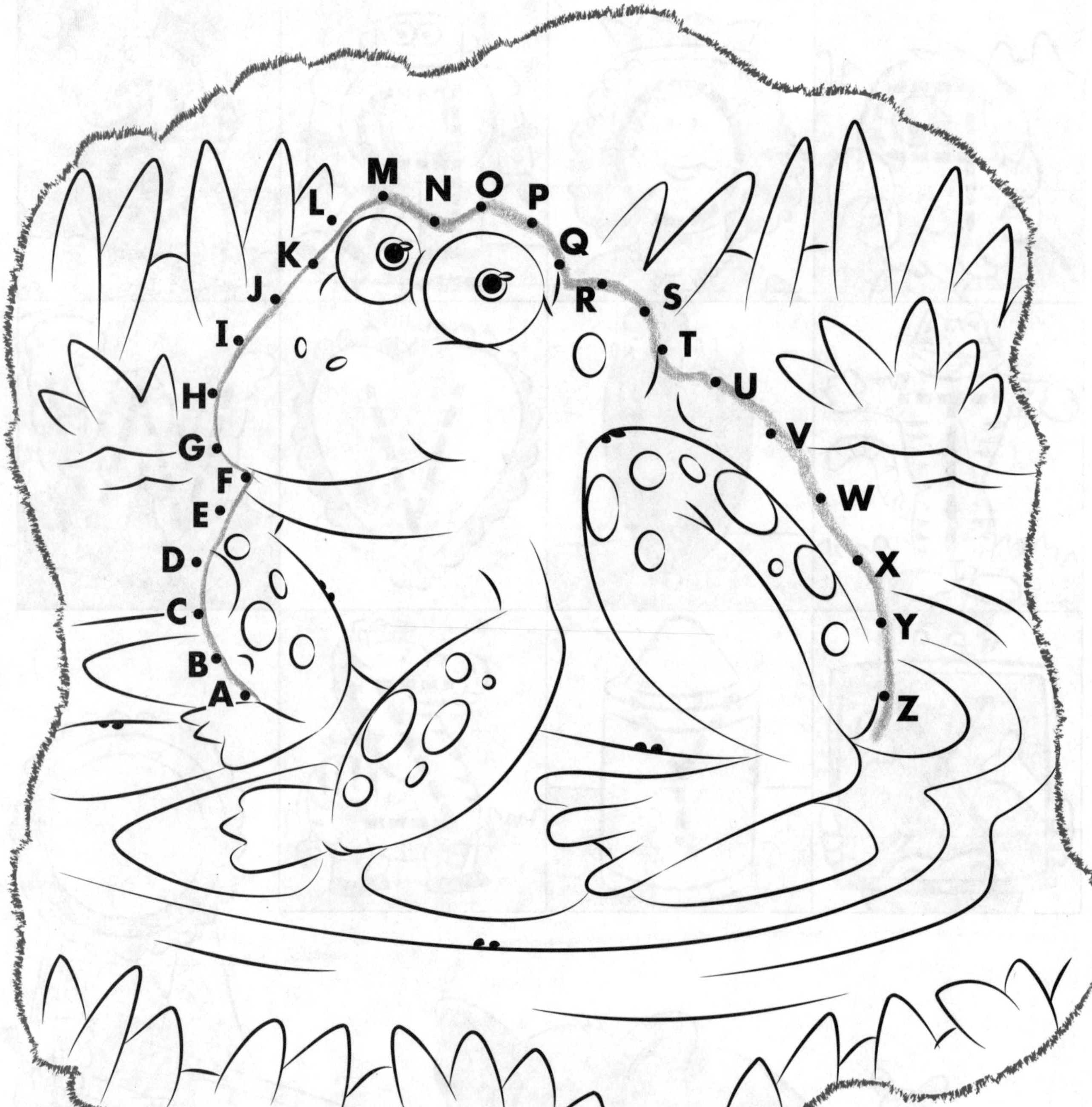

M N O P L K Q J R S I T U H G V F W E D X C Y B A Z

Parents: Ask your child to connect the letters in alphabetical order and then color the picture.

A to Z

A B C D E F G

H I J K L M N

O P Q R S T U

V W X Y Z

Parents: Use this chart to help your child practice saying the letters of the alphabet in the correct order. Name a letter, ask your child to point to it, and name the letters that come before and after. Repeat with other letters.

MATH

1 to 10

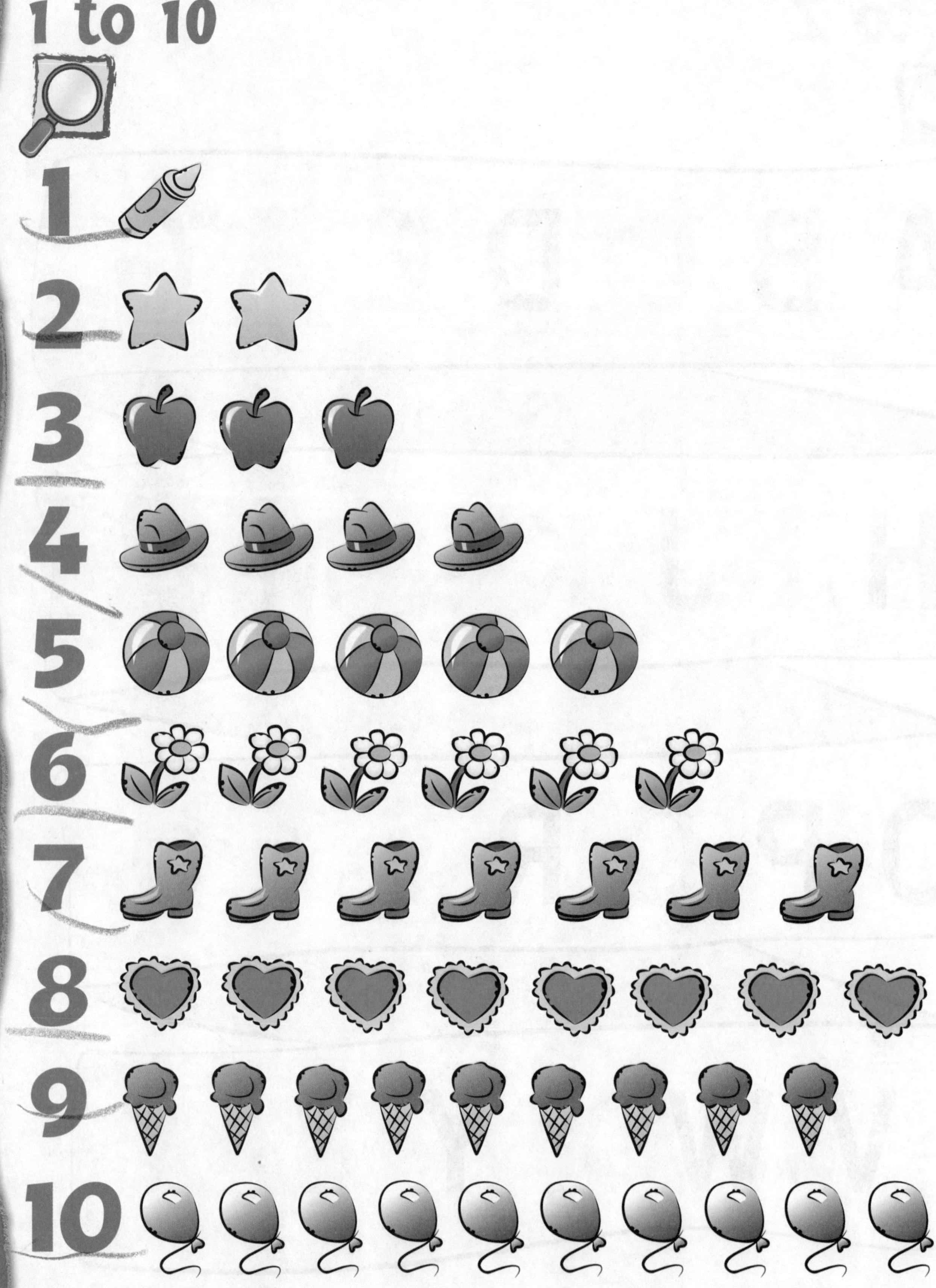

Parents: Use this chart to help your child practice numbers to 10. Have your child say each numeral and count the objects that follow.

One little bluebird sitting all alone;
It flew away and then there were none.

Counting Rhymes

One, two, buckle my shoe;

Three, four, shut the door.

Three little bluebirds sitting in a shoe;
One flew away and then there were two.

Two little bluebirds sitting in the sun;
One flew away and then there was one.

Five little bluebirds sitting on a door;
One flew away and then there were four.

Four little bluebirds sitting on a tree;
One flew away and then there were three.

Five, six, pick up sticks;

Seven, eight, lay them straight.

Nine, ten, a big fat hen!

1, 2, 3, 4, 5,
I caught a hare alive!

6, 7, 8, 9, 10,
I let it go again!

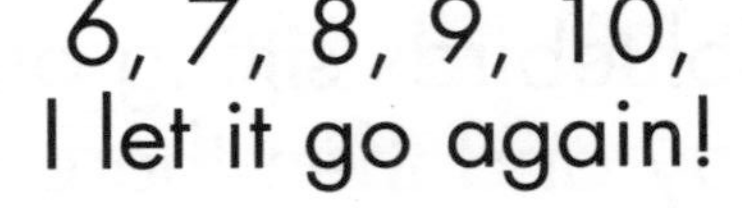

Month 9 Checklist

Hands-on activities to help prepare your child for school!

LANGUAGE

Opposites: pages 261-263

Use any of the activities for opposites suggested in previous checklists and try the ones below:

❑ Complete the worksheets.

❑ Let your child dunk a plastic (waterproof) doll or action figure in a pan of water to demonstrate wet. Then have him or her wipe the doll off to demonstrate dry.

❑ Make an opposites book using a spiral or other standard notebook. On facing pages, have your child paste opposite pictures—e.g., a *short* truck and a *long* truck.

MATH

Counting 9 and 10: pages 264-267

Matching Numerals and Number Words with Amounts: pages 268-269

Writing Numerals: page 270

With all early numbers work, using counters or other manipulatives is very helpful for young children.

❑ Complete the worksheets.

❑ With a bowl of fish-shaped crackers, ask your child to remove from the bowl, as he or she counts aloud, a specific number of fish.

❑ Practice using fingers to show amounts and for counting. If you have not done so, point out and discuss the meaning of the finger-counting panel on the right sides of pages 265 and 267. Then play a game where you say a number and your child holds up that many fingers. Speed makes the game more challenging.

PREREADING AND PREWRITING

Visual Discrimination: pages 271, 273, 275

Some of the worksheets in this month focus on the prereading skill of visual discrimination—the ability to look closely at a picture or scene and isolate the details. Use any of the activities for this skill from previous checklists and try the ones below:

❑ Complete the worksheets.
❑ Examine a family photo. Name particular details in the picture (e.g., Aunt Sue's pink hat) and ask your child to point to them. Discuss where the picture might have been taken, etc., based upon the visual clues.
❑ Let your child "read" a simple picture book by going through it page by page and telling the story the pictures show.

READING

Sounds of *m* and *p*: pages 272, 274

Matching Uppercase and Lowercase Letters *A/a* to *H/h*: pages 284-290

Helping a child learn the sound that goes with each letter is critical for both reading and spelling. Use any of the activities for learning sounds from previous checklists and try the ones below:

❑ Complete the worksheets.
❑ Say a familiar nursery rhyme slowly and ask your child to clap each time you read a word that begins with either the *m* or *p* sound. Good choices are "Little Miss Muffet" and "Peter Peter, Pumpkin Eater."
❑ Ask your child to pair uppercase and lowercase letters using alphabet blocks or magnetic letters.

WRITING

Lowercase Letters *a* to *h*: pages 276-283

❑ Complete the worksheets.
❑ Start an alphabet scrapbook. On each page, have your child write both the uppercase and lowercase forms of one letter and then draw or paste pictures that show objects with names that begin with that letter.
❑ If your child is having difficulty forming the lowercase letters, print the letters about one inch high using a very light pencil. Have your child trace over each letter using a yellow highlighter or crayon.

Wet and Dry

Parents: Ask your child to point to the wet dish and then to the dry one. Point to the words *wet* and *dry*. Explain that they are called opposites. Then say, "Find the wet bird and color it blue. Find the dry bird and color it yellow."

Long and Short

Color the long bench brown.

Color the short bench green.

Parents: Ask your child to point to the monkey wearing long pants and then to the monkey wearing short pants. Point to the words *long* and *short*. Explain that they are called opposites. Then say, "Color the long bench brown. Color the short bench green."

Opposites Review

Circle the opposite.

in

wet

short

Parents: Have your child tell about the first picture in each row. Point out and read the word under the picture. Then have your child circle the picture that shows its opposite.

Counting to 9

9 nine

Circle 9 .

Parents: (Top) Ask your child to say *nine* as he or she points to the numeral and number word and counts the nine rabbits. (Bottom) Then say, "Count the number of rabbits in each group and circle the picture with nine."

Showing 9

Color 9 carrots.

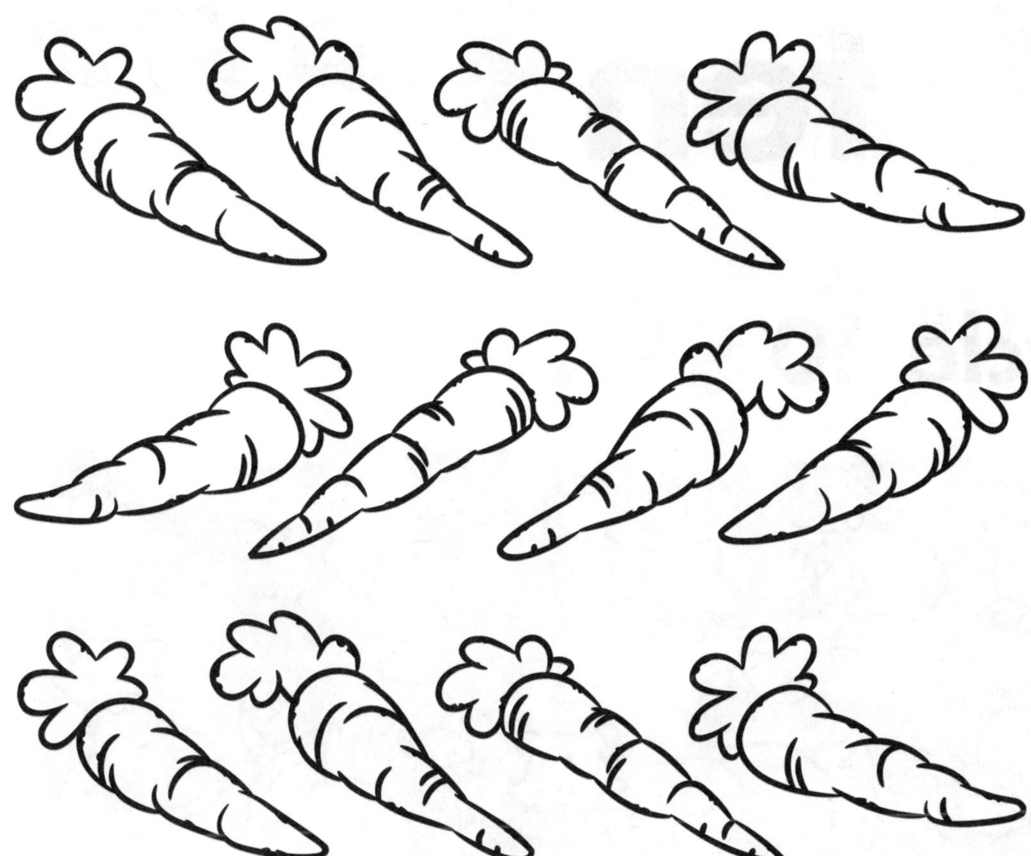

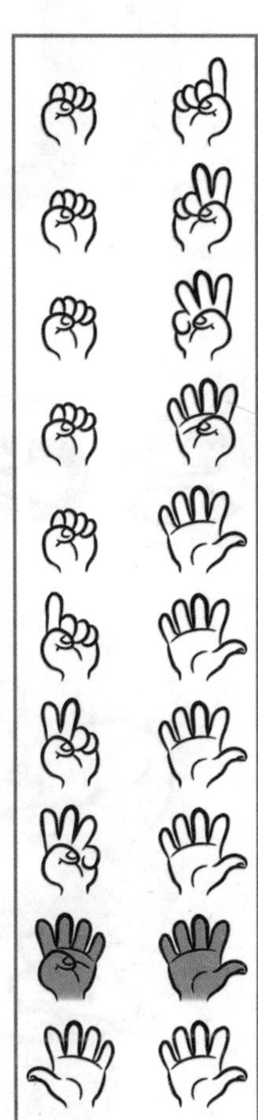

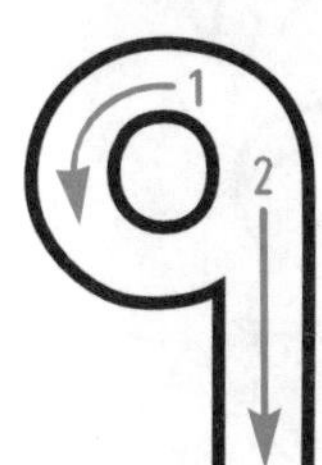

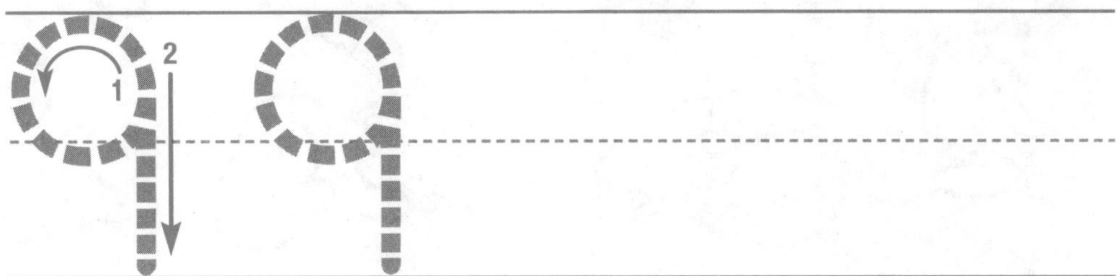

Parents: **Ask your child to say *nine* as he or she shows nine fingers. Help your child read the direction. Then have him or her color the correct number of carrots and use a finger to trace the hollow numeral and a pencil or crayon to trace and write more 9s.**

Counting to 10

10 ten

Circle 10 cats.

Parents: (Top) Ask your child to say *ten* as he or she points to the numeral and number word and counts the ten cats. (Bottom) Then say, "Count the number of cats in each group and circle the picture with ten."

Showing 10

Color 10 .

Parents: Ask your child to say *ten* as he or she shows ten fingers. Help your child read the direction. Then have him or her color the correct number of wind-up mice and use a finger to trace the hollow numeral and a pencil or crayon to trace and write more 10s.

MATH

Matching 1 to 10

Parents: **Have your child count the objects in each set and circle the correct number.**

Matching numerals with corresponding sets of objects

To the Stars!

4

9

5

8

Parents: Read the number at the left of the first row. Have your child count the number of rockets that have been colored. Then say, "Read the number in each row. Color that many things."

MATH

Writing 1 to 10

Write how many in each row.

5

2

6

8

9

Parents: Have your child count the objects in each row and write the number in the box.

Many Mushrooms

Circle 🍄🍄🍄🍄🍄 **.**

Parents: **Help your child find and circle the five *hidden* mushrooms. Then have him or her color the picture.**

Beginning Sound m

Color the things with names that begin with m.

Parents: **Point to the moon and say *moon*. Then ask, "What sound do you hear at the beginning of *mmm-moon*? That's the sound of the letter *m*." Then say, "Name the things in the picture. Listen for the sound of *m*. Color the things that begin with *m*."**

Pig Picnic

Circle **.**

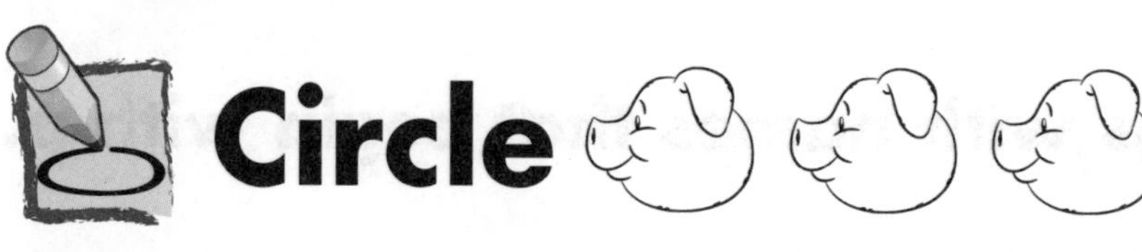

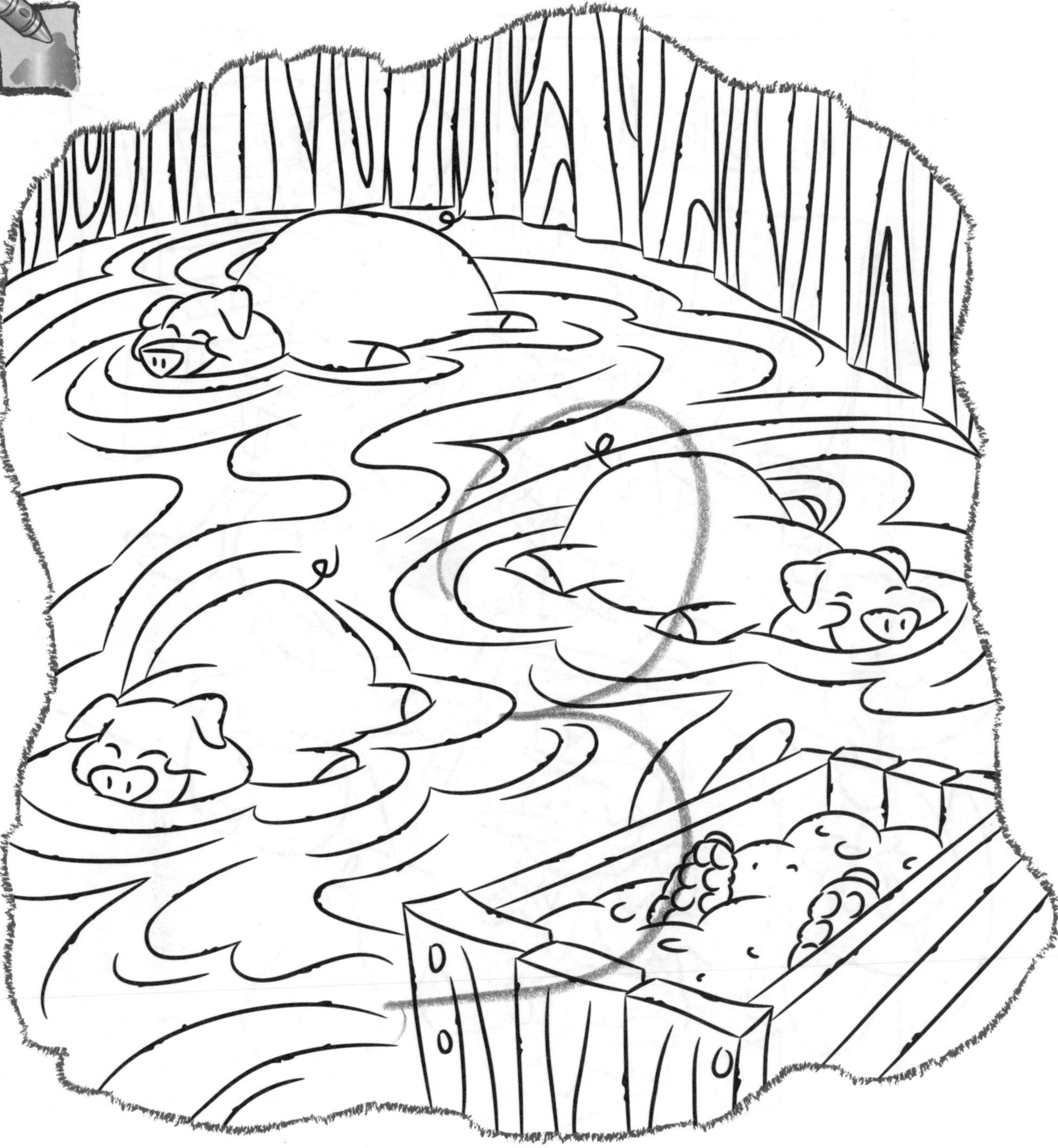

Parents: **Help your child find and circle the three *hidden* pigs. Then have him or her color the picture.**

Beginning Sound p

Color the things with names that begin with p.

Parents: **Point to the pear and say *pear*. Then ask, "What sound do you hear at the beginning of *ppp-pear*? That's the sound of the letter *p*." Then say, "Name the things in the picture. Listen for the sound of *p*. Color the things that begin with *p*."**

Swimming School

Circle .

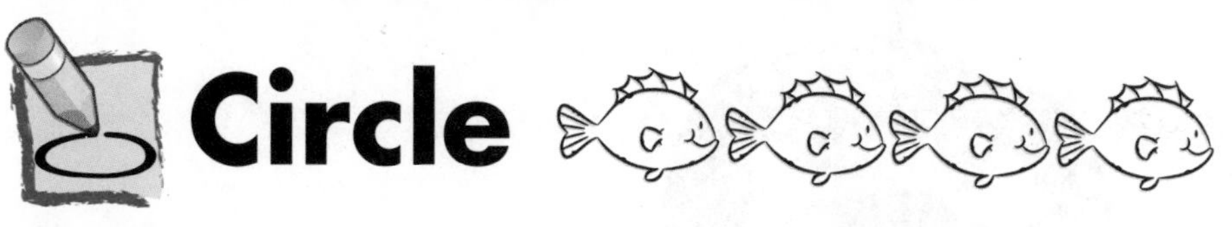

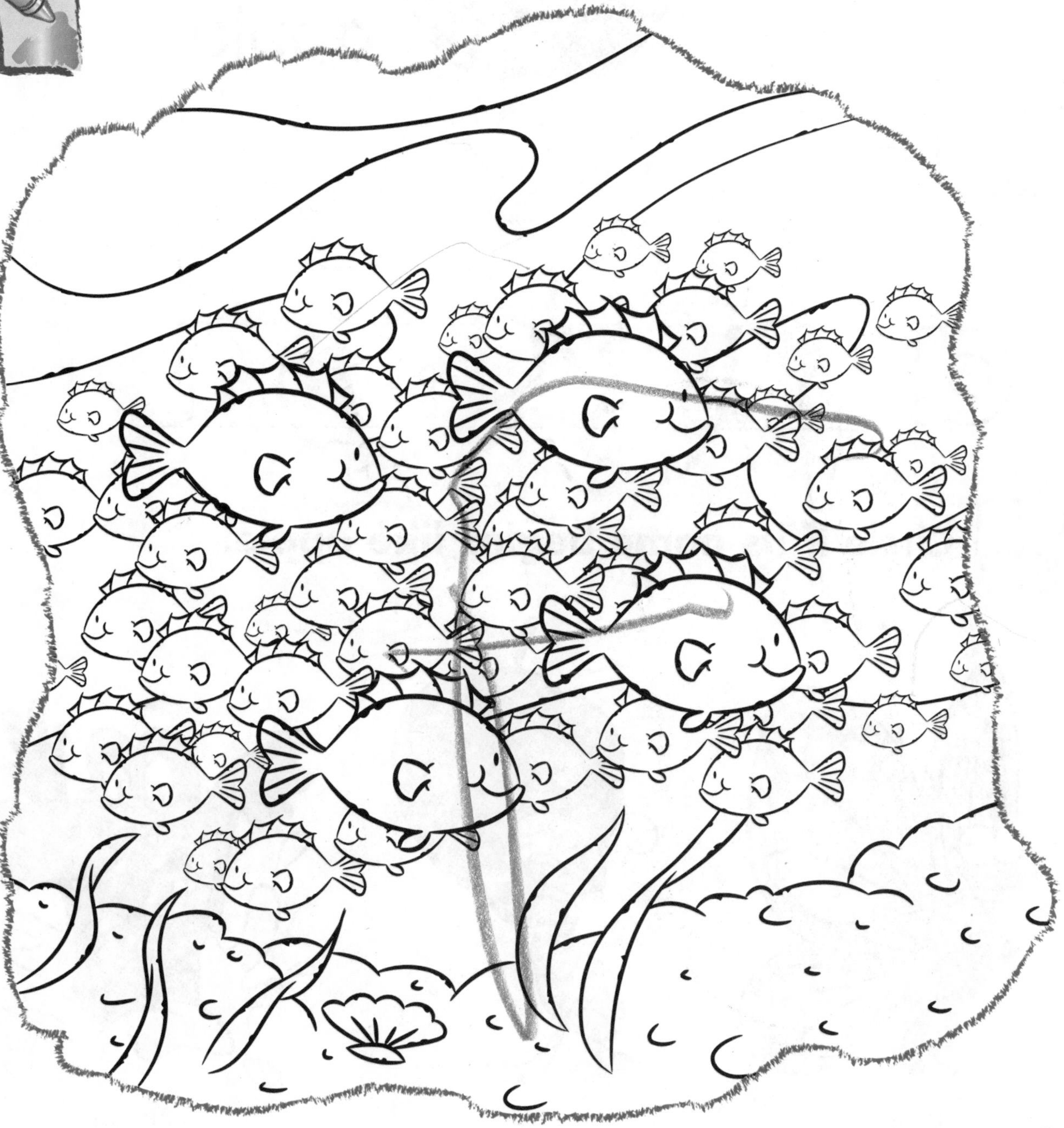

Parents: Help your child find and circle the four fish swimming in a different direction. Then have him or her color the picture.

WRITING

The Letter a

apple

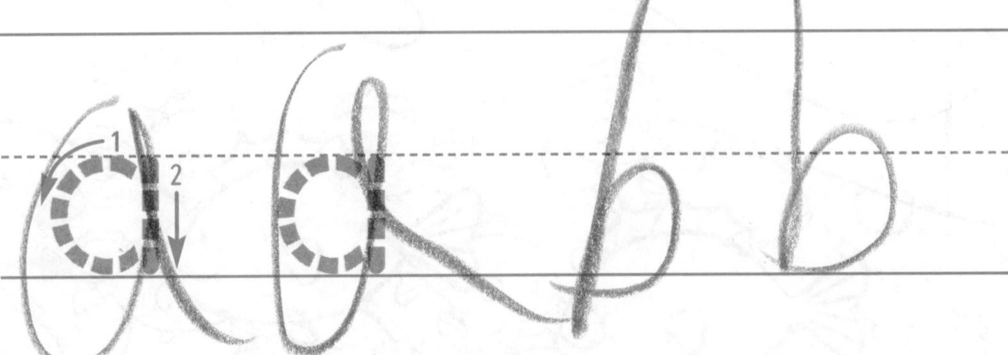

Circle if its name begins like apple.

butterfly

ant

alligator

Parents: Say, "*apple* begins with the letter *a*. Listen for the sound *a* makes at the beginning of *aaa-apple*. Say it!" Show your child how to trace the hollow letter with a finger. Have him or her use a pencil or crayon to trace and write the letter. Then ask your child to circle the pictures that begin with a.

Recognizing, tracing, and writing lowercase letters; recognizing letter sounds

The Letter b

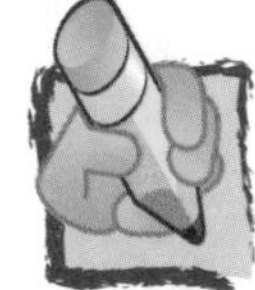

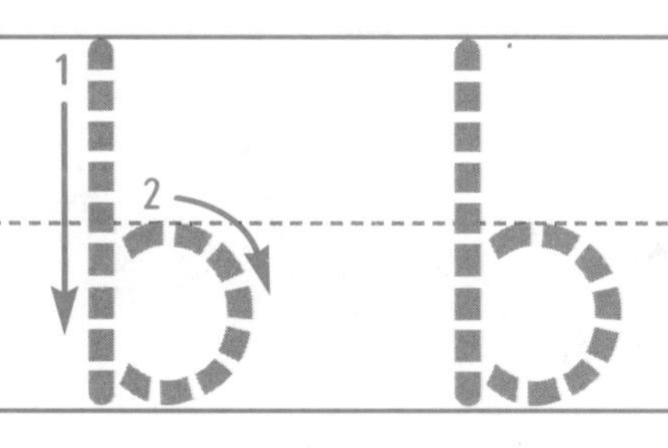

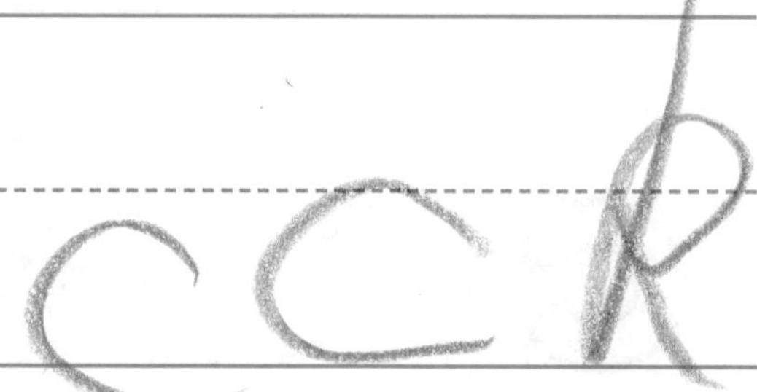

Circle if its name begins like boot.

bear

bee

giraffe

Parents: **Say, "*boot* begins with the letter *b*. Listen for the sound *b* makes at the beginning of *bbb-boot*. Say it!" Show your child how to trace the hollow letter with a finger. Have him or her use a pencil or crayon to trace and write the letter. Then ask your child to circle the pictures that begin with b.**

Recognizing, tracing, and writing lowercase letters; recognizing letter sounds

The Letter c

Circle if its name begins like cat.

cupcake

dog

cow

Parents: Say, "*cat* begins with the letter *c*. Listen for the sound *c* makes at the beginning of *ccc-cat*. Say it!" Show your child how to trace the hollow letter with a finger. Have him or her use a pencil or crayon to trace and write the letter. Then ask your child to circle the pictures that begin with c.

The Letter d

Parents: Say, "*dinosaur* begins with the letter *d*. Listen for the sound *d* makes at the beginning of *ddd-dinosaur*. Say it!" Show your child how to trace the hollow letter with a finger. Have him or her use a pencil or crayon to trace and write the letter. Then ask your child to circle the pictures that begin with d.

The Letter e

egg

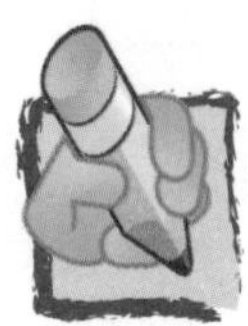

Circle if its name begins like egg.

sheep elf elephant

Parents: Say, "*egg* begins with the letter *e*. Listen for the sound *e* makes at the beginning of *eee-egg*. Say it!" Show your child how to trace the hollow letter with a finger. Have him or her use a pencil or crayon to trace and write the letter. Then ask your child to circle the pictures that begin with e.

The Letter f

fish

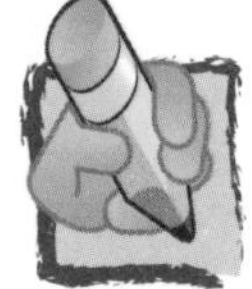

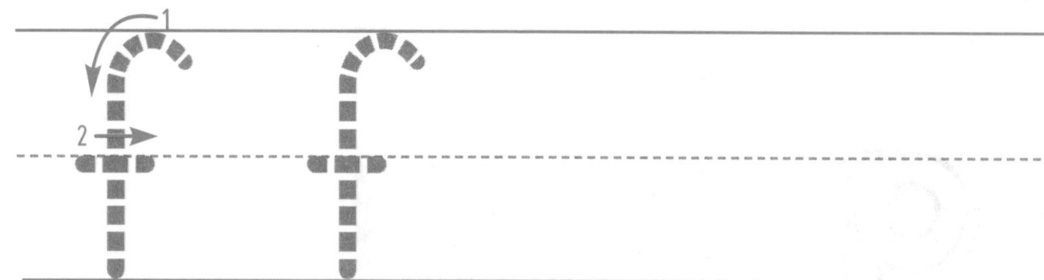

Circle if its name begins like fish.

firefighter

farmer

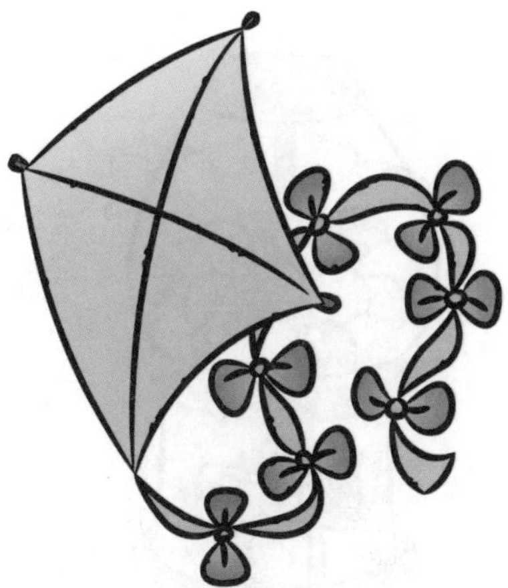

kite

Parents: Say, "*fish* begins with the letter *f*. Listen for the sound *f* makes at the beginning of *fff-fish*. Say it!" Show your child how to trace the hollow letter with a finger. Have him or her use a pencil or crayon to trace and write the letter. Then ask your child to circle the pictures that begin with f.

Recognizing, tracing, and writing lowercase letters; recognizing letter sounds

The Letter g

ghost

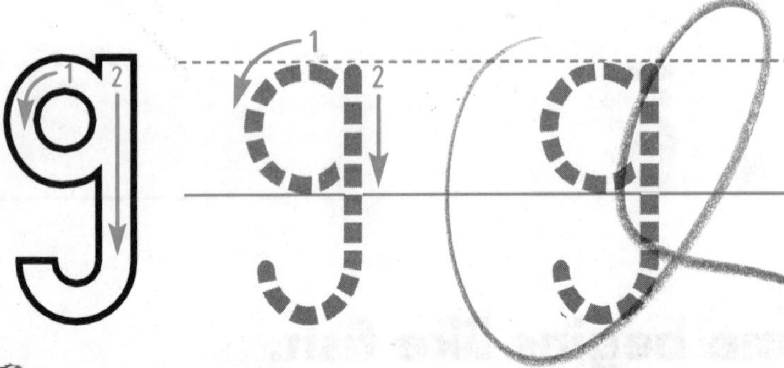

Circle if its name begins like ghost.

gumballs

girl

circus

Parents: ***Say, "ghost begins with the letter g. Listen for the sound g makes at the beginning of ggg-ghost. Say it!" Show your child how to trace the hollow letter with a finger. Have him or her use a pencil or crayon to trace and write the letter. Then ask your child to circle the pictures that begin with g.***

The Letter h

horse

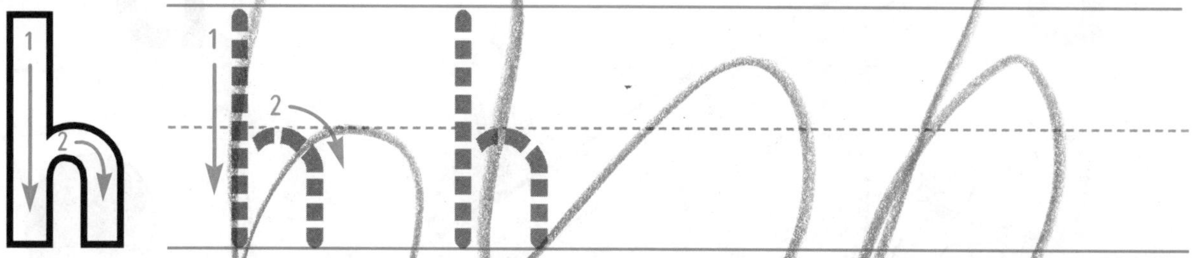

h h h

Circle if its name begins like horse.

house

barn

hen

Parents: Say, "*horse* begins with the letter *h*. Listen for the sound *h* makes at the beginning of *hhh-horse*. Say it!" Show your child how to trace the hollow letter with a finger. Have him or her use a pencil or crayon to trace and write the letter. Then ask your child to circle the pictures that begin with h.

Matching Letters I

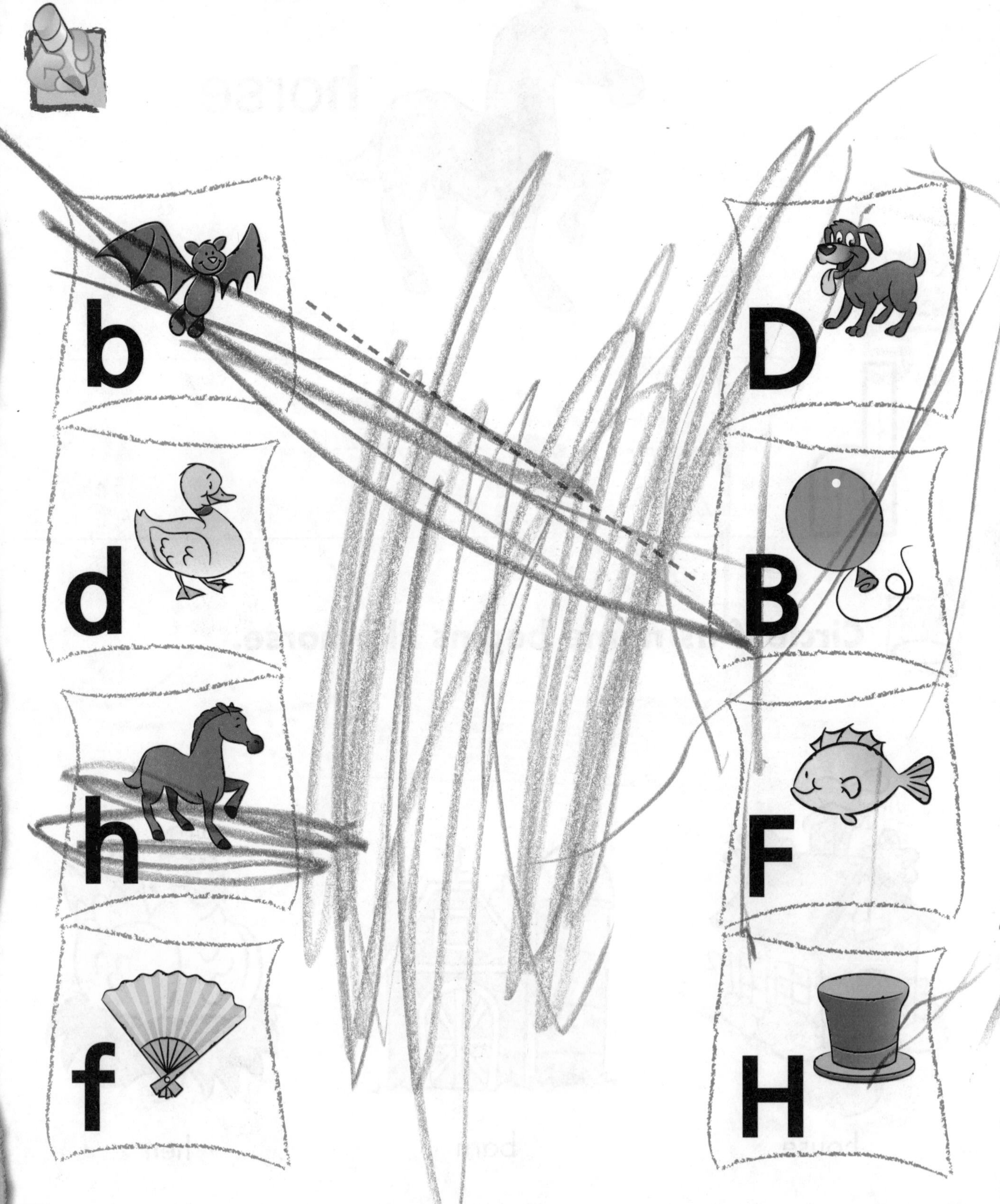

Parents: **Have your child name the letter and picture in each box. Then ask your child to draw a line from each box in the left-hand column to the box on the right with the same letter.**

Matching Letters II

READING

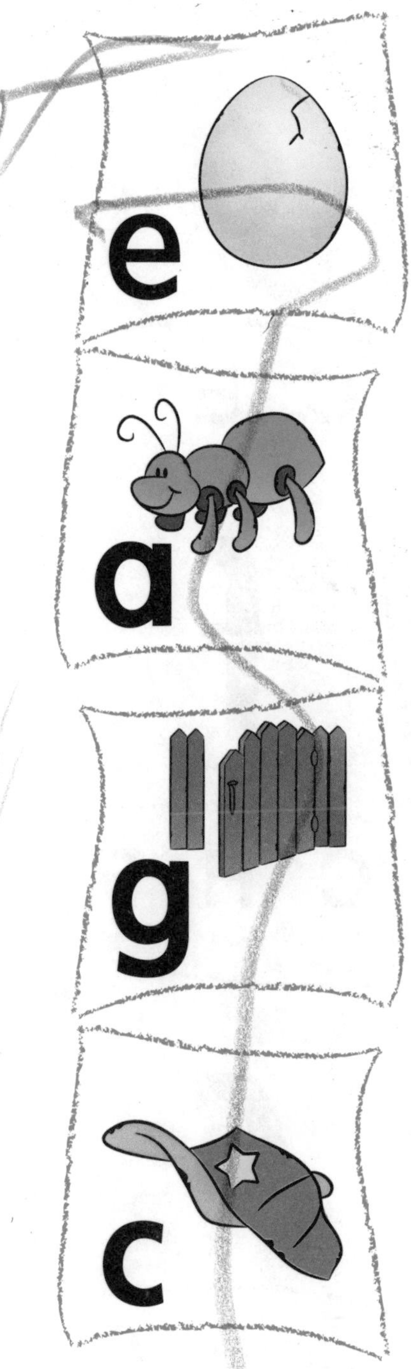

Parents: Have your child name the letter and picture in each box. Then ask your child to draw a line from each box in the left-hand column to the box on the right with the same letter.

Matching Letters III

Circle the matching uppercase letters.

g

G H E

d

D B A

e

C E A

a

A G E

b G A e a c h F B d

f

C H F

b

E B C

h

G B H

c

C F G

Parents: Ask your child to read aloud the large lowercase letter in each box before circling its capital (uppercase) form among the three letters below.

A to H Kaleidoscope

READING

Parents: **See page 288 for directions.**

A to H Kaleidoscope

Cut along the lines. Match each letter with a letter on page 289. Paste the pieces letter-side down.

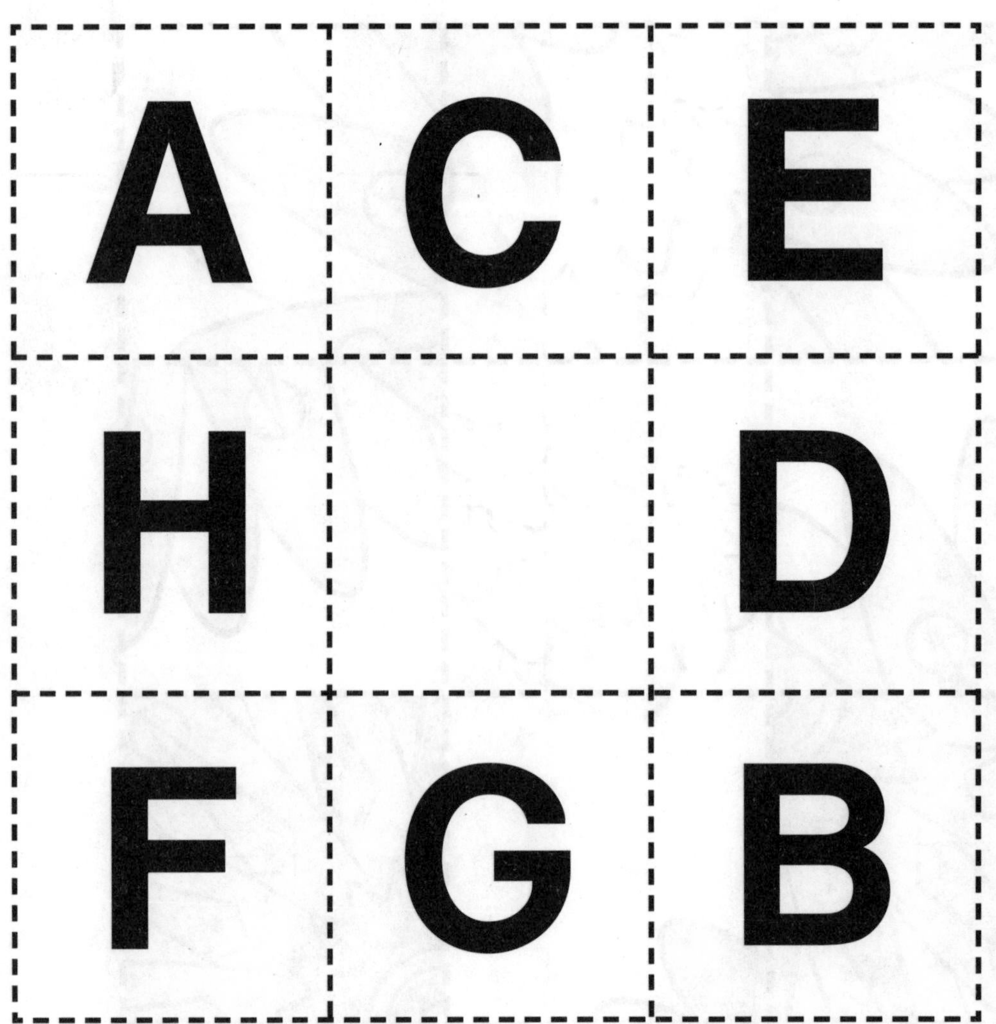

Parents: Help your child cut out the puzzle pieces and match the uppercase letters on the pieces with the lowercase letters in the squares of the puzzle on page 289. Make sure your child pastes each piece with the letter side facedown and the colored side up.

A to H Kaleidoscope

After you paste the pieces from page 288, color the rest of the picture.

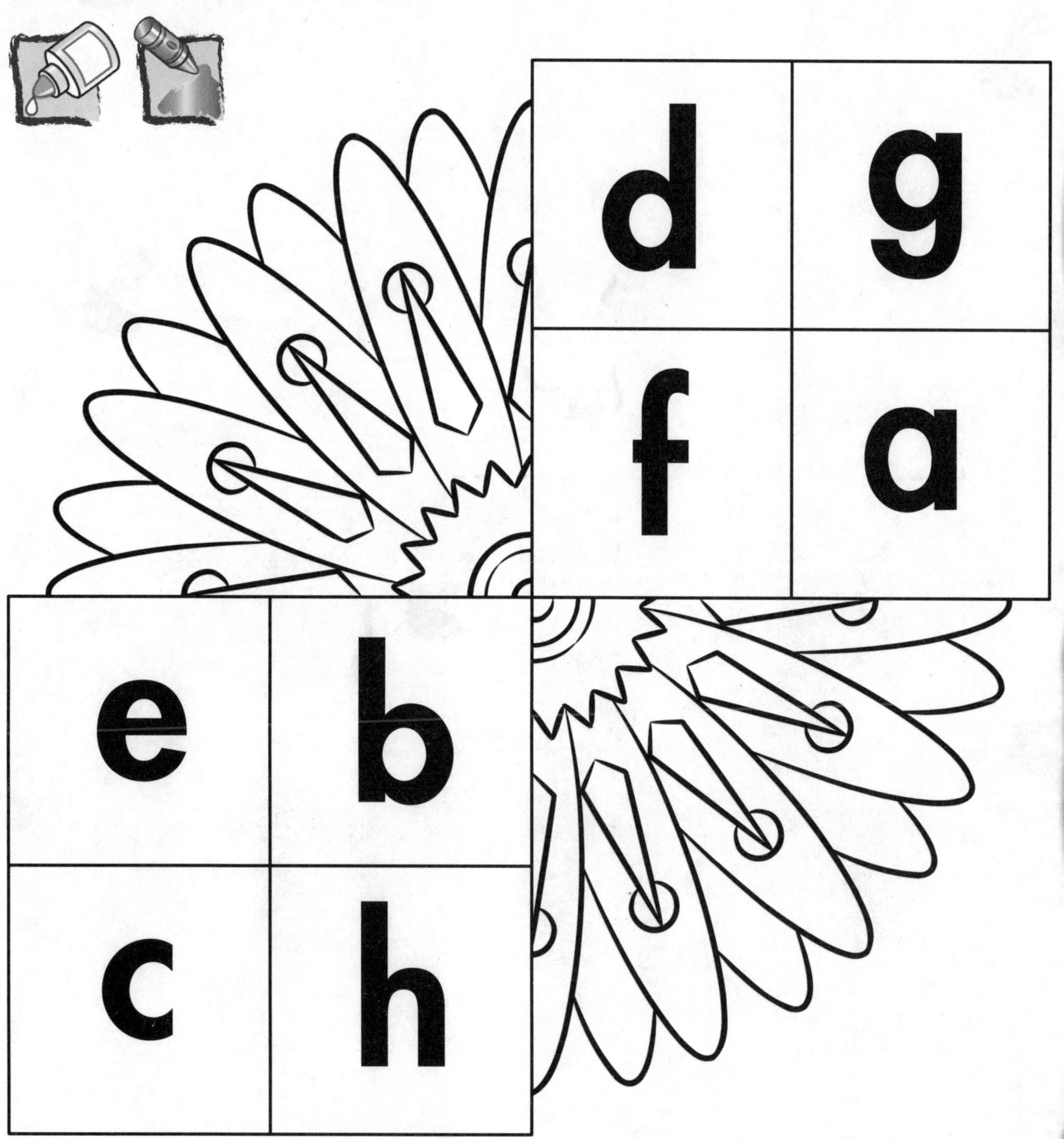

Parents: When the puzzle pieces from pages 287-288 are pasted down, encourage your child to identify the colors of different shapes in the design and to use the same colors when coloring matching shapes.

Month 10 Checklist

Hands-on activities to help prepare your child for school!

LANGUAGE

Opposites: pages 293-295

The best way to learn new words is to start using them in everyday speech. You can help your child practice using opposite words with the activities below:

- ❑ Complete the worksheets.
- ❑ Look at magazine pictures with your child. Ask questions about the pictures that encourage your child to answer using the correct opposite words. For example, with a picture that shows a dog under a table you might ask, "Where is the dog?" (It's *under* the table.)
- ❑ Play a game of opposites charades. To play, say a word, such as *over*, and ask the other player to pantomime its opposite (*under*).

MATH

Animal and Shape Patterns: pages 296, 301
Counting Patterns: pages 302-303

For this month, more complex patterns of shape and color, some of which involve counting, are introduced. It is a good idea to review counting to 10 before giving your child the worksheets.

- ❑ Complete the worksheets.
- ❑ Using cereal pieces of different shapes, colors, and sizes, help your child create patterns similar in complexity to the ones on the worksheets.
- ❑ Line up four or five blocks that vary in color or shape to make a pattern. Ask your child to add a block that continues the pattern. Repeat as long as there is interest.

PREREADING AND PREWRITING

Hidden Pictures: pages 304, 306

Learning to find things in pictures helps children improve visual discrimination skills, which must be finely developed before reading is possible.

❑ Complete the worksheets.

❑ Find a small object—e.g., a thimble, a feather, a top. Explain that you're about to play a game in which you hide the item in a room while the child is away. The child then comes back into the room and tries to find the item in less than two minutes. Let the child have a turn as the hider as well as the finder.

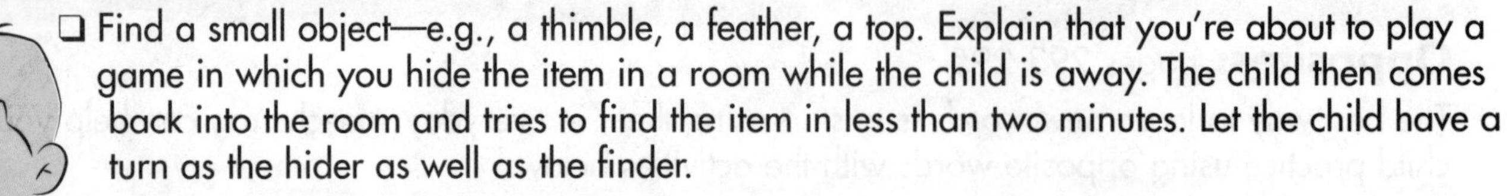

READING

Sounds of Letters *t* and *r*: pages 305, 307

Matching Uppercase and Lowercase Letters *I/i* to *P/p*: pages 316-321

This month, your child will continue to learn about letter sounds and will practice matching uppercase with lowercase forms.

❑ Complete the worksheets.

❑ Have your child watch in a mirror while making the sounds of *t* and *r* over and over. Talk about the position of the tongue against the teeth when making the *t* sound. Then ask, "Does your tongue touch your teeth when you make the *r* sound? Where does it stay when you make the *r* sound?"

❑ Look for uppercase and lowercase examples of the letters *Ii* through *Pp* on a page from a children's magazine. Find an uppercase letter, circle it, and then ask your child to find its lowercase counterpart and circle it. Use a different color of crayon for each pair.

WRITING

Lowercase Letters *i* to *p*: pages 308-315

If you began an alphabet scrapbook as suggested in last month's checklist, let your child continue to work on it. Include as many of the lowercase letter activities below in your child's schedule as you like:

❑ Complete the worksheets.

❑ Let your child trace over some of the large lowercase letters in this book using tissue paper.

❑ Each week, label a few items in your home with names that begin with any of the lowercase letters your child has mastered. Talk about the beginning sound of each name.

over

under

Color the monkey that's under brown.

Color the monkey that's over orange.

Parents: **Ask your child to point to the frog over, and then to the frog under, the lily pad. Point to the words *over* and *under*. Explain that they are called opposites. Then say, "Color the monkey under the climbing bars brown. Color the monkey over the bars orange."**

LANGUAGE

Big and Little

big

little

Color the big house blue.

Color the little house red.

Parents: Ask your child to point to the big clock and then to the little clock. Point to the words *big* and *little*. Explain that they are called opposites. Then say, "Find the big house and color it blue. Find the little house and color it red."

Opposites Review

Circle the opposites.

over

big

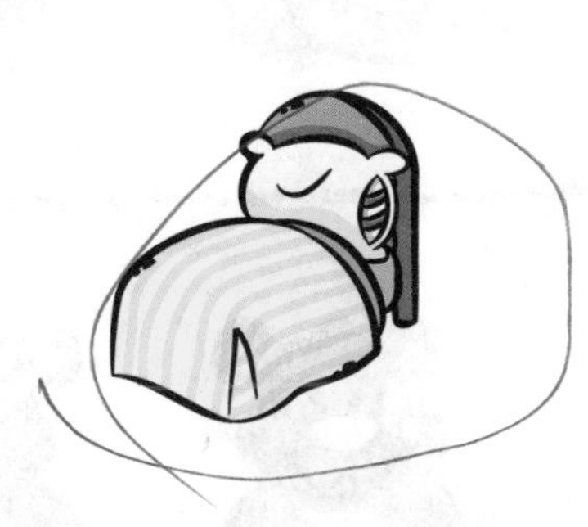

happy

Parents: Have your child tell about the first picture in each row. Point out and read the word under each picture. Then have your child circle the picture that shows its opposite.

MATH

Animals Patterns

Circle what comes next.

Parents: **In each row, have your child say the color and name of each animal. Then discuss the pattern in the row to help your child decide which animal to circle in the final box to continue the pattern.**

Parents: Remove pages 297–300 from this book. Then see directions for making mini books on the inside of the front cover.

1

There was one in the bed,
And the little one said,
"GOOD NIGHT!"

There were ten in the bed,
And the little one said,
"Roll over, roll over."
So they all rolled over,
And one fell out.

There were nine in the bed,
And the little one said,
"Roll over, roll over."
So they all rolled over,
And one fell out.

There were three in the bed,
And the little one said,
"Roll over, roll over."
So they all rolled over,
And one fell out.

There were two in the bed,
And the little one said,
"Roll over, roll over."
So they all rolled over,
And one fell out.

4

There were four in the bed,
And the little one said,
"Roll over, roll over."
So they all rolled over,
And one fell out.

8

There were eight in the bed,
And the little one said,
"Roll over, roll over."
So they all rolled over,
And one fell out.

There were seven in the bed,
And the little one said,
"Roll over, roll over."
So they all rolled over,
And one fell out.

There were six in the bed,
And the little one said,
"Roll over, roll over."
So they all rolled over,
And one fell out.

5

There were five in the bed,
And the little one said,
"Roll over, roll over."
So they all rolled over,
And one fell out.

Colored Shape Patterns

Draw and color what comes next.

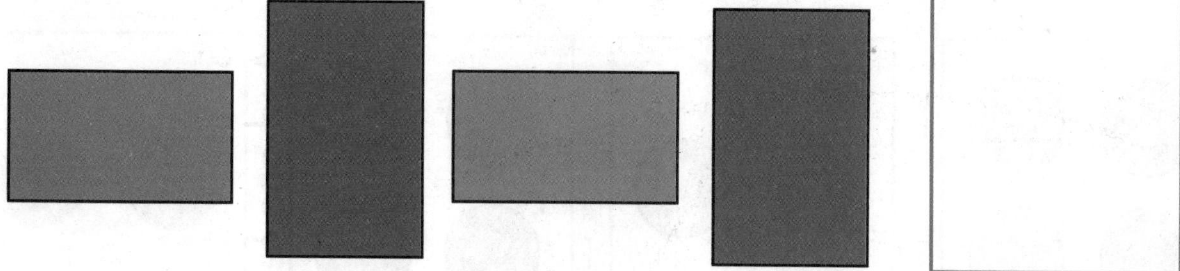

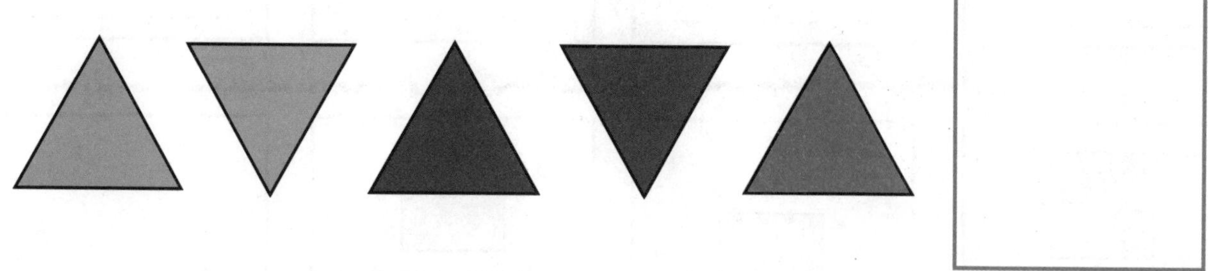

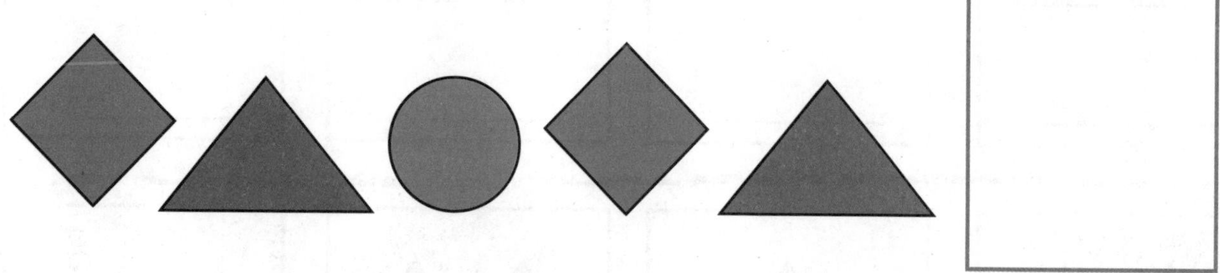

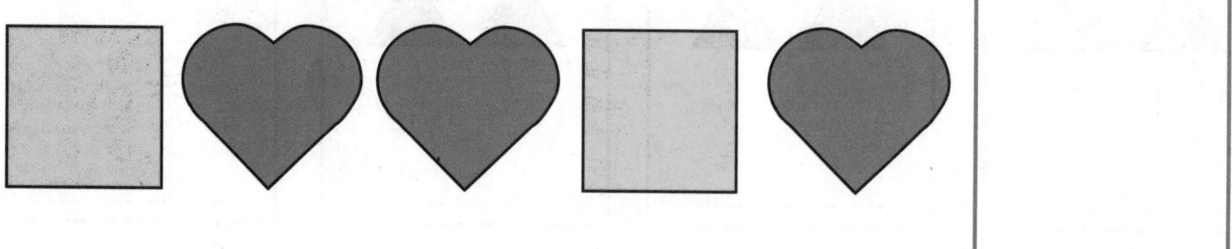

Parents: In each row, have your child say the color and shape of each object. Then discuss the pattern in the row to help your child decide which colored shape to draw in the empty box.

M A T H

Counting Patterns I

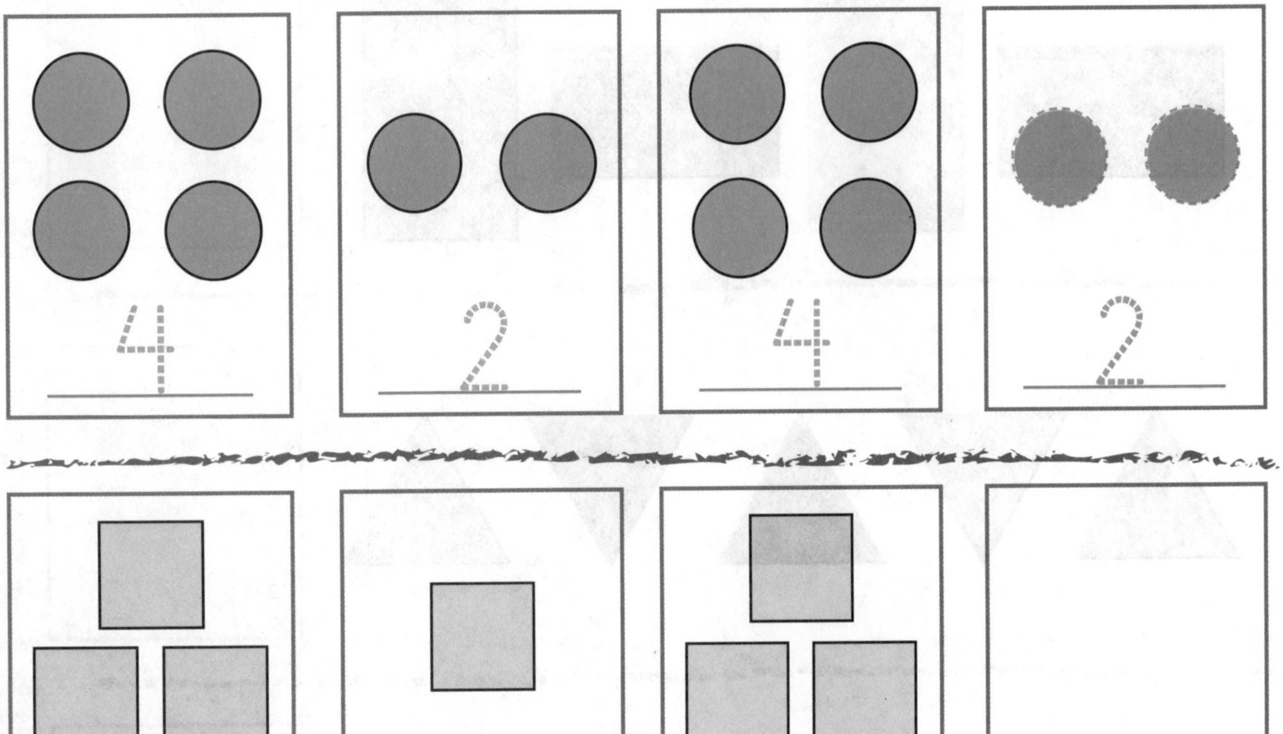

4 2 4 2

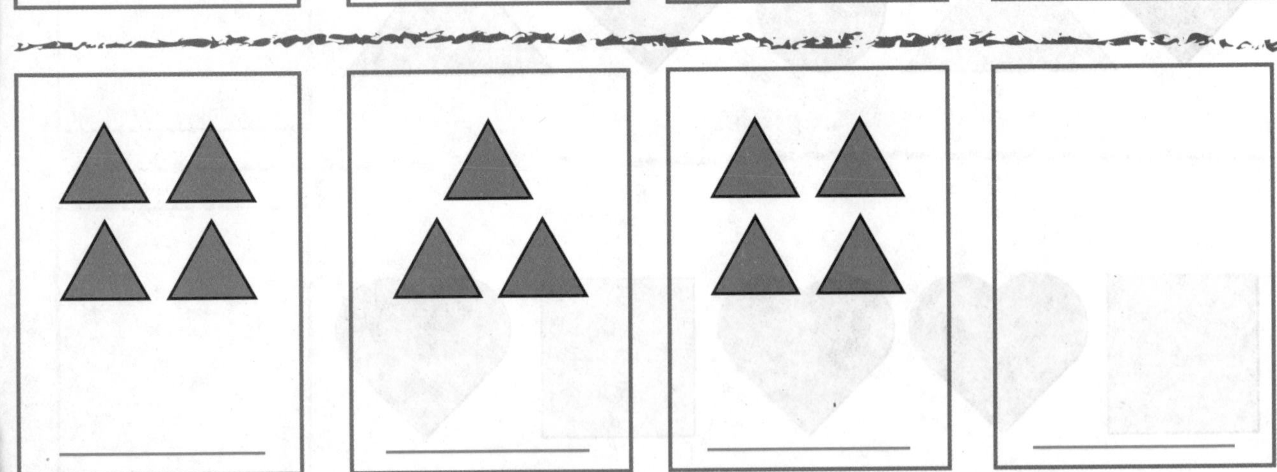

Parents: In each row, have your child count the shapes in each box and write the number. Then discuss the pattern in the row to help your child decide how many of the shapes to draw in the empty box and which number to write.

Counting Patterns II

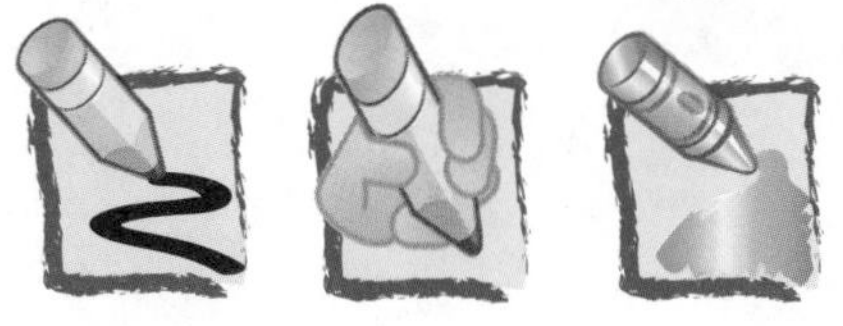

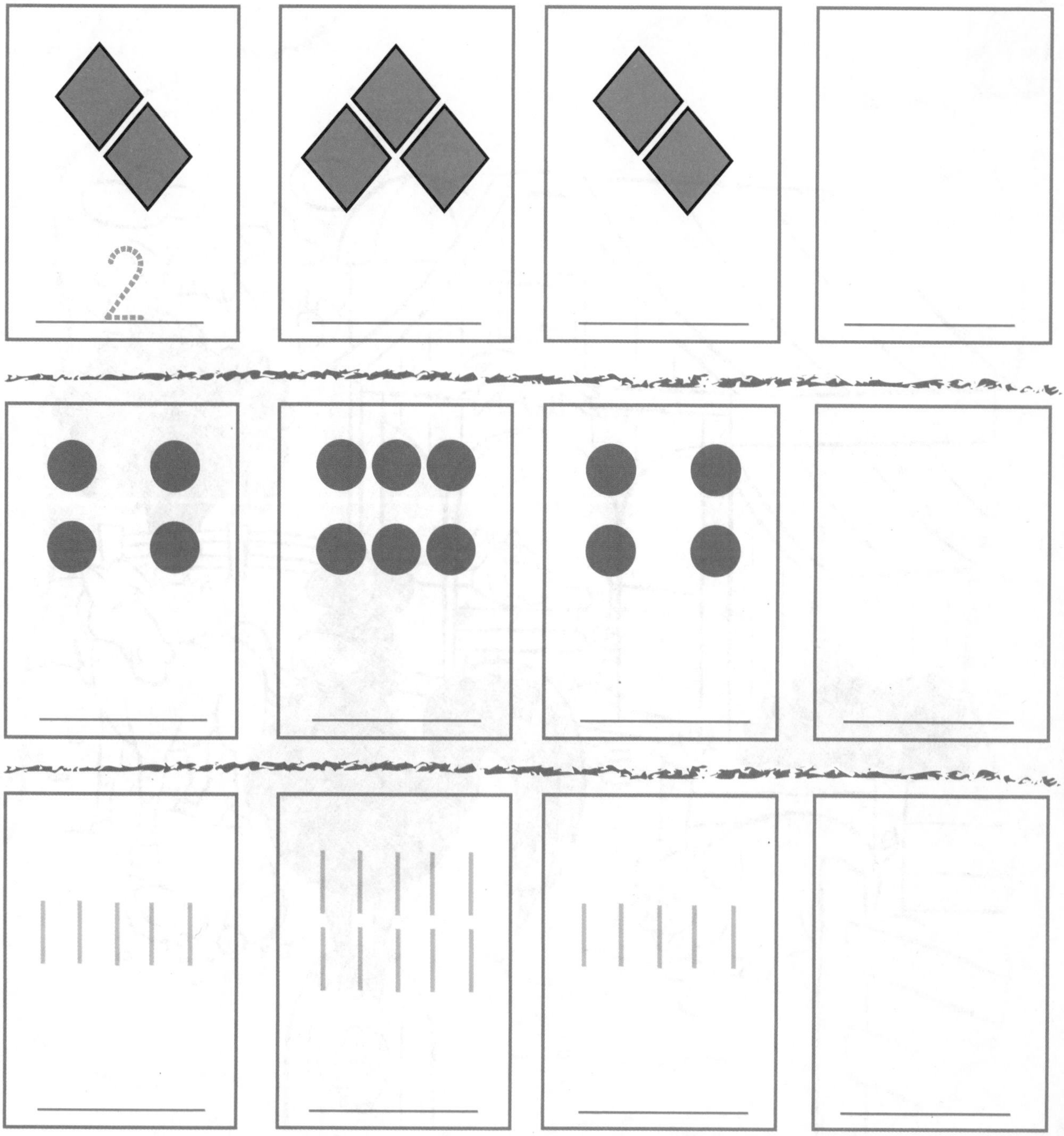

2

Parents: In each row, have your child count the shapes in each box and write the number. Then discuss the pattern in the row to help your child decide how many of the shapes to draw in the empty box and which number to write.

PREREADING

Timid Turkeys

Circle  **.**

Parents: Help your child find and circle the three hidden turkeys. Then have him or her finish coloring the picture.

Beginning Sound t

Color the things with names that begin with t.

TAXI

Parents: Point to the tiger and say, "*Tiger* begins with *t*. Listen for the sound *t* makes at the beginning of *ttt-tiger*. Say it!" Then ask your child to name each picture on the page, telling if the name begins with the *t* sound. Say, "If you hear the *t* sound, color the picture."

PREREADING

Rabbits on the Run

Parents: Help your child find and circle the four hidden rabbits. Then have him or her finish coloring the picture.

Beginning Sound r

Color the things with names that begin with r.

READING

Parents: Point to the rooster and say, "*Rooster* begins with *r*. Listen for the sound *r* makes at the beginning of *rrr-rooster*. Say it!" Then ask your child to name each picture on the page, telling if he or she hears the *r* sound. Say, "If you hear the *r* sound, color the picture."

The Letter i

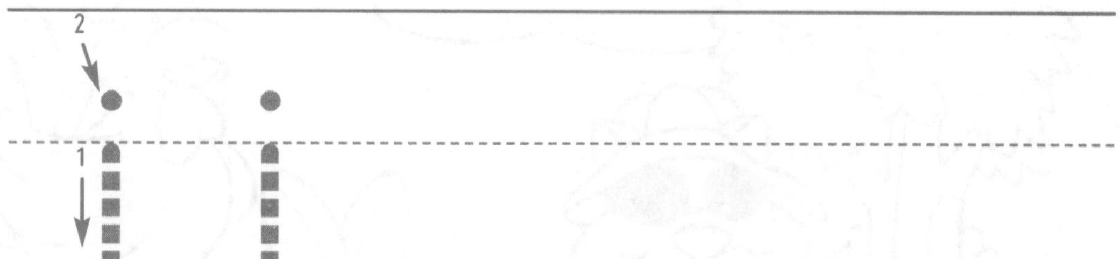

Circle if its name begins like igloo.

ink iguana frog

Parents: Say, "*igloo* begins with the letter *i.* Listen for the sound *i* makes at the beginning of *iii-igloo.* Say it!" Show your child how to trace the hollow letter with a finger. Have him or her use a pencil or crayon to trace and write the letter. Then ask your child to circle the pictures that begin with i.

Recognizing, tracing, and writing lowercase letters; recognizing letter sounds

The Letter j

jack-in-the-box

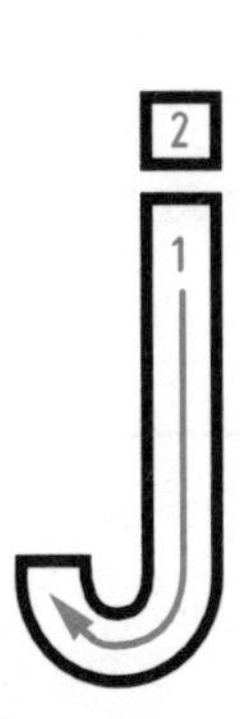

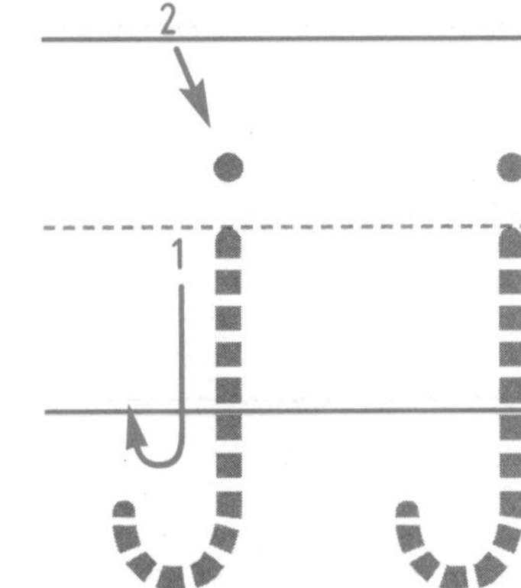

Circle if its name begins like jack-in-the-box.

jack-o'-lantern

fox

jacks

Parents: Say, "*jack-in-the-box* begins with the letter *j*. Listen for the sound *j* makes at the beginning of *jjj-jack-in-the-box*. Say it!" Show your child how to trace the hollow letter with a finger. Have him or her use a pencil or crayon to trace and write the letter. Then ask your child to circle the pictures that begin with j.

The Letter k

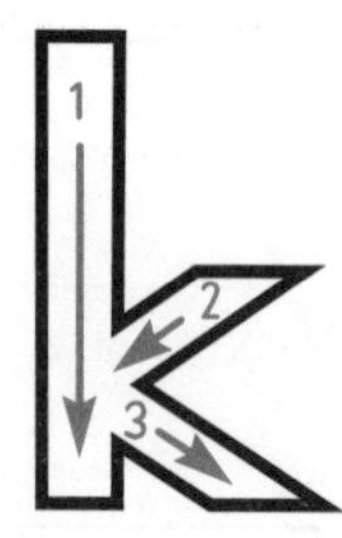

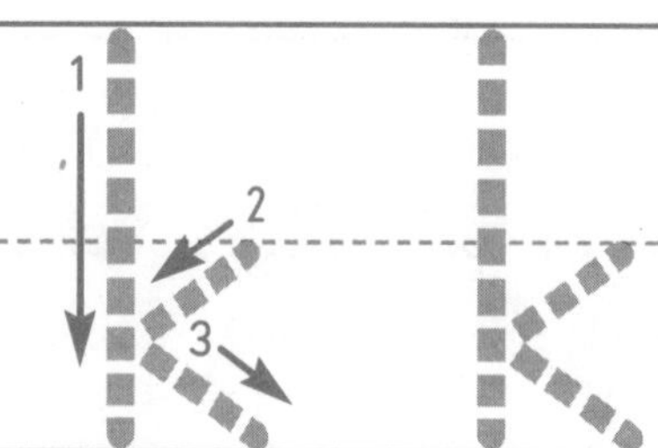

Circle if its name begins like kite.

bird

kangaroo

king

Parents: Say, "*kite* begins with the letter *k*. Listen for the sound *k* makes at the beginning of *kkk-kite*. Say it!" Show your child how to trace the hollow letter with a finger. Have him or her use a pencil or crayon to trace and write the letter. Then ask your child to circle the pictures that begin with k.

Recognizing, tracing, and writing lowercase letters; recognizing letter sounds

The Letter l

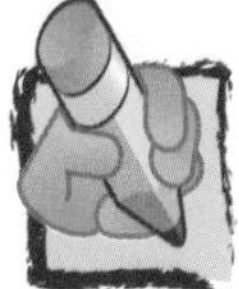

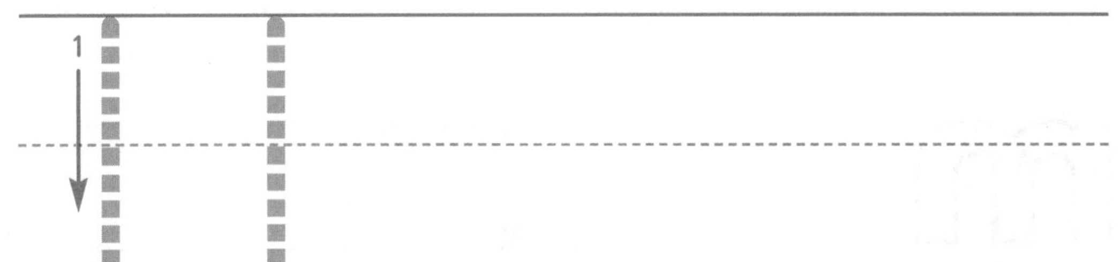

Circle if its name begins like lion.

lemon

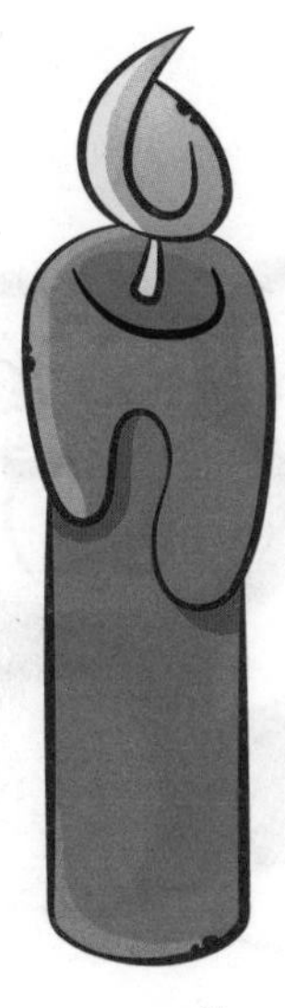

candle

lamp

Parents: Say, "*lion* begins with the letter *l*. Listen for the sound *l* makes at the beginning of *lll-lion*. Say it!" Show your child how to trace the hollow letter with a finger. Have him or her use a pencil or crayon to trace and write the letter. Then ask your child to circle the pictures that begin with l.

Recognizing, tracing, and writing lowercase letters; recognizing letter sounds

WRITING

The Letter m

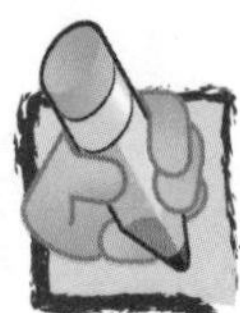

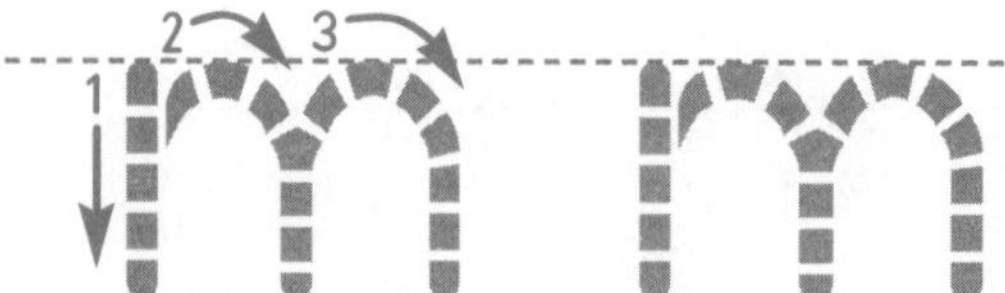

Circle if its name begins like mouse.

Parents: Say, "*mouse* begins with the letter *m*. Listen for the sound *m* makes at the beginning of *mmm-mouse*. Say it!" Show your child how to trace the hollow letter with a finger. Have him or her use a pencil or crayon to trace and write the letter. Then ask your child to circle the pictures that begin with m.

Recognizing, tracing, and writing lowercase letters; recognizing letter sounds

The Letter n

Circle if its name begins like net.

nest fish necklace

Parents: Say, "*net* begins with the letter *n*. Listen for the sound *n* makes at the beginning of *nnn-net*. Say it!" Show your child how to trace the hollow letter with a finger. Have him or her use a pencil or crayon to trace and write the letter. Then ask your child to circle the pictures that begin with n.

The Letter o

owl

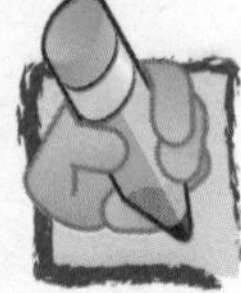

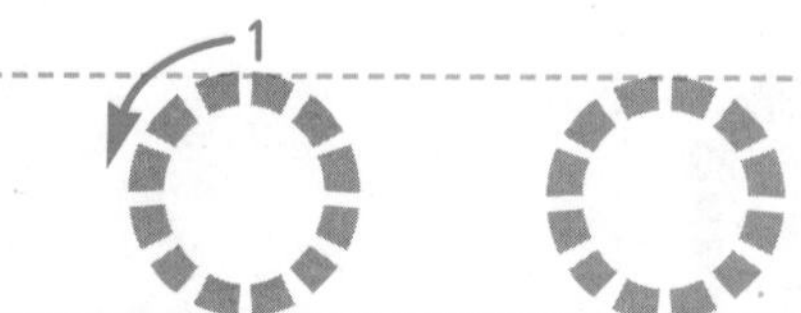

Circle if its name begins like owl.

bird octopus ox

Parents: Say, "*owl* begins with the letter *o*. Listen for the sound *o* makes at the beginning of *ooo-owl*. Say it!" Show your child how to trace the hollow letter with a finger. Have him or her use a pencil or crayon to trace and write the letter. Then ask your child to circle the pictures that begin with o.

Recognizing, tracing, and writing lowercase letters; recognizing letter sounds

The Letter p

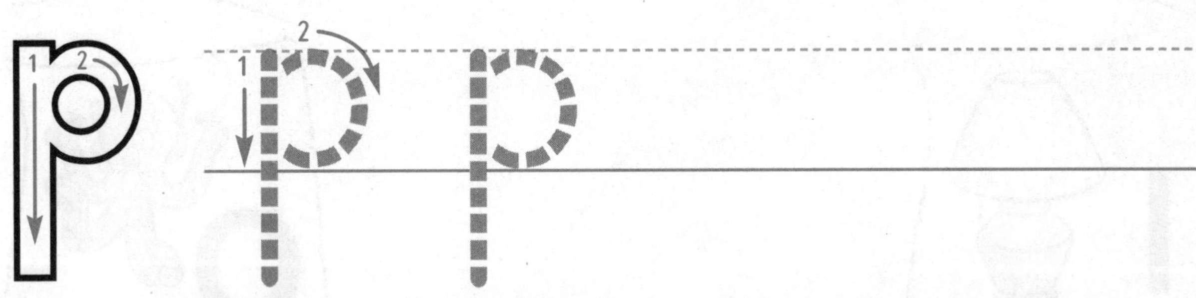

Circle if its name begins like pig.

parrot frog porcupine

Parents: Say, "*pig* begins with the letter *p*. Listen for the sound *p* makes at the beginning of *ppp-pig*. Say it!" Show your child how to trace the hollow letter with a finger. Have him or her use a pencil or crayon to trace and write the letter. Then ask your child to circle the pictures that begin with p.

READING

Matching Letters IV

i

l

o

p

L

O

I

P

Parents: Have your child name the letter and picture in each box. Then ask your child to draw a line from each box in the left-hand column to the box on the right with the same letter.

Matching Letters V

READING

Parents: Have your child name the letter and picture in each box. Then ask your child to draw a line from each box in the left-hand column to the box on the right with the same letter.

Matching Letters VI

Parents: Ask your child to read aloud the large lowercase letter in each box before circling its capital (uppercase) form among the three letters below.

I-P Kaleidoscope

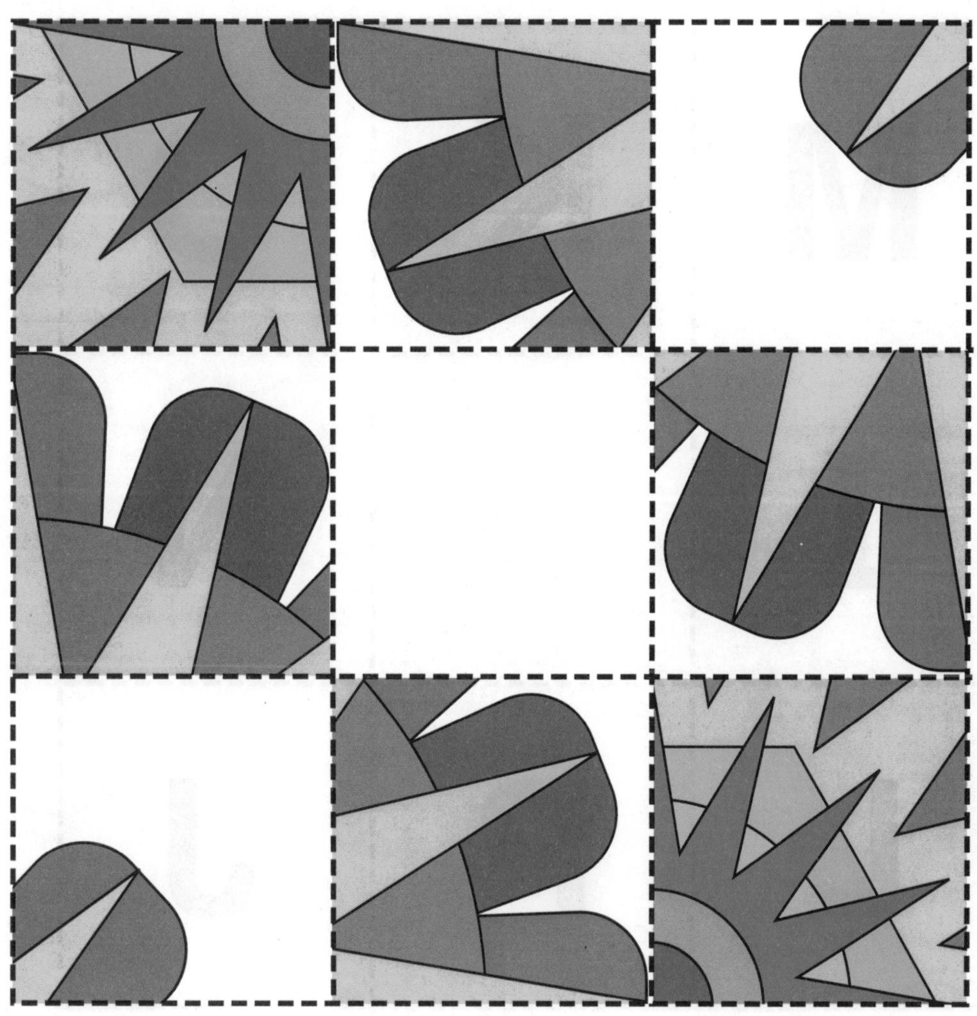

Parents: See page 320 for directions.

I-P Kaleidoscope

Cut along the lines. Match each letter with a letter on page 321. Paste the pieces letter-side down.

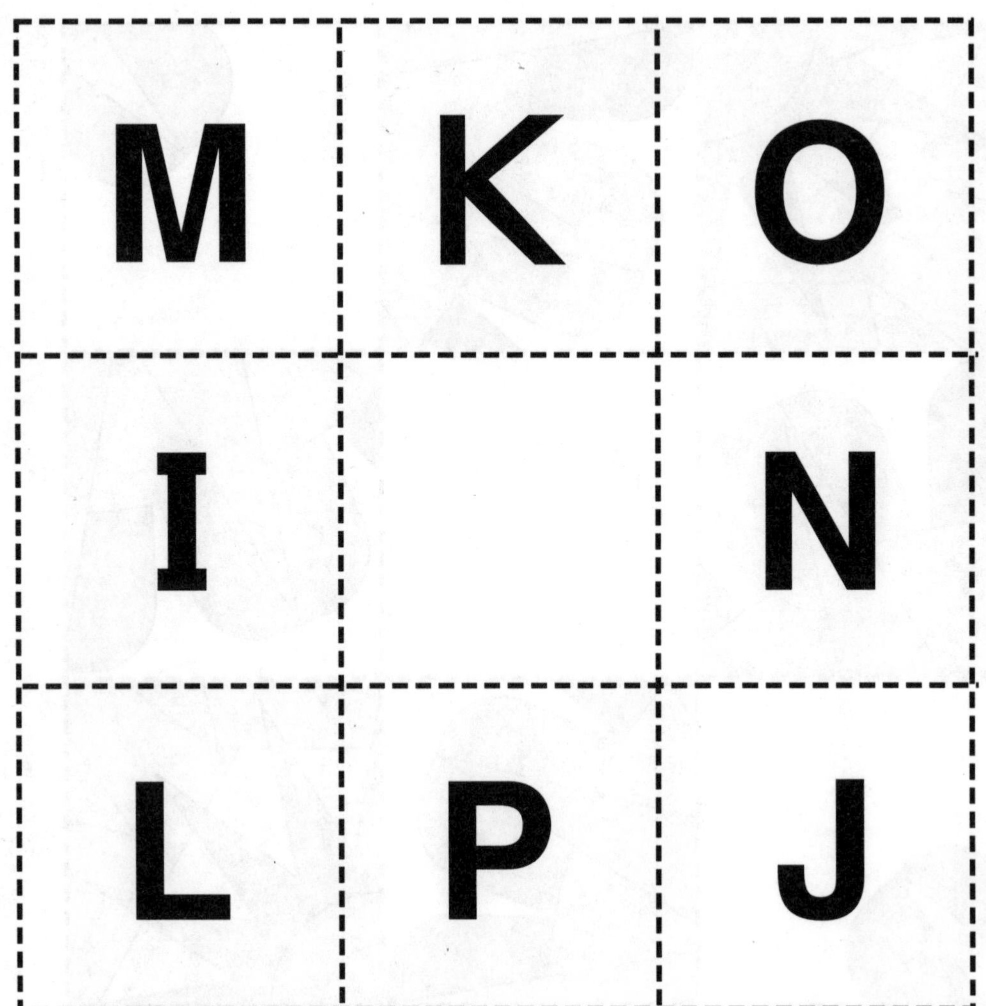

Parents: Help your child cut out the puzzle pieces and match the uppercase letters on the pieces with the lowercase letters in the squares of the puzzle on page 321. Make sure your child pastes each piece with the letter side facedown and the colored side up.

I-P Kaleidoscope

After you paste the pieces from page 320, color the rest of the picture.

n j

l p

k o

m i

Parents: When the puzzle pieces from pages 319-320 are pasted down, encourage your child to identify the colors of different shapes in the design and to use the same colors when coloring matching shapes.

Month 11 Checklist

Hands-on activities to help prepare your child for school!

MATH

Counting Forward and Backward: pages 325-327
Time, Money, and Measurement: pages 335-336

Some of the worksheets for this month focus on numeric order. Use any of the appropriate counting activities from previous checklists to help your child grasp this concept. The activities below will help you introduce money and measurement to your child:

- ❑ Complete the worksheets.
- ❑ Label each of four small paper cups with one of the following: 1¢, 5¢, 10¢, 25¢. Pile a mix of pennies, nickels, dimes, and quarters in front of the cups. Help your child sort the coins. Explain that ¢ means *cents*.
- ❑ Collect a number of measurement tools—a ruler, thermometer, clock, postal scale, yardstick, calendar, and so on. Explain to your child that all of these items are used to measure things. For each item, ask, "Do you know what it's used for?" Then give clues and ask the child to pick the appropriate item. Examples: "Which item tells time?" "Which item tells how hot something is?"
- ❑ To bring your preschooler's attention to clocks, help him or her find and count each clock or watch in your house. Talk about how these devices help us. Repeat this activity with calendars.
- ❑ The next time you're at the doctor, talk with your child about all the things the doctor or nurse use to measure us: thermometers to measure our temperature; scales to measure how heavy we are; rulers to measure how tall we are. At home, play "Doctor-Patient" with your youngster, letting the youngster be the doctor.

READING

Rhyming Words: pages 328-330
Matching Uppercase and Lowercase Letters Q/q to Z/z: pages 349-354

- ❑ Complete the worksheets.
- ❑ Help your child make up verses using rhyming words from the worksheets. For example, *king* and *ring*, from page 328, could be used as follows:

  There once was a king
  Who wore a big ring.
- ❑ Make a deck of uppercase and lowercase letters by printing each letter on an index card. Let your child decorate the cards by tracing over the letters with markers or glue and glitter. Use the deck for matching games for two or more players. Simply shuffle the cards, lay them out facedown, and then, in turn, each player turns two cards over. If the cards match (uppercase with lowercase letter), the player keeps them and turns over another pair. If they don't match, the player turns them back over and it's the next player's turn.

LANGUAGE

Telling a Story Using *First, Next, and Last:* pages 333-334

It's very important to encourage your child to talk about all kinds of things—because he or she will certainly have to speak in school. Learning to use *first*, *next*, and *last* helps a child organize what he or she needs to communicate:

- ❑ Complete the worksheets.
- ❑ Give your child instructions on how to do an everyday task (such as brushing teeth or setting the table) using the terms *first*, *next*, and *last*. Have your child repeat the instructions, or give instructions for another activity, also using *first*, *next*, and *last*.
- ❑ From children's magazines or other sources, find pictures that tell simple, three-part stories—e.g., before, during, and after a meal. Cut out each picture and put it on an index card. Shuffle the cards. Let your child put them in order, explaining what happened *first*, *next*, and *last*.

WRITING

Lowercase Letters q to z: pages 337-346
Lowercase Alphabet: pages 347-348

If you began an alphabet scrapbook with your child as suggested in Month 9's checklist, let the child continue to work on it. This month, add a front cover with a title, *The Alphabet*, and have your child sign/print his or her name.

- ❑ Complete the worksheets.
- ❑ Print a letter on an index card or construction paper. Help the child spread glue over the lines and then position yarn on the glue. When the card is dry, your child will have a tactile reminder of the letter shape.
- ❑ Help your youngster form waxed pipe cleaners into letter shapes. Press the pipe cleaner shapes onto paper.

Up to 10 and Down Again!

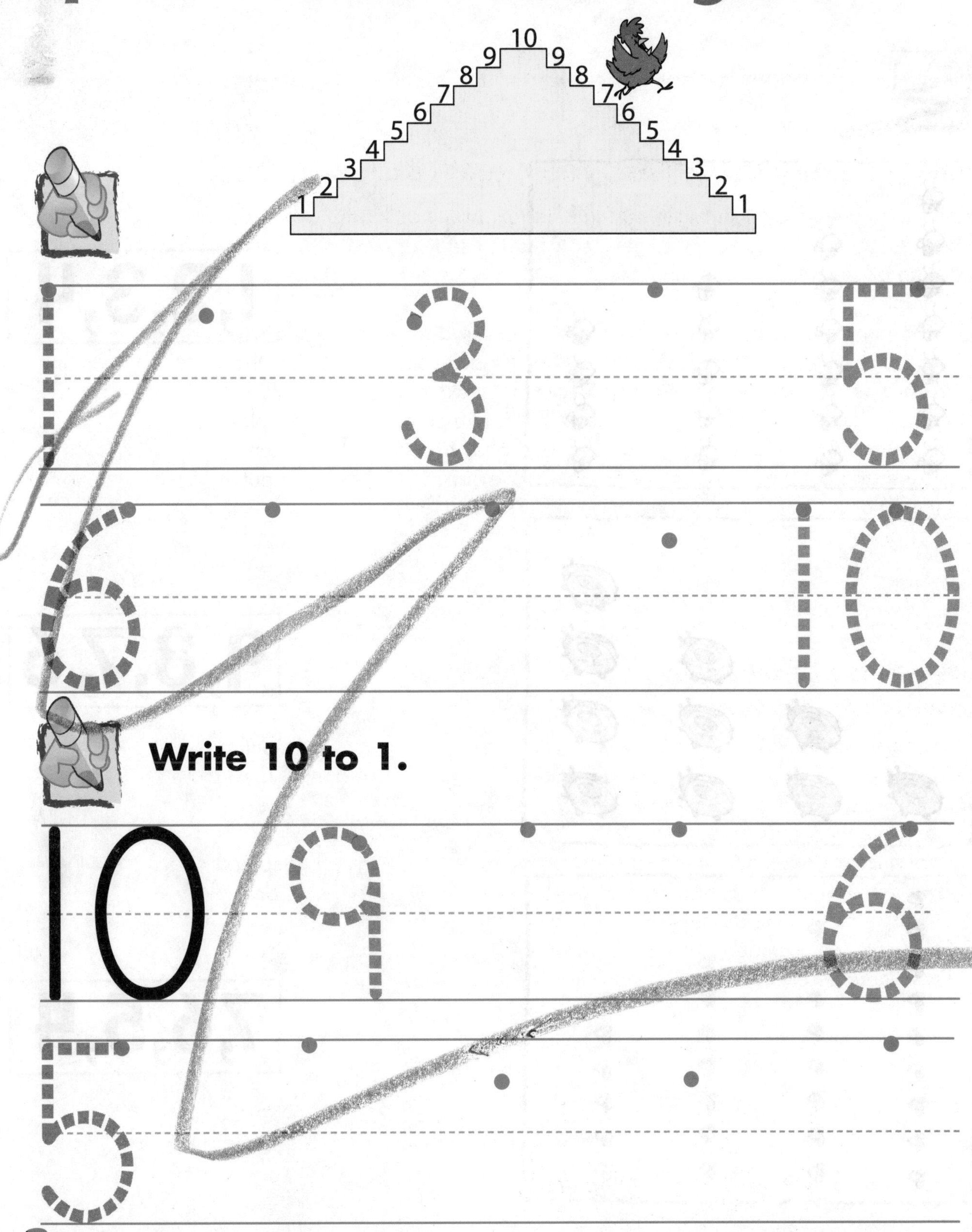

Parents: Count from 1 to 10 and 10 to 1 with your child, pointing to the staircase as you count; then let your child do it on his or her own. Have him or her write in missing numbers and trace over gray numbers on the write-on lines.

Matching Patterns

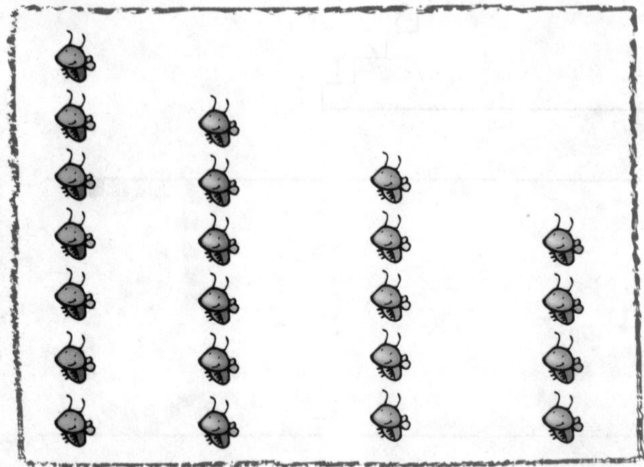

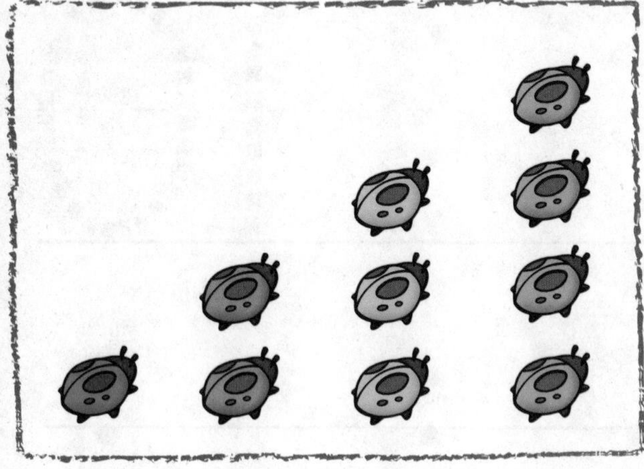

9,8,7,6

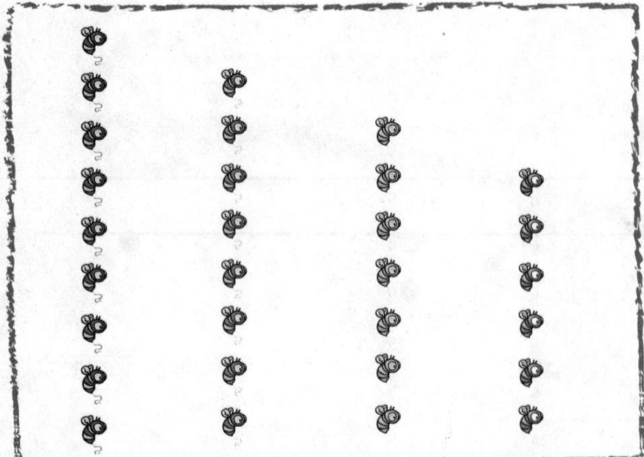

7,6,5,4

Parents: Point out the first box at the left and have your child count the insects in each stack in that box. Then ask your child to find the box at right with the same numbers in the same order, and draw a line between the boxes. Repeat with other boxes.

Number Patterns

1 2 3 4 5 6

10 9 8 7 6 ___

4 5 6 7 8 ___

7 6 5 4 3 ___

Parents: Have your child read Row 1, tell what number is needed next, and write that number on the line. Then have your child read Row 2, tell how this pattern is different from that of Row 1, and write the next number. Continue with the rest of the page.

Counting forward and backward; recognizing number order

-ing Rhymes

king

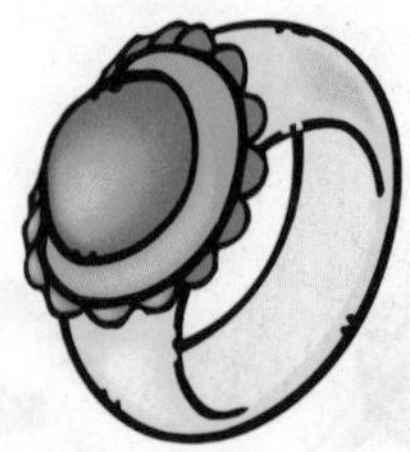

ring

Color the one that rhymes with *king*.

Color the ones with rhyming names.

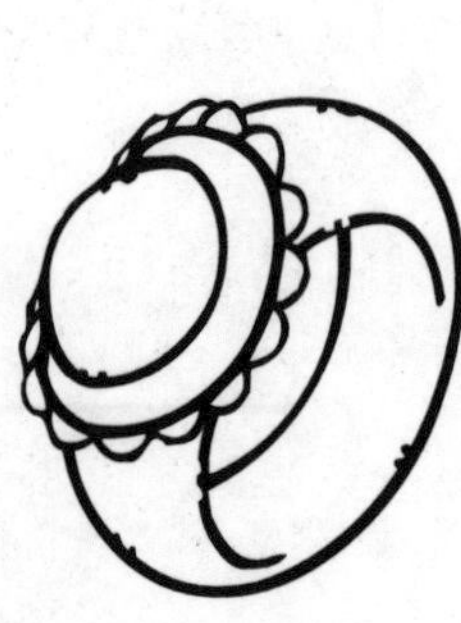

Parents: Point to each picture at the top of the page and say its name. Have your child do the same. Explain that those words rhyme because they both have the *-ing* sound at the end. Then help your child complete the rest of the page.

-ug Rhymes

bug

mug

Color the one that rhymes with *bug*.

Color the ones with rhyming names.

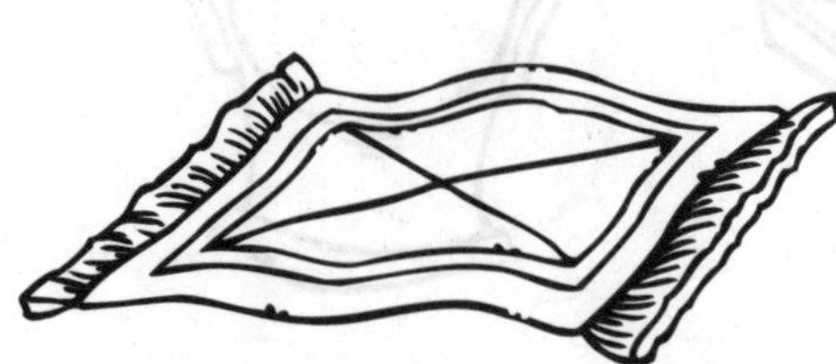

Parents: Point to each picture at the top of the page and say its name. Have your child do the same. Explain that those words rhyme because they both have the *-ug* sound at the end. Then help your child complete the rest of the page.

-ed Rhymes

bed

sled

Color the one that rhymes with *bed*.

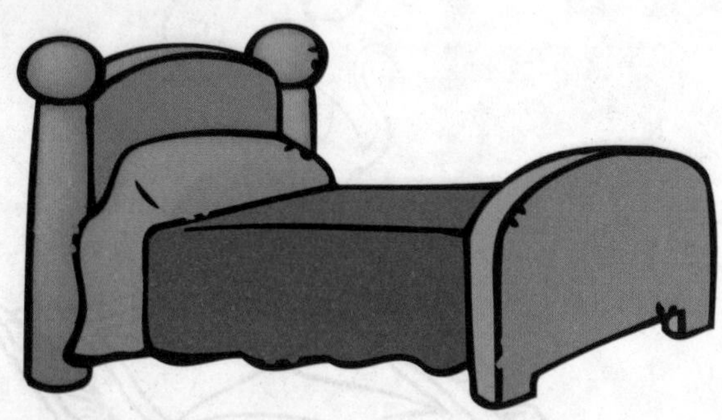

Color the ones with rhyming names.

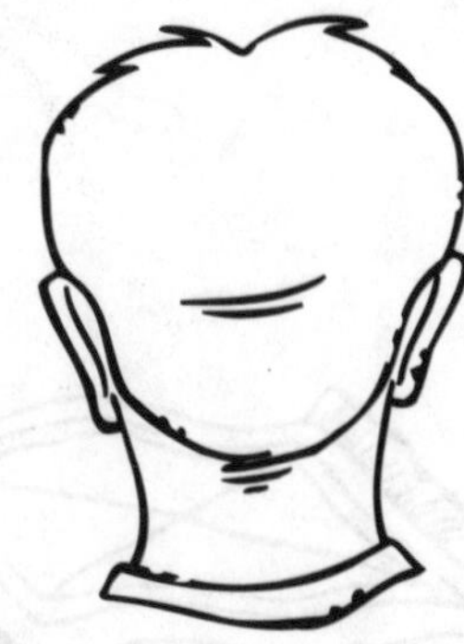

Parents: Point to each picture at the top of the page and say its name. Have your child do the same. Explain that those words rhyme because they both have the *-ed* sound at the end. Then have your child complete the rest of the page.

Finding Fossils

Parents: **Ask your child to use his or her index finger to find a path from the museum entrance to the dinosaur. Then have him or her use a pencil or crayon to draw the same path.**

PREREADING

Round Up

Circle [cow images] **.**

Parents: **Help your child find and circle the four hidden cows. Then have him or her finish coloring the picture.**

Baking & Planting Sequences

Parents: Help your child cut out the pictures and then arrange them to show what happened in time order. Encourage your child to tell a story about the pictures, using the words *first, next,* and *last*.

Playing & Drawing Sequences

Parents: Help your child cut out the pictures and then arrange them to show what happened in time order. Encourage your child to tell a story about the pictures, using the words *first, next,* and *last*.

Time and Money

Circle what doesn't belong in each row.

MARCH

S	M	T	W	T	F	S
				1	2	3
4	5	6	7	8	9	10
11	12	13	14	15	16	17
18	19	20	21	22	23	24
25	26	27	28	29	30	31

JUNE

S	M	T	W	T	F	S
				1	2	3
4	5	6	7	8	9	10
11	12	13	14	15	16	17
18	19	20	21	22	23	24
25	26	27	28	29	30	

Parents: Help your child identify the objects pictured in each row. Have your child circle the object that does not have anything to do with money in Row 1. Have your child circle the object that does not have anything to do with time in each of the other two rows.

Measurement

Circle what doesn't belong in each row.

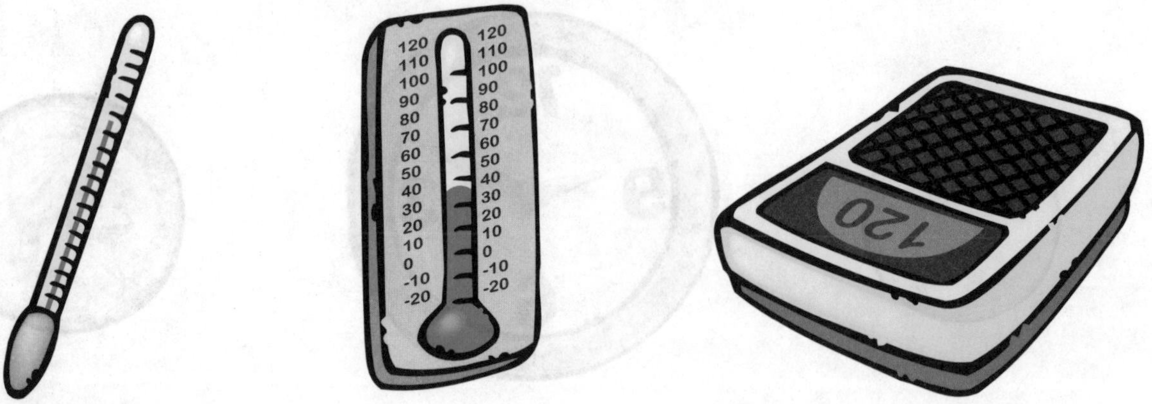

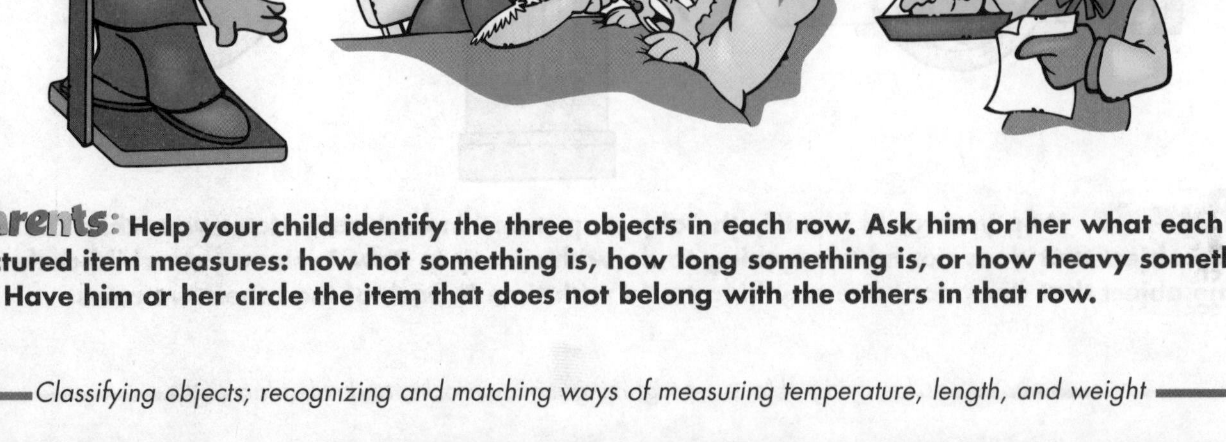

Parents: Help your child identify the three objects in each row. Ask him or her what each pictured item measures: how hot something is, how long something is, or how heavy something is. Have him or her circle the item that does not belong with the others in that row.

The Letter q

quilt

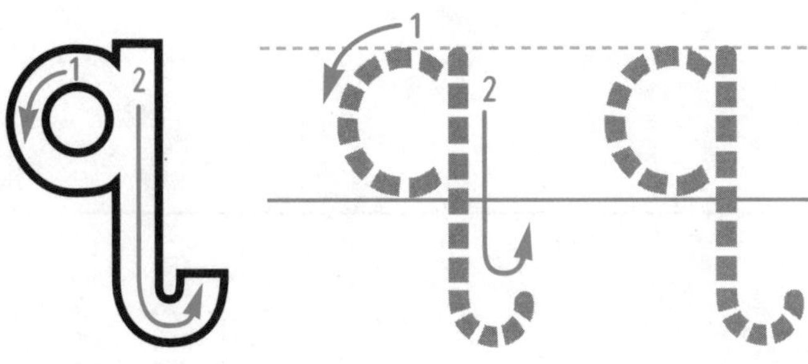

Circle if its name begins like quilt.

quarter

frog

queen

Parents: Say, "*quilt* begins with the letter *q*. Listen for the sound *q* makes at the beginning of *qqq-quilt*. Say it!" Show your child how to trace the hollow letter with a finger. Have him or her use a pencil or crayon to trace and write the letter. Then ask your child to circle the pictures that begin with q.

The Letter r

rabbit

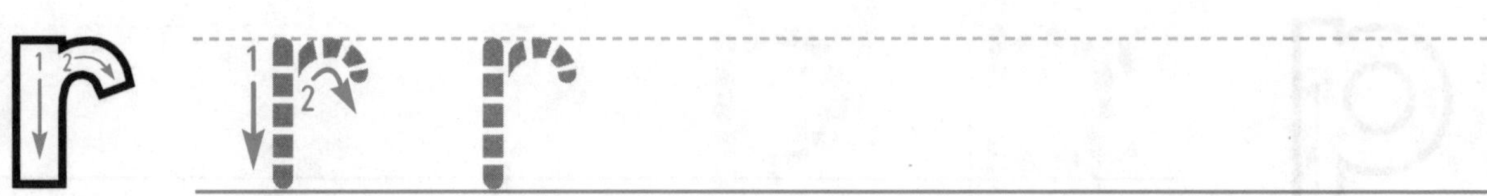

Circle if its name begins like rabbit.

robot boy rocket

Parents: Say, "*rabbit* begins with the letter *r*. Listen for the sound *r* makes at the beginning of *rrr-rabbit*. Say it!" Show your child how to trace the hollow letter with a finger. Have him or her use a pencil or crayon to trace and write the letter. Then ask your child to circle the pictures that begin with r.

Recognizing, tracing, and writing lowercase letters; recognizing letter sounds

The Letter s

sock

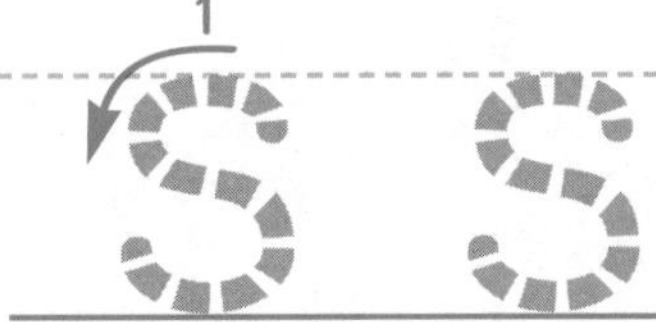

Circle if its name begins like sock.

seal sun doll

Parents: Say, "*sock* begins with the letter *s*. Listen for the sound *s* makes at the beginning of *sss-sock*. Say it!" Show your child how to trace the hollow letter with a finger. Have him or her use a pencil or crayon to trace and write the letter. Then ask your child to circle the pictures that begin with s.

The Letter t

Circle if its name begins like tiger.

Parents: Say, "*tiger* begins with the letter *t*. Listen for the sound *t* makes at the beginning of *ttt-tiger*. Say it!" Show your child how to trace the hollow letter with a finger. Have him or her use a pencil or crayon to trace and write the letter. Then ask your child to circle the pictures that begin with t.

The Letter u

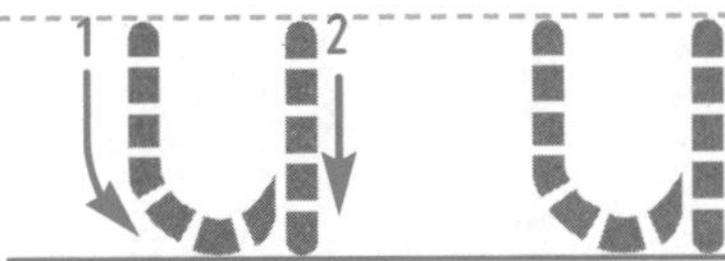

Circle if its name begins like umpire.

Parents: Say, "*umpire* begins with the letter *u*. Listen for the sound *u* makes at the beginning of *uuu-umpire*. Say it!" Show your child how to trace the hollow letter with a finger. Have him or her use a pencil or crayon to trace and write the letter. Then ask your child to circle the pictures that begin with u.

The Letter v

vase

Circle if its name begins like vase.

violets

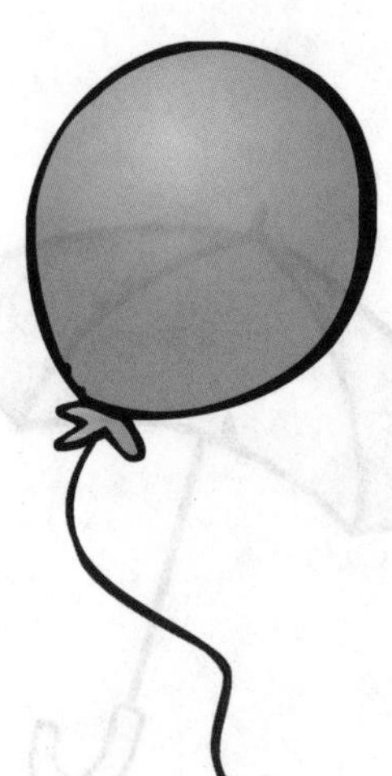

balloon

vegetables

Parents: Say, "*vase* begins with the letter *v*. Listen for the sound v makes at the beginning of *vvv-vase*. Say it!" Show your child how to trace the hollow letter with a finger. Have him or her use a pencil or crayon to trace and write the letter. Then ask your child to circle the pictures that begin with v.

Recognizing, tracing, and writing lowercase letters; recognizing letter sounds

The Letter w

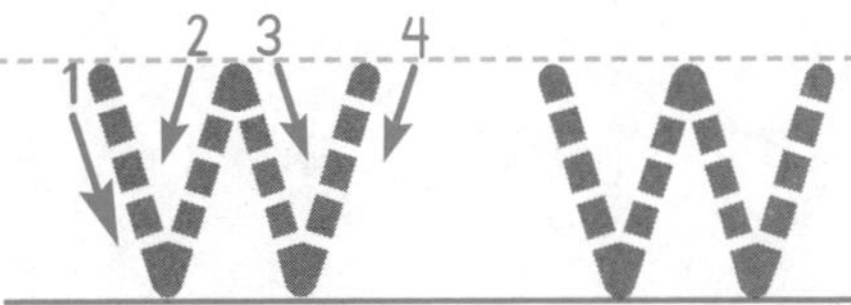

Circle if its name begins like worm.

apple walrus window

Parents: Say, "*worm* begins with the letter *w*. Listen for the sound *w* makes at the beginning of *www-worm*. Say it!" Show your child how to trace the hollow letter with a finger. Have him or her use a pencil or crayon to trace and write the letter. Then ask your child to circle the pictures that begin with w.

The Letter x

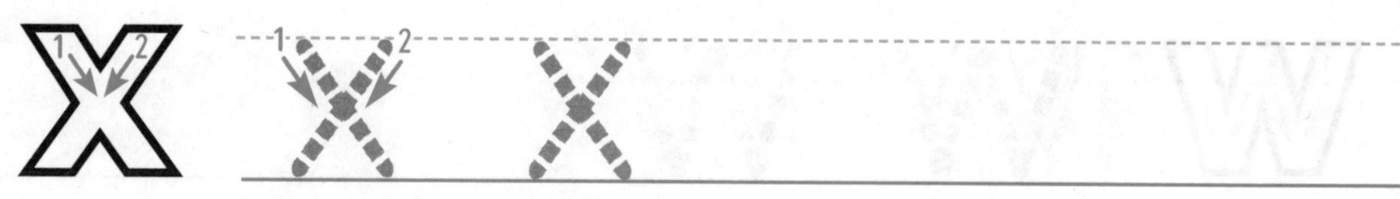

Circle if its name begins like x-ray.

fish xylophone x-ray

Parents: Say, "*x-ray* begins with the letter *x*. Listen for the sound *x* makes at the beginning of *xxx-x-ray*. Say it!" Show your child how to trace the hollow letter with a finger. Have him or her use a pencil or crayon to trace and write the letter. Then ask your child to circle the pictures that begin with x.

The Letter y

yarn

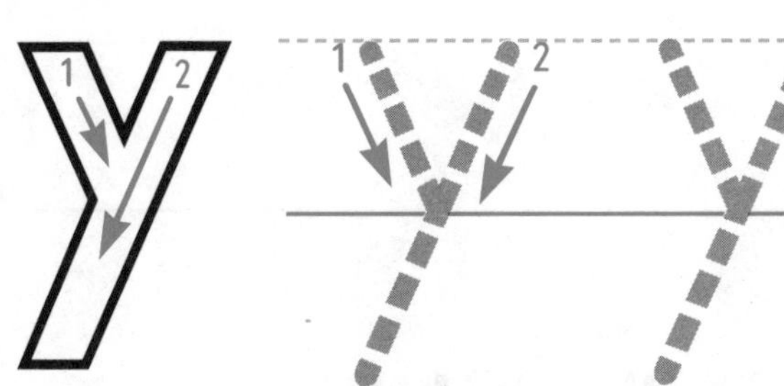

Circle if its name begins like yarn.

yak

yo-yo

parrot

Parents: Say, "*yarn* begins with the letter *y*. Listen for the sound *y* makes at the beginning of *yyy-yarn*. Say it!" Show your child how to trace the hollow letter with a finger. Have him or her use a pencil or crayon to trace and write the letter. Then ask your child to circle the pictures that begin with y.

The Letter z

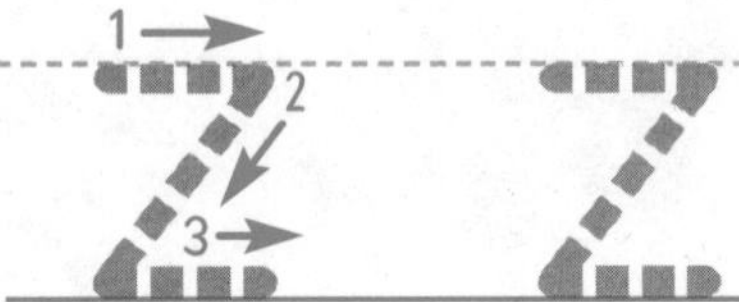

Circle if its name begins like zebra.

zipper　　baby　　zoo

Parents: Say, "*zebra* begins with the letter *z*. Listen for the sound *z* makes at the beginning of *zzz-zebra*. Say it!" Show your child how to trace the hollow letter with a finger. Have him or her use a pencil or crayon to trace and write the letter. Then ask your child to circle the pictures that begin with z.

abc Review

Parents: **Ask your child to point to and say the name of each object pictured on pages 347 and 348. Then ask, "What letter does the name begin with?" Have your child trace the letters *a* through *z* with a pencil and color the pictures.**

abc Review

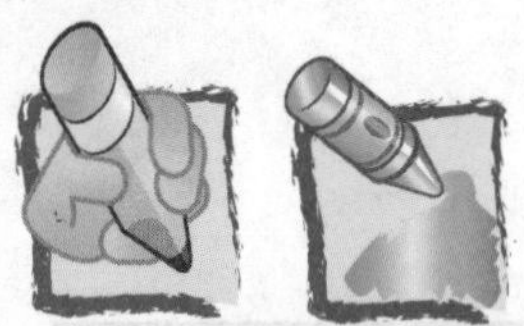

p q r s

t u v w

x y z

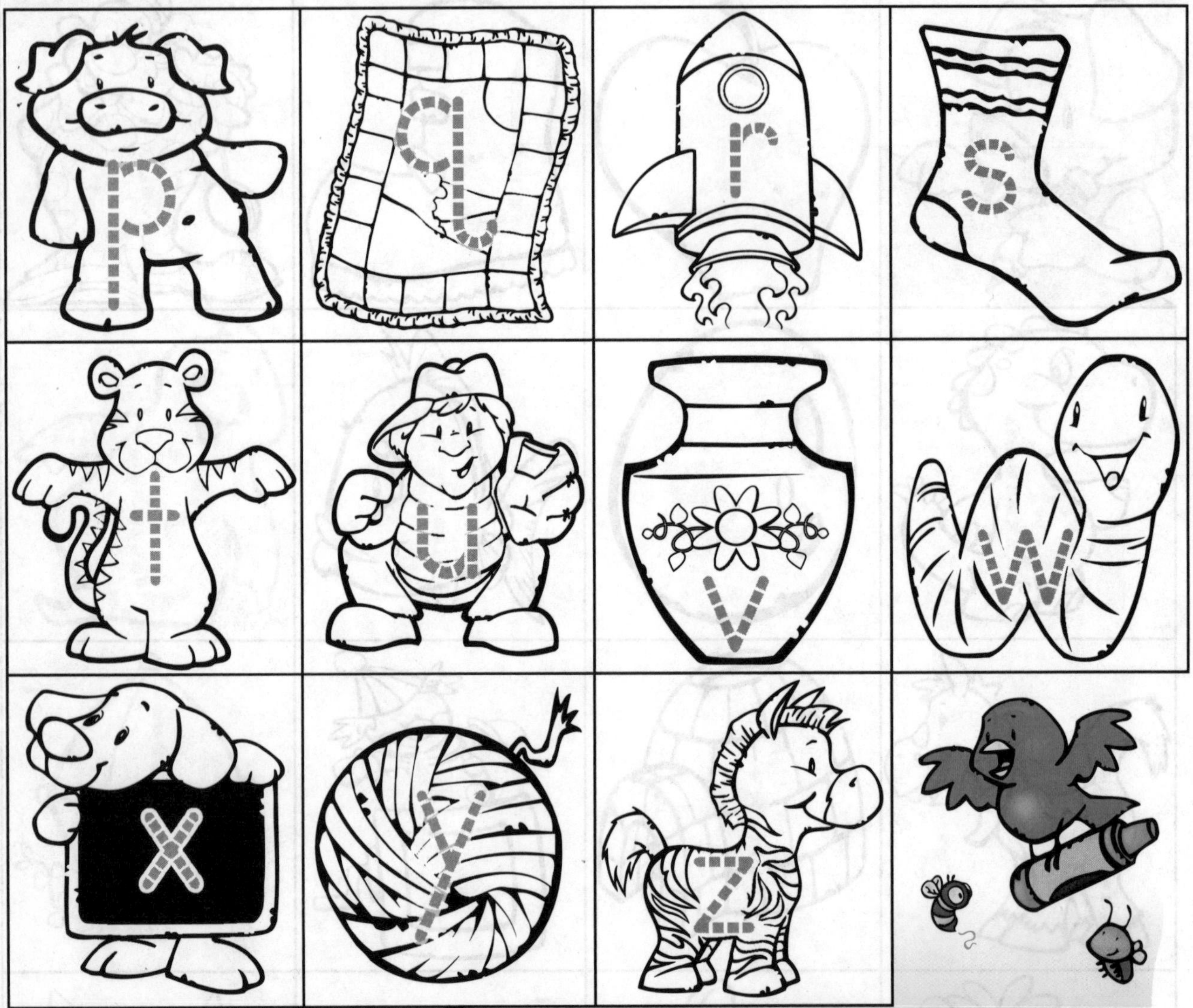

Matching Letters

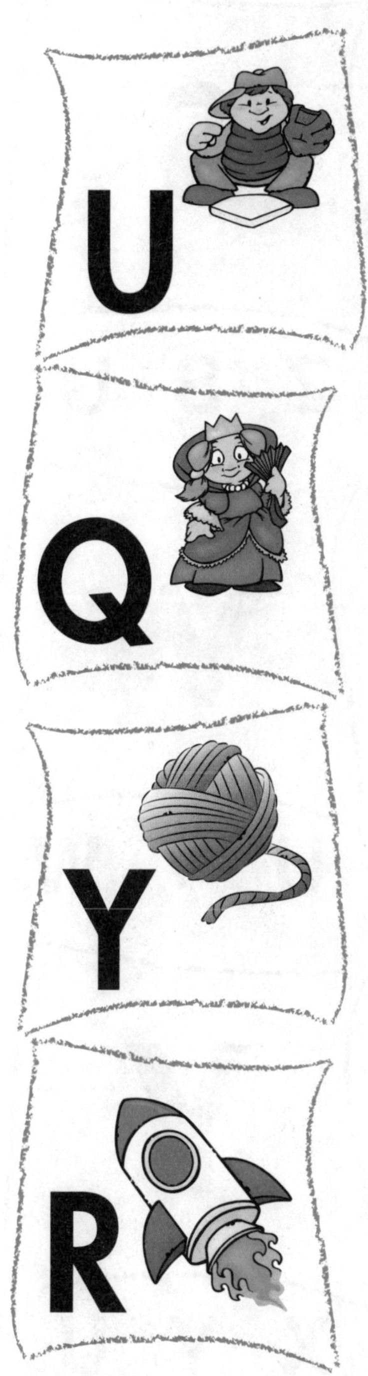

Parents: Have your child name the letter and picture in each box. Then ask your child to draw a line from each box in the left-hand column to the box on the right with the same letter.

READING

Matching Letters

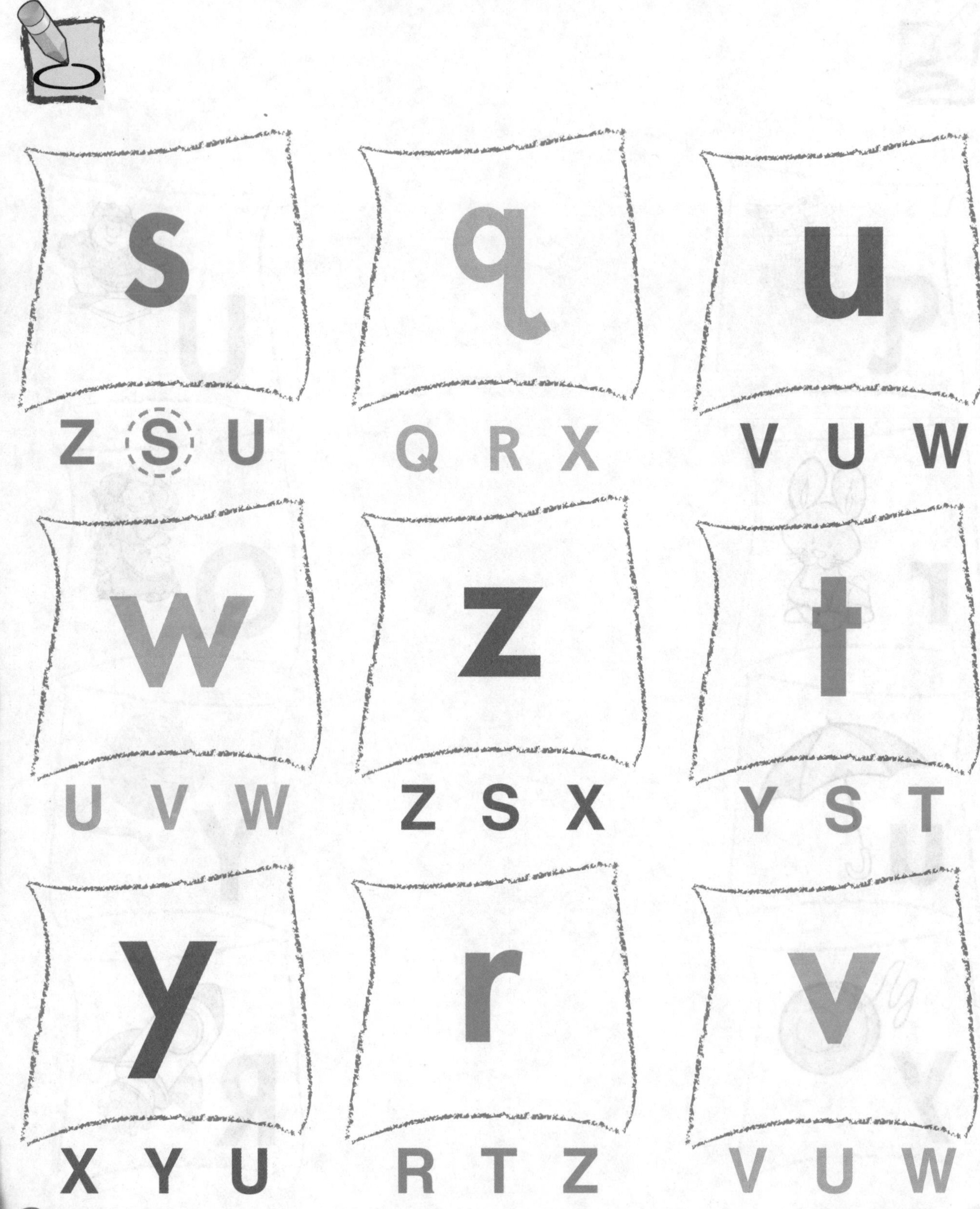

Parents: Ask your child to read the large lowercase letter in each box and to circle its capital (uppercase) form among the three letters below.

Q to Z Kaleidoscope

Parents: See page 352 for directions.

Q to Z Kaleidoscope

Cut along the lines. Match each letter with a letter on page 353. Paste the pieces letter side down.

U	W	T
Y	Q	Z
R	V	X
	S	

Parents: Help your child cut out the puzzle pieces and match the uppercase letters on the pieces with the lowercase letters in the squares of the puzzle on page 353. Make sure your child pastes each piece with the letter side facedown and the colored side up.

Q to Z Kaleidoscope

After you paste down the pieces from page 352, color the rest of the picture.

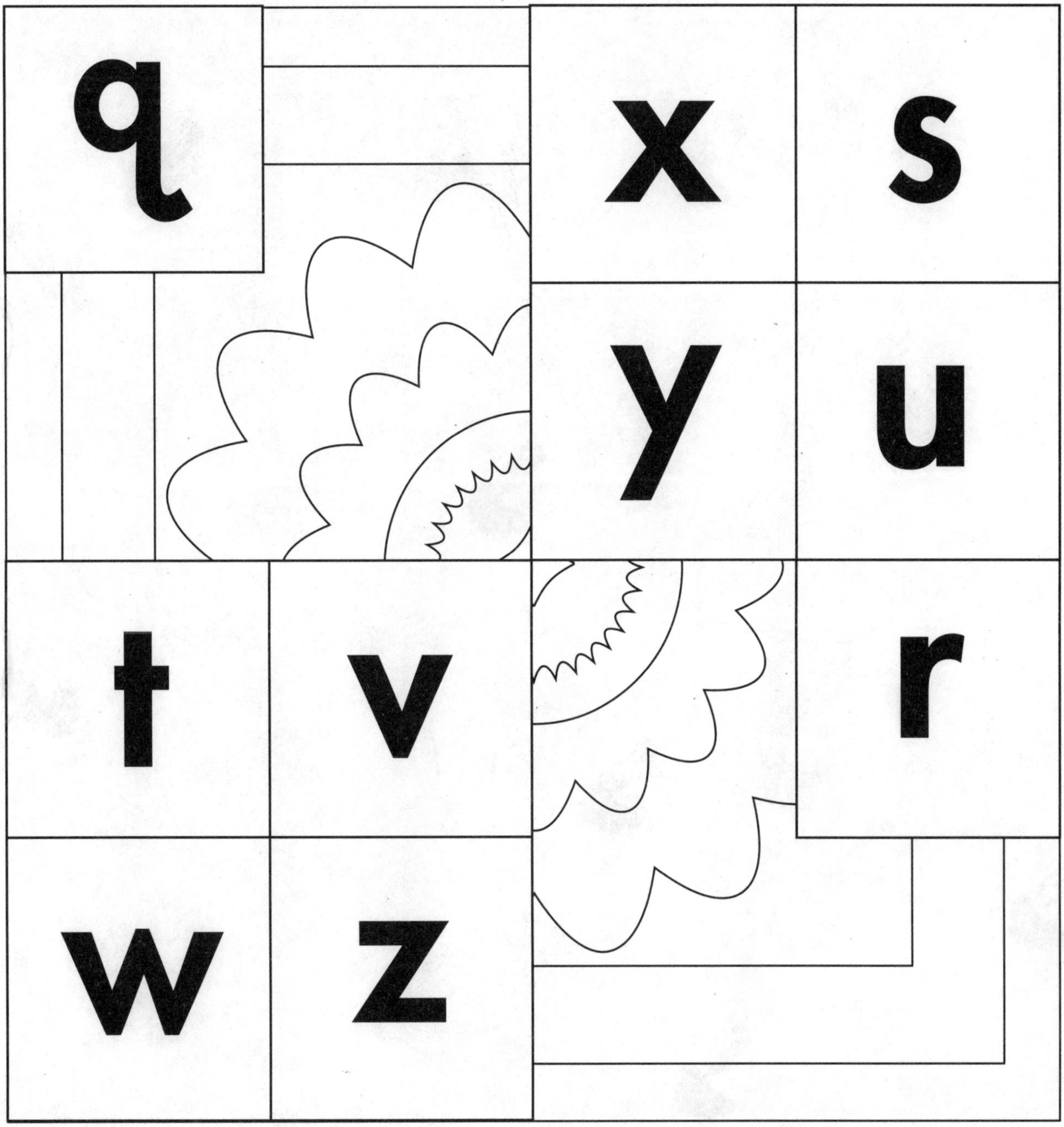

q x s

y u

t v r

w z

Parents: When the puzzle pieces from pages 351-352 are pasted down, encourage your child to identify the colors of different shapes in the design and to use the same colors when coloring matching shapes.

Month 12 Checklist

Hands-on activities to help prepare your child for school!

LANGUAGE

Opposites: pages 357-358

For this month, a couple of worksheets review opposites. Use the activity below and the ones from previous months to help your youngster practice using opposite words.

❑ Complete the worksheets.

❑ To the tune of "If you're happy and you know it...," sing this opposites song with your child, substituting new opposite pairs in each verse:
The opposite of empty is full.
Oh, the opposite of empty is full.
Well, the opposite of empty is full, full, full.
Yes, the opposite of empty is full!

MATH

Numerals and Number Words: pages 359-363

The worksheets for this month provide a way to review how much your child has learned about numbers over the past eleven months.

❑ Complete the worksheets.

❑ To practice counting, let your child count the dots on dominoes and place all the dominoes with the same amount of dots together. Or use an abacus to practice counting.

❑ Number words are some of the most important words in our language. They're among the first sight words that children learn. To help your child practice recognizing these words, point them out as you go about routines. For example, point them out in the supermarket, on billboards and street signs, in magazines and newspapers, and so on.

READING

Rhyming: pages 364, 369

Common Sight Words: pages 365-368, 370-380

Although preschoolers do not read and should not be pressured to try, there is much that can be done to prepare them for reading. Use the worksheets and activities for this month to help your child practice sight words:

- ❑ Complete the worksheets.
- ❑ Learning sight words can be an arduous process. Some children easily learn while others may not learn them until they've had in-depth phonics instruction. When you read to your child, pick out key words in the book and show them to your youngster. As you reread a story, encourage the child to say the words with you as you come to them. Remember to be patient—learning to read is not a race; never criticize your child's level of accomplishment; be generous with praise; and keep the story, not individual words, the focus of each reading session. At this point, you are planting seeds…the garden will come later.
- ❑ Make color-word index cards. First, make a circle of color on one side of the card and next to it write three words—e.g., red, one, it. Second, write the correct answer on the back of the card—e.g., red. Show the card to your child and ask him or her to choose the word that names the color. If the child uses the cards alone, he or she can check answers by looking at the back. Repeat this with number words, pet names, and so on.

SELF-CONCEPT

Self-Esteem: page 381

To reward your child for all the work that he or she has done while using this book, celebrate "graduation."

- ❑ Complete the graduation certificate.
- ❑ Have a family party with your child's favorite refreshments and award the certificate to him or her. Post favorite projects and pages from the book around the party room.

Opposites Review V

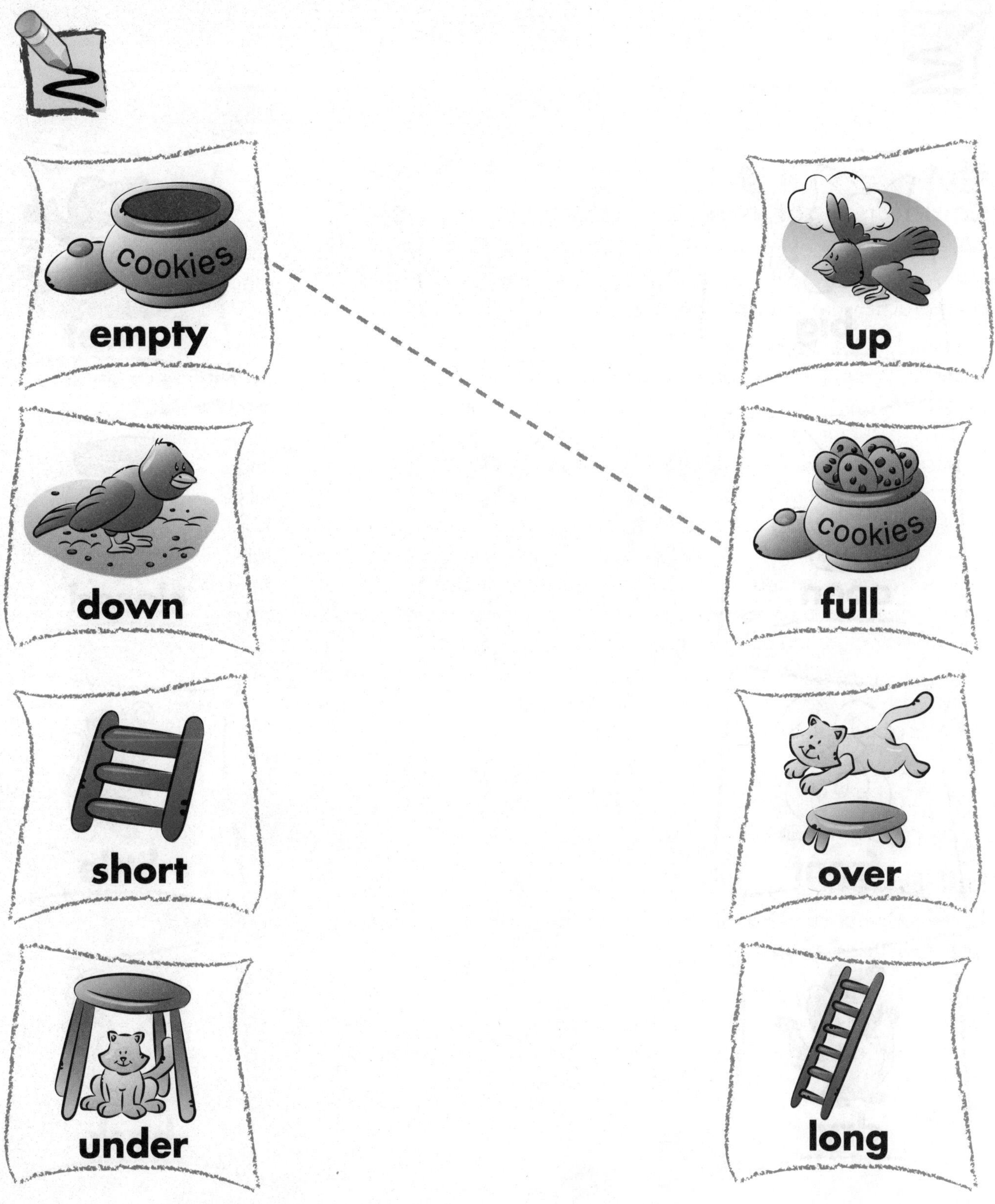

Parents: Talk about each picture and help your child see how it illustrates the word beneath it. Then have him or her draw a line from each picture in the left-hand column to a picture that shows its opposite in the right-hand column.

Opposites Review VI

big

wet

open

closed

front

little

dry

back

Parents: Talk about each picture and help your child see how it illustrates the word beneath it. Then have him or her draw a line from each picture in the left-hand column to a picture that shows its opposite in the right-hand column.

What Isn't Five?

Cross out what is not five.

2

5

five

1

Parents: Ask your child to describe each numeral, number word, and set of objects on the page, beginning with the circled word at the center. Then have him or her cross out every numeral, word, or set that does not match the central word, five.

M A T H

Mixed-up Sets

Cross out what does not belong.

7 seven two

Parents: Ask your child to draw an X through each numeral, number word, or group of objects that represents a number different from the other items in the box.

Sorry, Wrong Number

Cross out what does not belong.

8 **seven**

eight

10 **ten**

Parents: Ask your child to draw an X through each numeral, number word, or group of objects that represents a number different from the other items in the box.

Number Words

eight nine ten

three four five

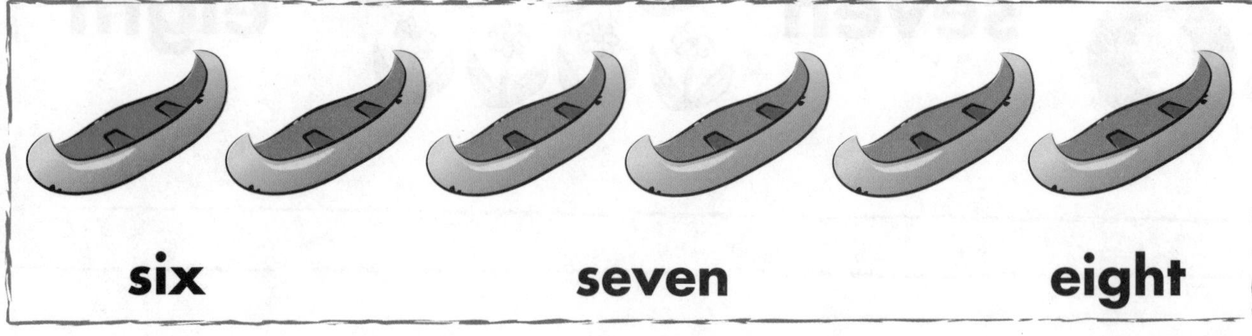

six seven eight

seven eight nine

Parents: Have your child count the number of objects in each box and circle the correct number word.

More Number Words

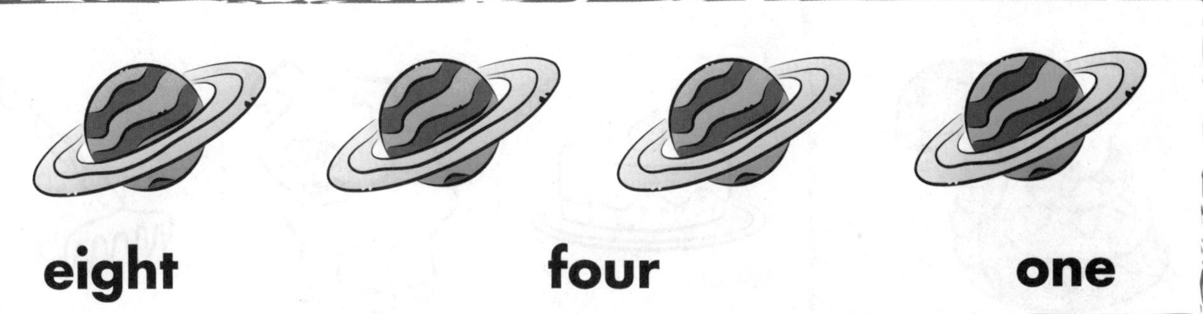

Parents: Have your child count the number of objects in each box and circle the correct number word.

Rhyme Time

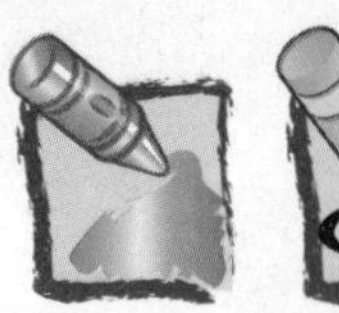

Circle and color the ones that rhyme.

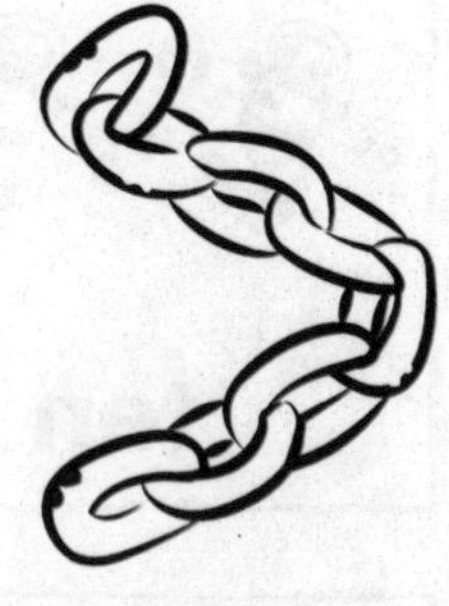

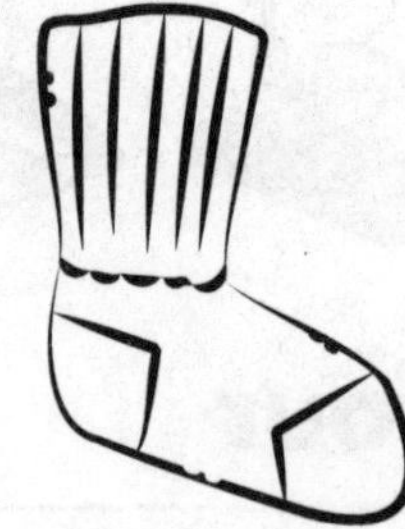

Parents: Have your child say the name of the first picture in each row, followed by the names of the other pictures. Ask, "Which names rhyme? Circle and color the pictures with names that rhyme with the first picture."

a b c d e f g h i j k l m n o p q r s t u v w x y z

My abc's are fun!
When I get to z,
I smile.
The alphabet is done!

apple to zebra

a is for apple,
b is for ball,
c is for cupcake,
d for doll.

u is for umpire,
v for vet,
w is for wagon,
x, y, z. . . you bet!

q is for queen,
r for rose,
s is for sailor,
t for toes.

e is for eggs,
f for five,
g is for goldfish,
h for hive.

i is for insect,
j for jam,
k is for kitchen,
l for lamb.

m is for monkey,
n for nurse,
o is for olives,
p for purse.

More Rhyme Time

Circle and color the ones that rhyme.

Parents: **Have your child say the name of the first picture in each row, followed by the names of the other pictures. Ask, "Which names rhyme? Circle and color the pictures with names that rhyme with the first picture."**

People Words

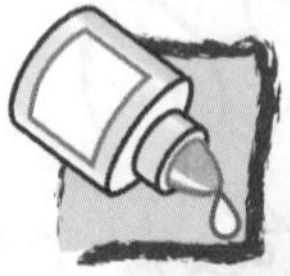

See page 375.

Parents: (Top) Point to the word below the boy and read aloud: "*b-o-y* spells *boy*." (Bottom) Ask your child to point to the word *boy* in the bottom picture, and then paste the correct picture from page 375 in the box. Follow the same steps for *girl*.

Pet Words

cat **dog**

See page 375.

dog **cat**

Parents: **(Top) Point to the word below the cat and read aloud: "*c-a-t* spells *cat*." (Bottom) Ask your child to point to the word *cat* in the bottom picture, and then paste the correct picture from page 375 in the box. Follow the same steps for *dog*.**

More Pet Words

fish

bird

See page 375.

bird

fish

Parents: **(Top) Point to the word below the fish and read aloud: "*f-i-s-h* spells *fish*." (Bottom) Ask your child to point to the word *fish* in the bottom picture, and then paste the correct picture from page 375 in the box. Follow the same steps for *bird*.**

Farm Animal Words

See page 375.

cow **pig**

Parents: (Top) Point to the word below the pig and read aloud: "*p-i-g* spells *pig*." (Bottom) Ask your child to point to the word *pig* in the bottom picture, and then paste the correct picture from page 375 in the box. Follow the same steps for *cow*.

READING

Animal Word Review

dog

cow

pig

cat

cow

cat

dog

pig

Parents: **Ask your child to look at the picture of the dog at the top left. Point to the word *dog* as you read it aloud. Ask your child to find the word *dog* on the right side and draw a line to connect the two. Do the same for the words *cow, pig,* and *cat.***

Cutouts for page 370-373.

Just Ducky!

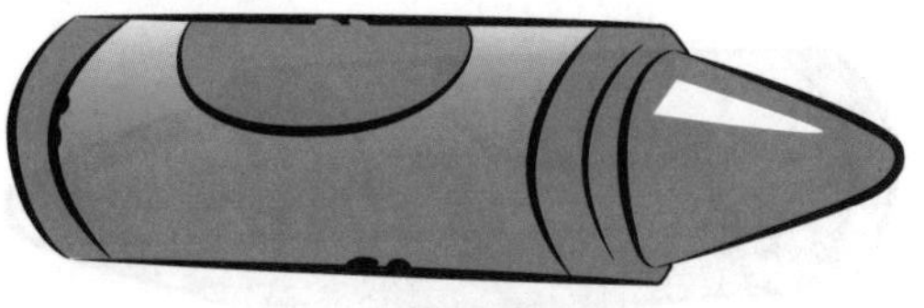

red

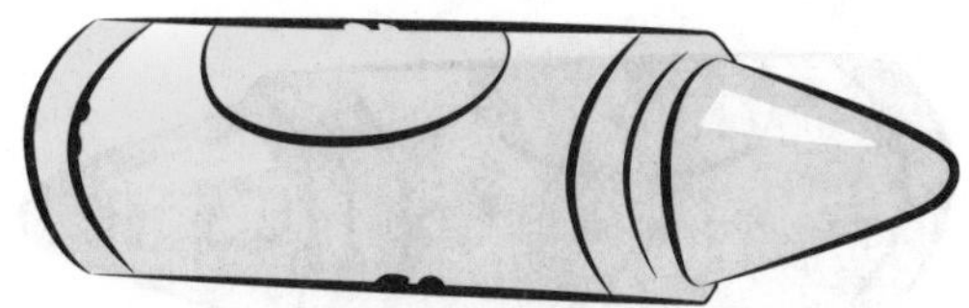

yellow

red

red

yellow

Parents: Point to the picture of the red crayon and then to the word *red* under it and say, "*r-e-d* spells *red*." Then say, "Find all the parts of the picture labeled *red* and color them." Repeat for *yellow*.

A Buggy Hello

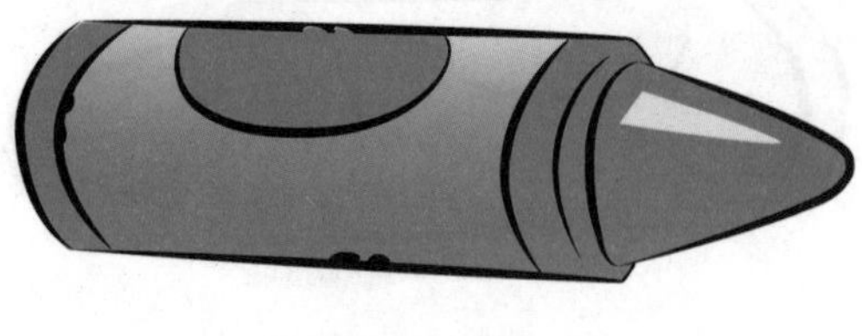

green

blue

green

blue

blue

green

green

Parents: **Point to the picture of the green crayon and then to the word *green* under it and say, "*g-r-e-e-n* spells *green*." Then say, "Find all the parts of the picture labeled *green* and color them." Repeat for *blue*.**

What's Cooking?

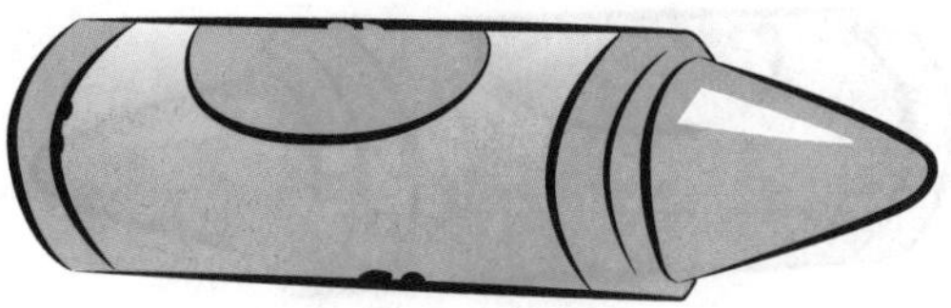

orange **black**

black

black

orange

black

black

orange

Parents: **Point to the picture of the orange crayon and then to the word *orange* under it and say, "*o-r-a-n-g-e* spells *orange*." Then say, "Find all the parts of the picture labeled *orange* and color them." Repeat for *black*.**

Sea Colors

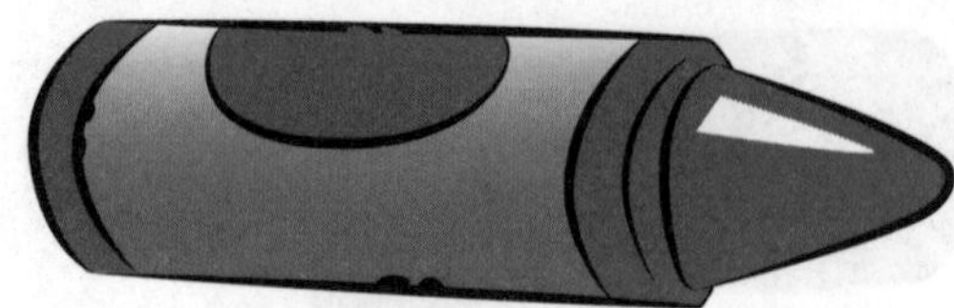

brown

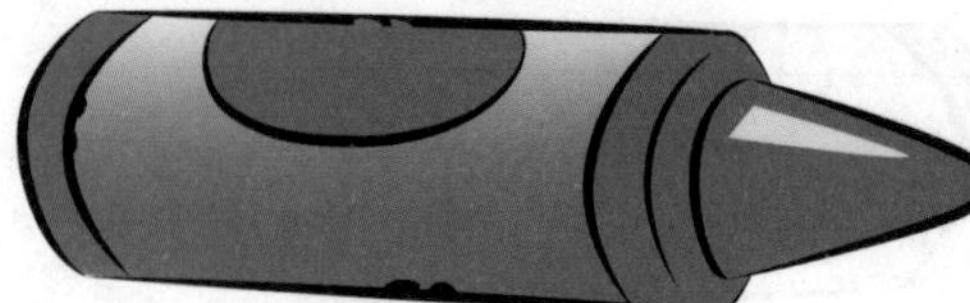

purple

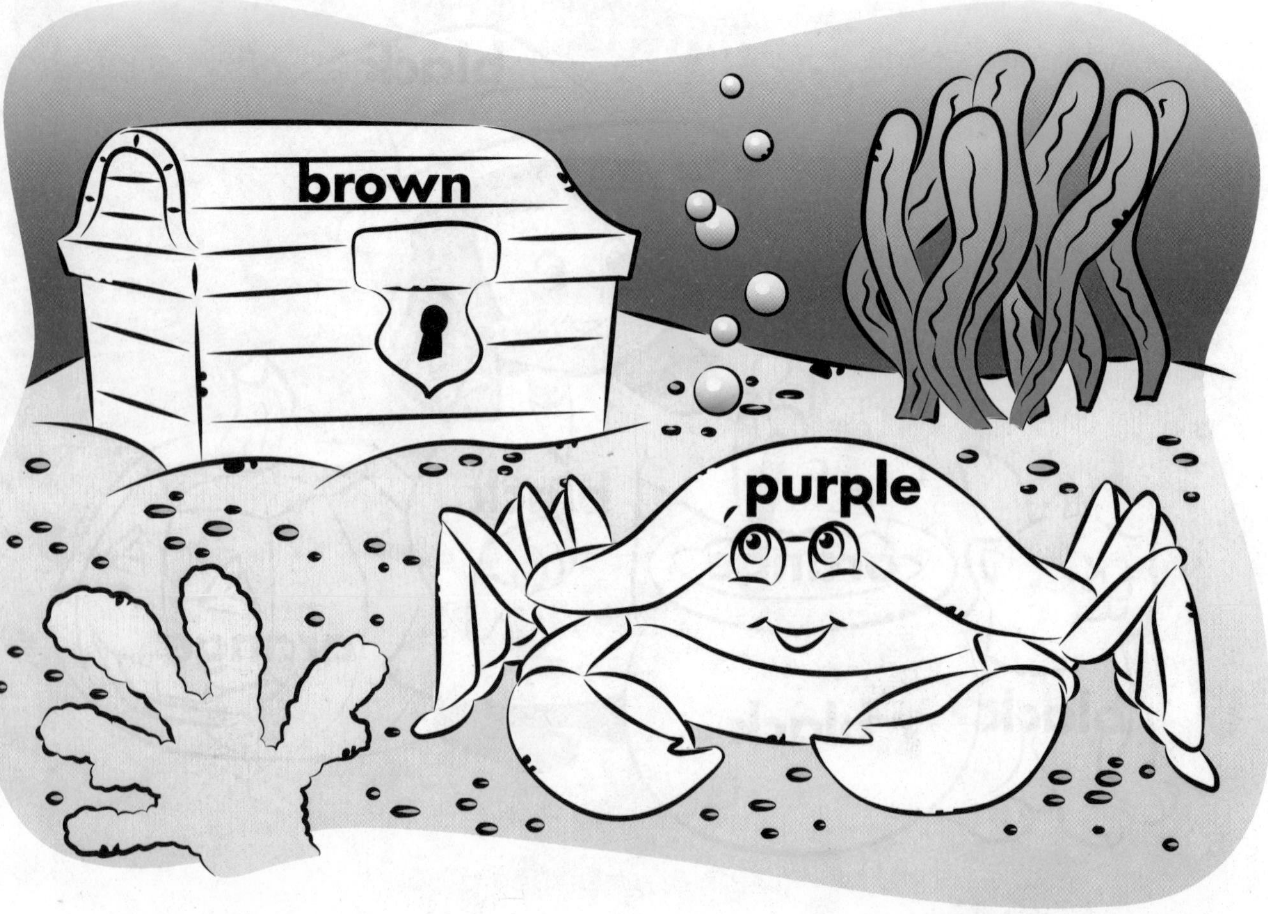

brown

purple

Parents: Point to the picture of the brown crayon and then to the word *brown* under it and say, "b-r-o-w-n spells *brown*." Then say, "Find the part of the picture labeled *brown* and color it." Repeat for *purple*.

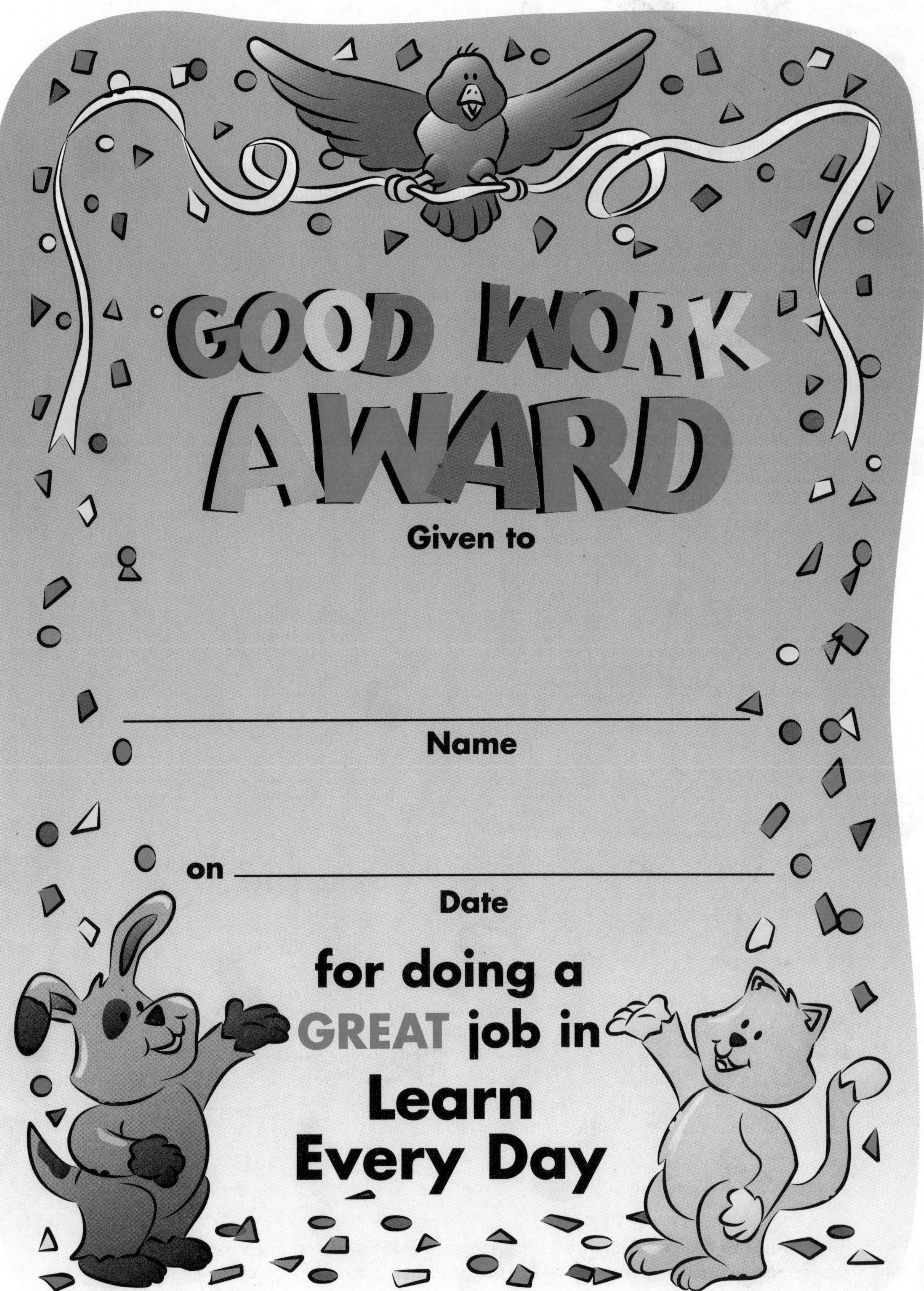
GOOD WORK
AWARD
Given to
Name
on
Date
for doing a
GREAT job in
Learn
Every Day

Index